Contents

Topic 10 — Using Resources

Practical Skills

Maths Skills

Exam Help

Reference

How to use this book

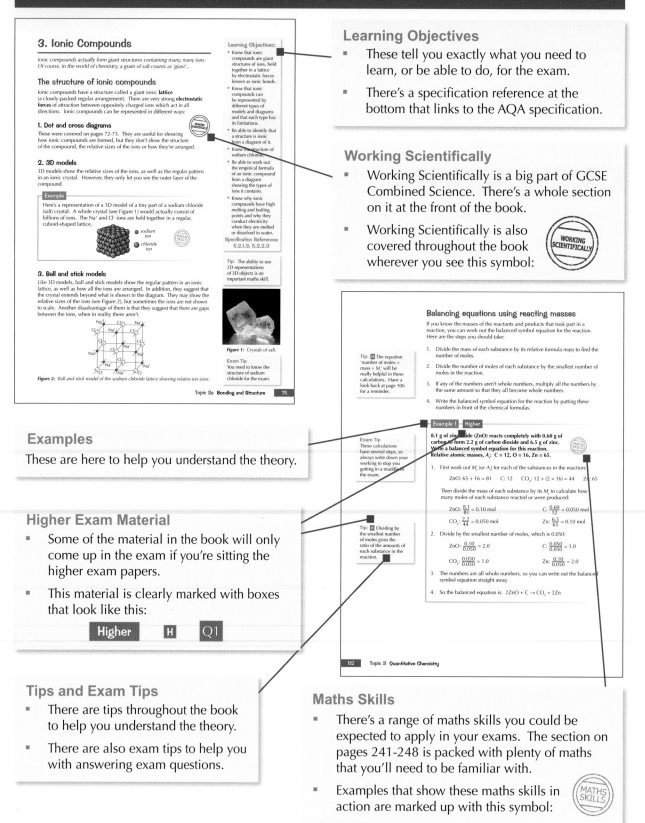

Learning Objectives

- These tell you exactly what you need to learn, or be able to do, for the exam.

- There's a specification reference at the bottom that links to the AQA specification.

Working Scientifically

- Working Scientifically is a big part of GCSE Combined Science. There's a whole section on it at the front of the book.

- Working Scientifically is also covered throughout the book wherever you see this symbol:

Examples

These are here to help you understand the theory.

Higher Exam Material

- Some of the material in the book will only come up in the exam if you're sitting the higher exam papers.

- This material is clearly marked with boxes that look like this:

    Higher **H** **Q1**

Tips and Exam Tips

- There are tips throughout the book to help you understand the theory.

- There are also exam tips to help you with answering exam questions.

Maths Skills

- There's a range of maths skills you could be expected to apply in your exams. The section on pages 241-248 is packed with plenty of maths that you'll need to be familiar with.

- Examples that show these maths skills in action are marked up with this symbol:

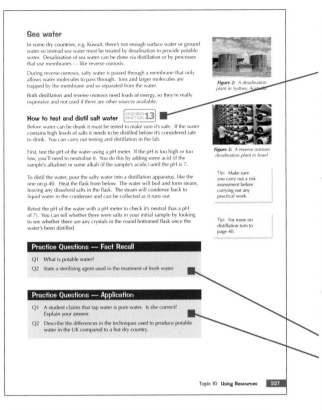

Required Practical Activities

There are some Required Practical Activities that you'll be expected to do throughout your course. You need to know all about them for the exams. The Required Practical Activities in this book are numbered 8-13, to match the AQA specification. They're all marked with stamps like this:

Practical Skills

There's also a whole section on pages 233-240 with extra details on practical skills you'll be expected to use in the Required Practical Activities, and apply knowledge of in the exams.

Practice Questions

- Fact recall questions test that you know the facts needed for your chemistry exams.

- Annoyingly, the examiners also expect you to be able to apply your knowledge to new situations — application questions give you plenty of practice at doing this.

- All the answers are in the back of the book.

Exam-style Questions

- Practising exam-style questions is really important — this book has some at the end of every topic to test you.

- They're the same style as the ones you'll get in the real exams.

- All the answers are in the back of the book, along with a mark scheme to show you how you get the marks.

- Higher-only questions are marked like this: **1.2**

Topic Checklist

Each topic has a checklist at the end with boxes that let you tick off what you've learnt.

Glossary

There's a glossary at the back of the book full of definitions you need to know for the exams, plus loads of other useful words.

Exam Help

There's a section at the back of the book stuffed full of things to help you with the exams.

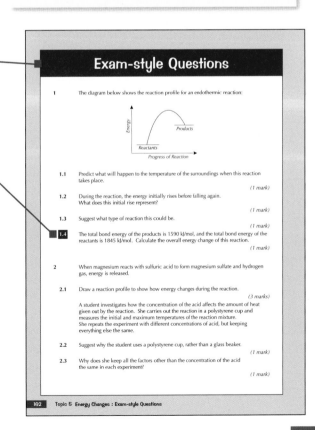

1. The Scientific Method

Science is all about finding things out and learning things about the world we live in. This topic is all about the scientific process — how a scientist's initial idea turns into a theory that is accepted by the wider scientific community.

Hypotheses

Scientists try to explain things. Everything. They start by observing something they don't understand — it could be anything, e.g. planets in the sky, a person suffering from an illness, what matter is made of... anything.

Then, they come up with a **hypothesis** — a possible explanation for what they've observed. (Scientists can also sometimes form a model too — a simplified description or a representation of what's physically going on — see next page).

The next step is to test whether the hypothesis might be right or not. This involves making a **prediction** based on the hypothesis and testing it by gathering evidence (i.e. data) from investigations. If evidence from experiments backs up a prediction, you're a step closer to figuring out if the hypothesis is true.

Testing a hypothesis

Normally, scientists share their findings in peer-reviewed journals, or at conferences. **Peer-review** is where other scientists check results and scientific explanations to make sure they're 'scientific' (e.g. that experiments have been done in a sensible way) before they're published. It helps to detect false claims, but it doesn't mean that findings are correct — just that they're not wrong in any obvious way.

Tip: Investigations include lab experiments and studies.

Once other scientists have found out about a hypothesis, they'll start basing their own predictions on it and carry out their own experiments. They'll also try to reproduce the original experiments to check the results — and if all the experiments in the world back up the hypothesis, then scientists start to think the hypothesis is true.

Tip: Sometimes it can take a really long time for a hypothesis to be accepted.

However, if a scientist somewhere in the world does an experiment that doesn't fit with the hypothesis (and other scientists can reproduce these results), then the hypothesis is in trouble. When this happens, scientists have to come up with a new hypothesis (maybe a modification of the old hypothesis, or maybe a completely new one).

Accepting a hypothesis

If pretty much every scientist in the world believes a hypothesis to be true because experiments back it up, then it usually goes in the textbooks for students to learn. Accepted hypotheses are often referred to as **theories**.

Our currently accepted theories are the ones that have survived this 'trial by evidence' — they've been tested many, many times over the years and survived (while the less good ones have been ditched). However... they never, never become hard and fast, totally indisputable fact. You can never know... it'd only take one odd, totally inexplicable result, and the hypothesising and testing would start all over again.

Example

Over time, scientists have come up with different hypotheses about the structure of the atom.

About 100 years ago we thought atoms looked like this.

Then we thought they looked like this.

And then we thought they looked like this.

Tip: There's lots more about the structure of the atom on pages 42-45.

Models

Models are used to describe or display how an object or system behaves in reality. They're often based on evidence collected from experiments, and should be able to accurately predict what will happen in other, similar experiments. There are different types of models that scientists can use to describe the world around them. Here are just a few:

- A **descriptive model** shows what's happening in a certain situation, without explaining why. It won't necessarily include details that could be used to predict the outcome of a different scenario. For example, a graph showing the rate of a reaction at different temperatures (see p.172) would be a descriptive model.

- A **representational model** is a simplified description or picture of what's going on in real life. It can be used to explain observations and make predictions. E.g. particle theory is a simplified way of explaining how particles behave in different states of matter (see p.97-98). It can be used to explain how changes of state occur.

- **Spatial models** are used to summarise how data is arranged within space. For example, a three-dimensional model of a covalent molecule would be a spatial model.

- **Computational models** use computers to make simulations of complex real-life processes, such as climate change. They're used when there are a lot of different variables (factors that change) to consider, and because you can easily change their design to take into account new data.

- **Mathematical models** can be used to describe the relationship between variables in numerical form (e.g. as an equation), and therefore predict outcomes of a scenario. For example, an equation can be written to predict how the pH of a solution will change if the concentration of H^+ ions in the solution changes.

Tip: Like hypotheses, models have to be tested before they're accepted by other scientists. You can test models by using them to make a prediction, and then carrying out an investigation to see whether the results match the prediction.

Figure 1: A spatial model showing how the atoms are arranged in a water molecule.

Tip: Mathematical models are made using patterns found in data and also using information about known relationships between variables.

All models have limitations on what they can explain or predict. Climate change models have several limitations — for example, it's hard to take into account all the biological and chemical processes that influence climate. It can also be difficult to include regional variations in climate.

Communicating results

Some scientific discoveries show that people should change their habits, or they might provide ideas that could be developed into new technology. So scientists need to tell the world about their discoveries.

> **Example**
>
> Several technologies are being developed that make use of fullerenes (see p.88-89). These include drug delivery systems for use in medicine. Information about these systems needs to be communicated to doctors so they can make use of them, and to patients, so they can make informed decisions about their treatment.

Reports about scientific discoveries in the media (e.g. newspapers or television) aren't peer-reviewed. This means that, even though news stories are often based on data that has been peer-reviewed, the data might be presented in a way that is over-simplified or inaccurate, leaving it open to misinterpretation.

It's important that the evidence isn't presented in a **biased** way. This can sometimes happen when people want to make a point, e.g. they overemphasise a relationship in the data. (Sometimes without knowing they're doing it.) There are all sorts of reasons why people might want to do this.

> **Examples**
>
> - They want to keep the organisation or company that's funding the research happy. (If the results aren't what they'd like they might not give them any more money to fund further research.)
> - Governments might want to persuade voters, other governments or journalists to agree with their policies about a certain issue.
> - Companies might want to 'big up' their products, or make impressive safety claims.
> - Environmental campaigners might want to persuade people to behave differently.

There's also a risk that if an investigation is done by a team of highly-regarded scientists it'll be taken more seriously than evidence from less well known scientists. But having experience, authority or a fancy qualification doesn't necessarily mean the evidence is good — the only way to tell is to look at the evidence scientifically (e.g. is it repeatable, valid, etc.).

Tip: New scientific discoveries are usually communicated to the public in the news or via the internet. They might be communicated to governments and large organisations via reports or meetings.

Tip: If you're reading an article about a new scientific discovery, always think about how the study was carried out. It may be that the sample size was very small, and so the results aren't representative (see page 10 for more on sample sizes).

Tip: An example of bias is a newspaper article describing details of data supporting an idea without giving any of the evidence against it.

2. Scientific Applications and Issues

New scientific discoveries can lead to lots of exciting new ways of using science in our everyday lives. Unfortunately, these developments may also come with social, economic or moral problems that need to be considered.

Using scientific developments

Lots of scientific developments go on to have useful applications.

Examples

- An alloy is a mixture of a metal and another element. Alloys are harder than pure metals. This discovery has meant that scientists have been able to develop materials that are harder than pure metals, and so can be used for different purposes.

- The discovery that long-chain alkanes will break down if heated in the presence of steam has meant that cracking has been developed to increase the supply of more useful, short chain hydrocarbons.

Tip: There's lots more about alloys on page 91, and there's more about cracking on pages 194-195.

Issues created by science

Scientific knowledge is increased by doing experiments. And this knowledge leads to scientific developments, e.g. new technologies or new advice. These developments can create issues though. For example, they could create political issues, which could lead to developments being ignored, or governments being slow to act if they think responding to the developments could affect their popularity with voters.

Example

Some governments were pretty slow to accept the fact that human activities are causing global warming, despite all the evidence. This is because accepting it means they've got to do something about it, which costs money and could hurt their economy. This could lose them a lot of votes.

Tip: See pages 209-211 for more on global warming.

Scientific developments can cause a whole host of other issues too.

Examples

- **Economic issues:** Society can't always afford to do things scientists recommend (e.g. investing heavily in alternative energy sources) without cutting back elsewhere.

- **Social issues:** Decisions based on scientific evidence affect people — e.g. should fossil fuels be taxed more highly (to invest in alternative energy)? Would the effect on people's lifestyles be acceptable?

- **Environmental issues:** Human activity often affects the environment. For example, building a dam to produce electricity will change the local habitat so some species might be displaced. But it will also reduce our need for fossil fuels, so will help to reduce climate change.

- **Personal issues:** Some decisions will affect individuals. For example, someone might support alternative energy, but object if a wind farm is built next to their house.

Figure 1: *A dam used to produce electricity. This could be a potential alternative to fossil fuels, but some people have concerns about how it could affect the surrounding habitat.*

3. Limitations of Science

Science has taught us an awful lot about the world we live in and how things work — but science doesn't have the answer for everything.

Questions science hasn't answered yet

We don't understand everything. And we never will. We'll find out more, for sure — as more hypotheses are suggested, and more experiments are done. But there'll always be stuff we don't know.

Examples

- Today we don't know as much as we'd like about the impacts of global warming. How much will sea levels rise? And to what extent will weather patterns change?

- We also don't know anywhere near as much as we'd like about the universe. Are there other life forms out there? And what is the universe made of?

In order to answer scientific questions, scientists need data to provide evidence for their hypotheses. Some questions can't be answered yet because the data can't currently be collected, or because there's not enough data to support a theory. But eventually, as we get more evidence, we probably will be able to answer these questions. By then, there'll be loads of new questions to answer though.

Questions science can't answer

There are some questions that all the experiments in the world won't help us answer — for example, the "should we be doing this at all?" type questions.

Example

Think about new drugs which can be taken to boost your 'brain power'.

- Some people think they're good as they could improve concentration or memory. New drugs could let people think in ways beyond the powers of normal brains.

- Other people say they're bad — they could give you an unfair advantage in exams. And people might be pressured into taking them so that they could work more effectively, and for longer hours.

The question of whether something is morally or ethically right or wrong can't be answered by more experiments — there is no "right" or "wrong" answer. The best we can do is get a consensus from society — a judgement that most people are more or less happy to live by. Science can provide more information to help people make this judgement, and the judgement might change over time. But in the end it's up to people and their conscience.

Figure 1: *Global warming could cause weather patterns to change — which may result in longer, hotter droughts in some areas.*

Tip: Some experiments have to be approved by ethics committees before scientists are allowed to carry them out. This stops scientists from getting wrapped up in whether they <u>can</u> do something before anyone stops to think about whether they <u>should</u> do it.

4. Risks and Hazards

A lot of things we do could cause us harm. But some things are more hazardous than they at first seem, whereas other things are less hazardous than they at first seem. This may sound confusing, but it'll all become clear...

What are risks and hazards?

A **hazard** is something that could potentially cause harm. All hazards have a **risk** attached to them — this is the chance that the hazard will cause harm.

The risks of some things seem pretty obvious, or we've known about them for a while, like the risk of causing acid rain by polluting the atmosphere, or of having a car accident when you're travelling in a car.

New technology arising from scientific advances can bring new risks. These risks need to be thought about alongside the potential benefits of the technology, in order to make a decision about whether it should be made available to the general public.

> **Example**
>
> Technology is being developed that captures carbon dioxide produced by burning fuels before it's released into the atmosphere. The carbon dioxide can then be stored in cracks underground. This should help to prevent global warming.
>
> However, the full effects of storing carbon dioxide underground aren't known. For example, storing a gas at high pressure underground could increase the risk of earthquakes. Also, if the carbon dioxide leaked, it could cause humans or animals to suffocate, or contaminate drinking water.
>
> So people need to weigh up the risks against the benefits of using carbon capture and storage.

Tip: There's more about global warming on pages 209-210 and more about reducing carbon dioxide emissions on page 212.

Estimating risk

You can estimate the risk based on how many times something happens in a big sample (e.g. 100 000 people) over a given period (e.g. a year). For example, you could assess the risk of a driver crashing by recording how many people in a group of 100 000 drivers crashed their cars over a year.

To make a decision about an activity that involves a hazardous event, we don't just need to take into account the chance of the event causing harm, but also how serious the consequences would be if it did.

The general rule is that, if an activity involves a hazard that's very likely to cause harm, with serious consequences if it does, that activity is considered high-risk.

> **Example 1**
>
> If you go for a run, you may sprain an ankle. But most sprains recover within a few days if they're rested, so going for a run would be considered a low-risk activity.

┌─ Example 2 ───

If you go skiing, you may fall and break a bone. This would take many weeks to heal, and may cause further complications later on in life. So skiing would be considered higher risk than running.

Perceptions of risk

Not all risks have the same consequences, e.g. if you chop veg with a sharp knife you risk cutting your finger, but if you go scuba-diving you risk death. You're much more likely to cut your finger during half an hour of chopping than to die during half an hour of scuba-diving. But most people are happier to accept a higher probability of an accident if the consequences are short-lived and fairly minor.

People tend to be more willing to accept a risk if they choose to do something (e.g. go scuba diving), compared to having the risk imposed on them (e.g. having a nuclear power station built next door).

People's perception of risk (how risky they think something is) isn't always accurate. They tend to view familiar activities as low-risk and unfamiliar activities as high-risk — even if that's not the case. For example, cycling on roads is often high-risk, but many people are happy to do it because it's a familiar activity. Air travel is actually pretty safe, but a lot of people perceive it as high-risk. People may over-estimate the risk of things with long-term or invisible effects, e.g. ionising radiation.

Tip: Risks people choose to take are called 'voluntary risks'. Risks that people are forced to take are called 'imposed risks'.

Reducing risk in investigations

Part of planning an investigation is making sure that it's safe. To make sure your experiment is safe you must identify all the **hazards**. Hazards include:

Tip: You can find out about potential hazards by looking in textbooks, doing some internet research, or asking your teacher.

- Microorganisms: e.g. some bacteria can make you ill.

- Chemicals: e.g. sulfuric acid can burn your skin and alcohols catch fire easily.

- Fire: e.g. an unattended Bunsen burner is a fire hazard.

- Electricity: e.g. faulty electrical equipment could give you a shock.

Once you've identified the hazards you might encounter, you should think of ways of reducing the risks from the hazards.

Figure 1: Scientists wearing safety goggles to protect their eyes during an experiment.

┌─ Examples ───

- If you're working with sulfuric acid, always wear gloves and safety goggles. This will reduce the risk of the acid coming into contact with your skin and eyes.

- If you're using a Bunsen burner, stand it on a heatproof mat. This will reduce the risk of starting a fire.

5. Designing Investigations

To be a good scientist you need to know how to design a good experiment, including how to make sure you get good quality results.

Making predictions from a hypothesis

Scientists observe things and come up with hypotheses to explain them. To decide whether a **hypothesis** might be correct you need to do an investigation to gather evidence, which will help support or disprove the hypothesis. The first step is to use the hypothesis to come up with a **prediction** — a statement about what you think will happen that you can test.

> **Example**
>
> If your hypothesis is 'increasing temperature causes reactions to go faster', then your prediction might be 'a reaction carried out at a high temperature will finish faster than the same reaction carried out at a low temperature'.

Once a scientist has come up with a prediction, they'll design an investigation to see if there are patterns or relationships between two variables. For example, to see if there's a pattern or relationship between the variables 'temperature of reaction' and 'time taken for reaction to finish'.

Tip: A variable is just something in the experiment that can change.

Repeatable and reproducible results

Results need to be **repeatable** and **reproducible**. Repeatable means that if the same person does an experiment again using the same methods and equipment, they'll get similar results. Reproducible means that if someone else does the experiment, or a different method or piece of equipment is used, the results will be similar.

Tip: Data that's repeatable and reproducible is <u>reliable</u> and scientists are more likely to have confidence in it.

> **Example**
>
> In 1998, a scientist claimed to have found a link between the MMR vaccine (for measles, mumps and rubella) and autism. This meant many parents stopped their children from being vaccinated, leading to a rise in the number of children catching measles. However, the results have never been reproduced. Health authorities have now decided that the vaccine is safe.

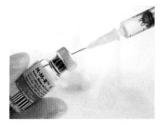

Ensuring the test is valid

Valid results are repeatable, reproducible and answer the original question.

Figure 1: *The MMR vaccine.*

> **Example**
>
> **Do power lines cause cancer?**
>
> Some studies have found that children who live near overhead power lines are more likely to develop cancer. What they'd actually found was a **correlation** (relationship) between the variables "presence of power lines" and "incidence of cancer". They found that as one changed, so did the other.
>
> But this data isn't enough to say that the power lines cause cancer, as there might be other explanations. For example, power lines are often near busy roads, so the areas tested could contain different levels of pollution. As the studies don't show a definite link they don't answer the original question.

Tip: Peer review (see page 2) is used to make sure that results are valid before they're published.

Tip: See page 17 for more on correlation.

Ensuring it's a fair test

In a lab experiment you usually change one variable and measure how it affects another variable. To make it a fair test, everything else that could affect the results should stay the same (otherwise you can't tell if the thing you're changing is causing the results or not — the data won't be valid).

Tip: For the results of an investigation to be valid the investigation must be a fair test.

> **Example**
>
> You might change only the temperature of a chemical reaction and measure how this affects the rate of reaction. You need to keep, for example, the concentration of the reactants the same, otherwise you won't know if any change in the rate of reaction is caused by the change in temperature, or a difference in reactant concentration.

Tip: You'd also need to keep other factors the same for this to be a fair test, such as the volumes of reactants and the surface area of any solid reactants.

The variable you change is called the **independent variable**. The variable you measure when you change the independent variable is called the **dependent variable**. The variables that you keep the same are called **control variables**.

> **Example**
>
> In the rate of reaction example, temperature is the independent variable, the rate of the reaction is the dependent variable and the concentrations of reactants, the volumes of reactants etc. are control variables.

Controlling variables in a study

A study is an investigation that doesn't take place in the lab. It's important that a study is a fair test, just like a lab experiment. It's a lot trickier to control the variables in a study than it is in a lab experiment though. Sometimes you can't control them all, but you can use a **control group** to help. This is a group of whatever you're studying (people, crops, animals, etc.) that's kept under the same conditions as the group in the experiment, but doesn't have anything done to it.

Tip: A pesticide is a chemical that can be used to kill insects and other pests.

> **Example**
>
> If you're studying the effect of pesticides on crop growth, pesticide is applied to one field but not to another field (the control field). Both fields are planted with the same crop, and are in the same area (so they get the same weather conditions).
>
> The control field is there to try and account for variables like the weather, which don't stay the same all the time, but could affect the results.

Sample size

Data based on small samples isn't as good as data based on large samples. A sample should be representative of the whole population (i.e. it should share as many of the various characteristics in the population as possible) — a small sample can't do that as well.

The bigger the sample size the better, but scientists have to be realistic when choosing how big.

Example

If you were studying the effects of a chemical used to sterilise water on the people drinking it, it'd be great to study everyone who was drinking the water (a huge sample), but it'd take ages and cost a bomb. It's more realistic to study a thousand people, with a mixture of ages, gender, and race.

Tip: It's hard to spot anomalies if your sample size is too small.

Trial runs

It's a good idea to do a **trial run** (a quick version of your experiment) before you do the proper experiment. Trial runs are used to figure out the range (the upper and lower limits) of independent variable values used in the proper experiment. If there was no change in the dependent variable between your upper and lower values in the trial run, then you might increase the range until there was an observable change. Or if there was a large change, you might want to make your higher and lower values closer together.

Tip: If you don't have time to do a trial run, you could always look at the data other people have got doing a similar experiment and use a range and interval values similar to theirs.

Example

For a rate of reaction experiment, you might do a trial run with a temperature range of 10-50 °C. If there was no reaction at the lower end (e.g. 10-20 °C), you might narrow the range to 20-50 °C for the proper experiment.

Trial runs can be used to figure out appropriate intervals (gaps) between the values too. The intervals can't be too small (otherwise the experiment would take ages), or too big (otherwise you might miss something).

Example

If using 1 °C intervals doesn't give you much change in the rate of reaction each time you might decide to use 5 °C intervals, e.g 20, 25, 30, 35, 40, 45, 50 °C...

Trial runs can also help you figure out whether or not your experiment is repeatable.

Tip: Consistently repeating the results is crucial for checking that your results are repeatable.

Example

If you repeat it three times and the results are all similar, the experiment is repeatable.

---

6. Collecting Data

Once you've designed your experiment, you need to get on and do it. Here's a guide to making sure the results you collect are good.

Getting good quality results

When you do an experiment you want your results to be **repeatable**, **reproducible** and as **accurate** and **precise** as possible.

To check repeatability you need to repeat the readings and check that the results are similar — you should repeat each reading at least three times. To make sure your results are reproducible you can cross check them by taking a second set of readings with another instrument (or a different observer).

Tip: For more on means see page 14.

Your data also needs to be accurate. Really accurate results are those that are really close to the true answer. The accuracy of your results usually depends on your method — you need to make sure you're measuring the right thing and that you don't miss anything that should be included in the measurements. For example, estimating the amount of gas released from a reaction by counting the bubbles isn't very accurate because you might miss some of the bubbles and they might have different volumes. It's more accurate to measure the volume of gas released using a gas syringe.

Tip: Sometimes, you can work out what result you should get at the end of an experiment (the theoretical result) by doing a bit of maths. If your experiment is accurate there shouldn't be much difference between the theoretical result and the result you actually get.

Your data also needs to be precise. Precise results are ones where the data is all really close to the mean (average) of your repeated results (i.e. not spread out).

Example

Look at the data in this table. Data set 1 is more precise than data set 2 because all the data in set 1 is really close to the mean, whereas the data in set 2 is more spread out.

Repeated measurement	Data set 1	Data set 2
1	12	11
2	14	17
3	13	14
Mean	13	14

Choosing the right equipment

When doing an experiment, you need to make sure you're using the right equipment for the job. The measuring equipment you use has to be sensitive enough to measure the changes you're looking for.

Example

If you need to measure changes of 1 cm³ you need to use a measuring cylinder that can measure in 1 cm³ steps — it'd be no good trying with one that only measures 10 cm³ steps, it wouldn't be sensitive enough.

***Figure 1:** Different types of measuring cylinder and glassware — make sure you choose the right one before you start an experiment.*

The smallest change a measuring instrument can detect is called its **resolution**. For example, some mass balances have a resolution of 1 g, some have a resolution of 0.1 g, and some are even more sensitive.

Also, equipment needs to be **calibrated** by measuring a known value. If there's a difference between the measured and known value, you can use this to correct the inaccuracy of the equipment.

| Example |

If a known mass is put on a mass balance, but the reading is a different value, you know that the mass balance has not been calibrated properly.

Tip: Calibration is a way of making sure that a measuring device is measuring things accurately — you get it to measure something you know has a certain value and set the device to say that amount.

Errors

Random errors

The results of an experiment will always vary a bit due to **random errors** — unpredictable differences caused by things like human errors in measuring.

| Example |

Errors made when reading from a measuring cylinder are random. You have to estimate or round the level when it's between two marks — so sometimes your figure will be a bit above the real one, and sometimes a bit below.

You can reduce the effect of random errors by taking repeat readings and finding the mean. This will give you a more precise result.

Tip: Repeating the experiment in the exact same way and calculating a mean won't correct a systematic error.

Systematic errors

If a measurement is wrong by the same amount every time, it's called a **systematic error**.

| Example |

If you measured from the very end of your ruler instead of from the 0 cm mark every time, all your measurements would be a bit small.

Just to make things more complicated, if a systematic error is caused by using equipment that isn't zeroed properly it's called a **zero error**. You can compensate for some of these errors if you know about them though.

Tip: If there's no systematic error, then doing repeats and calculating a mean can make your results more accurate.

| Example |

If a mass balance always reads 1 gram before you put anything on it, all your measurements will be 1 gram too heavy. This is a zero error. You can compensate for this by subtracting 1 gram from all your results.

Figure 2: *A mass balance that has been set to zero.*

Anomalous results

Sometimes you get a result that doesn't seem to fit in with the rest at all. These results are called **anomalous results** (or outliers).

Tip: A zero error is a specific type of systematic error.

| Example |

The entry in the table that's circled is an anomalous result because it's much larger than any of the other data values.

Experiment	A	B	C	D	E	F
Rate of reaction (cm³/s)	10.5	11.2	10.8	85.4	10.6	11.1

You should investigate anomalous results and try to work out what happened. If you can work out what happened (e.g. you measured something totally wrong) you can ignore them when processing your results.

Tip: There are lots of reasons why you might get an anomalous result, but usually they're due to human error rather than anything crazy happening in the experiment.

7. Processing Data

Once you've collected some data, you might need to process it.

Organising data

It's really important that your data is organised. Tables are dead useful for organising data. When you draw a table, use a ruler, make sure each column has a heading (including the units) and keep it neat and tidy.

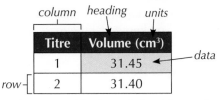

Figure 1: *Table showing the volume of acid needed to neutralise an alkali.*

Tip: If you're recording your data as decimals, make sure you give each value to the same number of decimal places.

Processing your data

When you've collected data from a number of repeats of an experiment, it's useful to summarise it using a few handy-to-use figures.

Mean and range

When you've done repeats of an experiment, you should always calculate the **mean** (a type of average). To do, this add together all the data values and divide by the total number of values in the sample.

You might also need to calculate the **range** (how spread out the data is). To do this, find the largest number and subtract the smallest number from it.

Tip: You should ignore anomalous results when calculating the mean, range, median or mode — see page 13 for more on anomalous results.

Example

Look at the data in the table below. The mean and range of the data for each test tube has been calculated.

Test tube	Repeat (g)			Mean (g)	Range (g)
	1	**2**	**3**		
A	28	37	31	(28 + 37 + 31) ÷ 3 = 32	37 − 28 = 9
B	47	51	61	(47 + 51 + 61) ÷ 3 = 53	61 − 47 = 14

Median and mode

There are two more types of average, other than the mean, that you might need to calculate. These are the **median** and the **mode**.

- To calculate the median, put all your data in numerical order — the median is the middle value.

- The number that appears most often in a data set is the mode.

Tip: If you have an even number of values, the median is halfway between the middle two values.

Example

The results of a study investigating the pH of water from different places along a river are shown below:

8, 6, 5, 4, 6, 7, 7, 5, 7

First put the data in numerical order: 4, 5, 5, 6, 6, 7, 7, 7, 8

There are 9 values, so the median is the 5th number, which is **6**.

7 comes up 3 times. None of the other numbers come up more than twice. So the mode is **7**.

Uncertainty

When you repeat a measurement, you often get a slightly different figure each time you do it due to random error. This means that each result has some **uncertainty** to it. The measurements you make will also have some uncertainty in them due to limits in the resolution of the equipment you use. This all means that the mean of a set of results will also have some uncertainty to it. Here's how to calculate the uncertainty of a mean result:

$$\text{uncertainty} = \frac{\text{range}}{2}$$

The larger the range, the less precise your results are and the more uncertainty there will be in your results. Uncertainties are shown using the '±' symbol.

Tip: Since uncertainty affects precision, you'll need to think about it when you come to evaluating your results (see page 21).

> **Example**
>
> The table below shows the results of an experiment to determine the volume of carbon dioxide produced by a reaction.
>
> | Repeat | 1 | 2 | 3 | mean |
> |---|---|---|---|---|
> | Volume of CO_2 produced (cm^3) | 20.10 | 19.80 | 20.00 | 19.97 |
>
> 1. The range is: $20.10 - 19.80 = 0.30 \ cm^3$
> 2. So the uncertainty of the mean is: range ÷ 2 = 0.30 ÷ 2 = $0.15 \ cm^3$. You'd write this as **19.97 ± 0.15 cm^3**

Measuring a greater amount of something helps to reduce uncertainty. For example, in a rate of reaction experiment, measuring the amount of product formed over a longer period compared to a shorter period will reduce the percentage uncertainty in your results.

Rounding to significant figures

The first **significant figure** (s.f.) of a number is the first digit that isn't a zero. The second, third and fourth significant figures follow on straight after the first (even if they're zeros). When you're processing your data you may well want to round any really long numbers to a certain number of significant figures.

Exam Tip
If a question asks you to give your answer to a certain number of significant figures, make sure you do this, or you might not get all the marks.

> **Example**
>
> 0.6874976 rounds to **0.69** to **2 s.f.** and to **0.687** to **3 s.f.**

When you're doing calculations using measurements given to a certain number of significant figures, you should try to give your answer to the lowest number of significant figures that was used in the calculation. If your calculation has multiple steps, only round the final answer, or it won't be as accurate.

> **Example**
>
> For the calculation: $1.2 \div 1.85 = 0.648648648...$
>
> 1.2 is given to 2 significant figures. 1.85 is given to 3 significant figures. So the answer should be given to 2 significant figures.
>
> Round the final significant figure (0.6<u>4</u>8) up to 5: $1.2 \div 1.85 = $ **0.65 (2 s.f.)**

Tip: When rounding a number, if the next digit after the last significant figure you're using is less than 5 you should round it <u>down</u>, and if it's 5 or more you should round it <u>up</u>.

The lowest number of significant figures in the calculation is used because the fewer digits a measurement has, the less accurate it is. Your answer can only be as accurate as the least accurate measurement in the calculation.

8. Graphs and Charts

It can often be easier to see trends in data by plotting a graph or chart of your results, rather than by looking at numbers in a table.

Plotting your data on a graph or chart

One of the best ways to present your data after you've processed it is to plot your results on a graph or chart. The type of graph or chart you use depends on the type of data you've collected.

Bar charts and histograms

If either the independent or dependent variable is **categoric** or **discrete**, you should use a bar chart to display the data (see Figure 1). If the independent variable is **continuous**, the frequency data should be shown on a histogram. Histograms may look like bar charts, but it's the area of the bars that represents the frequency (rather than height). The height of each bar is called the **frequency density** and is found by dividing the frequency by the class width. (The class width is just the width of the bar on the histogram, see Figure 1.)

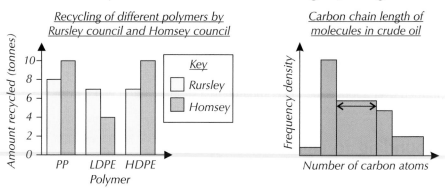

Figure 1: *An example of a bar chart (left) and a histogram (right).*

Graphs

If the independent and the dependent variables are **continuous** you should use a graph to display the data. Here are the golden rules for drawing graphs:

- Draw it nice and big (covering at least half of the graph paper).

- Put the independent variable (the thing you change) on the x-axis (the horizontal one).

- Put the dependent variable (the thing you measure) on the y-axis (the vertical one).

- Label both axes and remember to include the units.

- To plot the points, use a sharp pencil and make a neat little cross.

- In general, you shouldn't join the dots up. You need to draw a line of best fit (or a curve of best fit if your points make a curve). When drawing a line (or curve), try to draw the line through or as near to as many points as possible, ignoring anomalous results.

- If you've got more than one set of data, include a key.

- Give your graph a title explaining what it is showing.

Tip: Categoric data is data that comes in distinct categories, such as 'type of material (e.g. wood, metal, paper) and 'state of matter' (e.g. solid, liquid, gas)'. Discrete data can only take certain values, because there are no in-between values, e.g. 'number of people' (because you can't have half a person). Continuous data is numerical data that can have any value within a range, e.g. length, volume, temperature.

Tip: Frequency is just the number of times that something occurs. It's often shown in a frequency table.

Tip: A frequency diagram is a histogram where the width of all the bars are the same and frequency is plotted on the y-axis, rather than frequency density.

Tip: If you're not in an exam, you can use a computer to plot your line graph and draw your line of best fit for you.

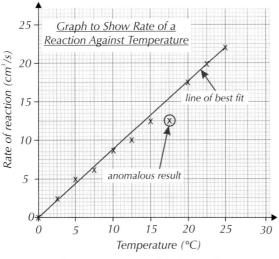

Tip: Use the biggest data values you've got to draw a sensible scale on your axes. Here, the highest rate of reaction is 22 cm³/s, so it makes sense to label the y-axis up to 25 cm³/s.

Figure 2: *An example of a graph.*

Correlations

Graphs are used to show the relationship between two variables.
Data can show three different types of **correlation** (relationship):

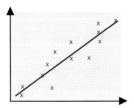

Positive correlation
As one variable increases the other increases.

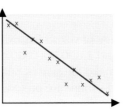

Negative correlation
As one variable increases the other decreases.

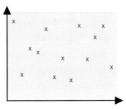

No correlation
There's no relationship between the two variables.

Tip: Just because two variables are correlated doesn't mean that the change in one is causing the change in the other. There might be other factors involved — see pages 20-21 for more.

9. Units

Using the correct units is important when you're drawing graphs or calculating values with an equation. Otherwise your numbers don't really mean anything.

S.I. units

Lots of different units can be used to describe the same quantity. For example, volume can given in terms of cubic feet, cubic metres or pints. It would be confusing if different scientists used different units to define quantities, as it would be hard to compare people's data. To stop this happening, scientists have come up with a set of standard units, called **S.I. units**, that all scientists use to measure their data. Here are some S.I. units you'll see in chemistry:

Tip: S.I. stands for 'Système International', which is French for 'international system'.

Quantity	S.I. Base Unit
mass	kilogram, kg
length	metre, m
time	second, s
amount of substance	mole, mol

Figure 1: *Some common S.I. units used in chemistry.*

Scaling prefixes

Quantities come in a huge range of sizes. For example, the volume of a swimming pool might be around 2 000 000 000 cm³, while the volume of a cup is around 250 cm³. To make the size of numbers more manageable, larger or smaller units are used. There are prefixes that can be used in front of units to make them bigger or smaller:

prefix	tera (T)	giga (G)	mega (M)	kilo (k)	deci (d)	centi (c)	milli (m)	micro (µ)	nano (n)
multiple of unit	10^{12}	10^9	1 000 000 (10^6)	1000	0.1	0.01	0.001	0.000001 (10^{-6})	10^{-9}

Figure 2: *Scaling prefixes used with units.*

These prefixes are called **scaling prefixes** and they tell you how much bigger or smaller a unit is than the base unit. So one kilometre is one thousand metres.

Converting between units

Exam Tip
If you're going from a smaller unit to a larger unit, your number should get smaller.
If you're going from a larger unit to a smaller unit, your number should get larger.
This is a handy way to check you've done the conversion correctly.

To swap from one unit to another, all you need to know is what number you have to divide or multiply by to get from the original unit to the new unit — this is called the **conversion factor** and is equal to the number of times the smaller unit goes into the larger unit.

- To go from a bigger unit to a smaller unit, you multiply by the conversion factor.

- To go from a smaller unit to a bigger unit, you divide by the conversion factor.

There are some conversions that'll be particularly useful for your chemistry exams. Here they are...

Mass can have units of kg and g.

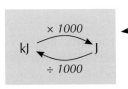

Energy can have units of J and kJ.

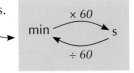

Time can have units of min and s.

Volume can have units of m³, dm³ and cm³.

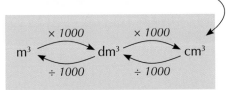

Concentration can have units of g/dm³ and g/cm³.

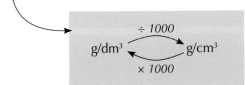

Exam Tip
Before you put values into an equation, you need to make sure they have the right units.

Exam Tip
Being familiar with these common conversions could save you time when it comes to doing calculations in the exam.

Examples

- To go from dm³ to cm³, you'd multiply by 1000.

    2 dm³ is equal to 2 × 1000 = **2000 cm³**

- To go from grams to kilograms, you'd divide by 1000.

    3400 g is equal to 3400 ÷ 1000 = **3.4 kg**

(MATHS SKILLS)

10. Conclusions and Evaluations

So... you've planned an amazing experiment, you've done the experiment, collected some data and have processed and presented your data in a sensible way. Now it's time to figure out what your data actually tells you.

How to draw conclusions

Drawing conclusions might seem pretty straightforward — you just look at your data and say what pattern or relationship you see between the dependent and independent variables.

But you've got to be really careful that your conclusion matches the data you've got and doesn't go any further. You also need to be able to use your results to justify your conclusion (i.e. back up your conclusion with some specific data).

When writing a conclusion, you need to refer back to the original hypothesis and say whether the data supports it or not.

Example

A scientist carried out an experiment to determine which of two catalysts increased the rate of a reaction more. The scientist hypothesised that catalyst B would make the reaction go faster than catalyst A. The results of the experiment are shown in the table.

Catalyst	Rate of reaction (cm^3/s)
A	13.5
B	19.5
No catalyst	5.5

The conclusion of this experiment would be that catalyst B makes this reaction go faster than catalyst A, so the data supports the hypothesis.

The justification for this conclusion is that the rate of this reaction was 6 cm^3/s faster using catalyst B compared with catalyst A.

You can't conclude that catalyst B increases the rate of any other reaction more than catalyst A — the results might be completely different.

Correlation and causation

If two things are correlated (i.e. there's a relationship between them) it doesn't necessarily mean that a change in one variable is causing the change in the other — this is really important, don't forget it. There are three possible reasons for a correlation:

1. Chance

Even though it might seem a bit weird, it's possible that two things show a correlation in a study purely because of chance.

Example

One study might find a correlation between the number of people with breathing problems and the distance they live from a cement factory. But other scientists don't get a correlation when they investigate it — the results of the first study are just a fluke.

Tip: Graphs are useful for seeing whether two variables are correlated (see page 17).

Tip: Causation just means one thing is causing another.

2. They're linked by a third variable

A lot of the time it may look as if a change in one variable is causing a change in the other, but it isn't — a third variable links the two things.

Example

There's a correlation between water temperature and shark attacks. This isn't because warm water makes sharks crazy. Instead, they're linked by a third variable — the number of people swimming (more people swim when the water's hotter, and with more people in the water shark attacks increase).

3. Causation

Sometimes a change in one variable does cause a change in the other.

Example

There's a correlation between smoking and lung cancer.
This is because chemicals in tobacco smoke cause lung cancer.

You can only conclude that a correlation is due to cause if you've controlled all the variables that could be affecting the result. (For the smoking example, this would include age and exposure to other things that cause cancer.)

Evaluation

This is the final part of an investigation. Here you need to evaluate (assess) the following things about your experiment and the data you gathered.

- **The method**: Was it valid? Did you control all the other variables to make it a fair test?

- **The quality of your results:** Was there enough evidence to reach a valid conclusion? Were the results repeatable, reproducible, accurate and precise?

- **Anomalous results**: Were any of the results anomalous? If there were none then say so. If there were any, try to explain them — were they caused by errors in measurement? Were there any other variables that could have affected the results? You should comment on the level of uncertainty in your results too..

Once you've thought about these points you can decide how much confidence you have in your conclusion. For example, if your results are repeatable, reproducible and valid and they back up your conclusion then you can have a high degree of confidence in your conclusion.

You can also suggest any changes to the method that would improve the quality of the results, so that you could have more confidence in your conclusion. For example, you might suggest changing the way you controlled a variable, or increasing the number of measurements you took. Taking more measurements at narrower intervals could give you a more accurate result.

You could also make more predictions based on your conclusion, then further experiments could be carried out to test them.

Tip: Lots of things are correlated without being directly related. E.g. the level of carbon dioxide (CO_2) in the atmosphere and the amount of obesity have both increased over the last 100 years, but that doesn't mean increased atmospheric CO_2 is causing people to become obese.

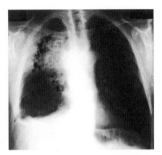

Figure 1: *A coloured chest X-ray of a smoker who has lung cancer.*

Tip: When suggesting improvements to the investigation, always make sure that you say why you think this would make the results better.

Learning Objectives:

- Know that everything is made up of atoms.
- Be able to compare the scale of atoms with other objects.
- Be able to describe the structure of an atom.
- Know that atoms are tiny, with a radius of 0.1 nm.
- Know the nucleus has a radius 10 000 times smaller than an atom.
- Know the relative charges and masses of protons, neutrons and electrons.
- Know that atoms have the same number of protons as electrons, so they have no overall charge.

Specification References
5.1.1.1, 5.1.1.4, 5.1.1.5

1. Atoms

Atoms are the basis of all of chemistry. So you really need to know what they are. Luckily, these pages are here to help out with that...

The structure of the atom

Atoms are the tiny particles that everything is made up of — they have a radius of about 0.1 nanometer (that's 1×10^{-10} metres). Atoms are so tiny that a 50p piece contains about 77 400 000 000 000 000 000 000 of them. There are quite a few different (and equally useful) models of the atom — but chemists tend to like the nuclear model best. The nuclear model shows atoms as having a small **nucleus** surrounded by **electrons** (see Figure 1).

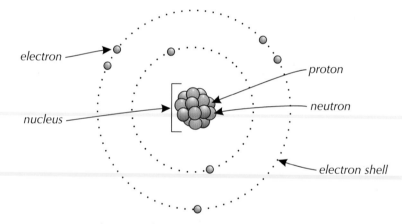

Figure 1: *The nuclear model of the atom.*

The nucleus and electrons

The nucleus is in the middle of the atom. It contains **protons** and **neutrons**. Protons are positively charged. Neutrons have no charge (they're neutral). So the nucleus has a positive charge overall because of the protons. But size-wise it's tiny compared to the rest of the atom — the radius is 1×10^{-14} m, that's about 1/10 000 of the size of an atom.

The electrons move around the nucleus. They're negatively charged. They're tiny, but they cover a lot of space. They occupy **shells** around the nucleus. Electrons don't have much mass at all compared to protons and neutrons, so nearly all of the mass of an atom is located in the nucleus. Figure 2 shows the relative electrical charges and relative masses of protons, neutrons and electrons.

Particle	Proton	Neutron	Electron
Relative charge	+1	0	−1
Relative mass	1	1	Very small

Figure 2: *The relative charges and masses of protons, neutrons and electrons.*

Tip: A nanometer (nm) is one billionth of a metre. Shown in standard form, that's 1×10^{-9} m. Standard form is used for showing really <u>large</u> or really <u>small</u> numbers. There's more on standard form in the maths skills section.

Tip: A <u>shell</u> is just an area where electrons are found. At GCSE you'll usually see them drawn as circles around the nucleus. Shells are sometimes called <u>energy levels</u>.

Electrical charge

The number of protons always equals the number of electrons in an atom. The charge on the electrons (–1) is the same size as the charge on the protons (+1) — but opposite. This means atoms have no charge overall — they are neutral.

Tip: Don't worry about the way the electrons are arranged in the shells for now. You do need to know this stuff but it's all covered for you on pages 44-45.

Tip: Protons, neutrons and electrons are all types of <u>subatomic particle</u>.

Tip: An ion is an atom or group of atoms that has <u>lost</u> or <u>gained</u> electrons.

Example

This atom has 7 protons and 7 electrons. Each proton has a charge of +1, so the total charge of the nucleus is +7. (neutrons have no charge, remember).

As there are 7 electrons and each electron has a charge of –1, the charge of the nucleus is cancelled out. The atom doesn't have a charge overall.

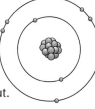

If some electrons are added or removed, the atom becomes charged and is then an **ion**. For example, an ion with a 2– charge has two more electrons than protons (see pages 70-71 for more on ions).

Practice Questions — Fact Recall

Q1 Describe the structure of an atom. Use the terms 'proton', 'neutron', 'electron', 'nucleus' and 'shell' in your answer.

Q2 What is the relative size of the nucleus compared to the atom?

Q3 What is the relative charge of...

a) a proton?

b) a neutron?

c) an electron?

Q4 What is the relative mass of a proton?

Q5 Atoms are uncharged particles. Explain why.

Practice Questions — Application

Q1 An atom of fluorine has 9 protons in its nucleus. How many electrons does the atom have?

Q2 An atom of silver contains 47 protons. How many electrons does an atom of silver contain?

Q3 An atom of selenium contains 34 electrons. How many protons does an atom of selenium contain?

Learning Objectives:
- Know that an element is made up of only one type of atom.
- Know that the atom is the smallest part of an element that can exist.
- Know that all atoms of an element have the same number of protons, and atoms of different elements have different numbers of protons.
- Recall that there are roughly 100 known elements.
- Know that elements can be represented by symbols.
- Understand nuclear symbols and know what atomic number and mass number represent.
- Know how to work out the number of protons, neutrons and electrons in an atom of an element.

Specification References
5.1.1.1, 5.1.1.4, 5.1.1.5

You may have heard of elements before, but as they're so important to chemistry, you're going to learn a whole lot more about them.

Elements

Atoms can have different numbers of protons, neutrons and electrons. It's the number of protons in the nucleus that decides what type of atom it is.

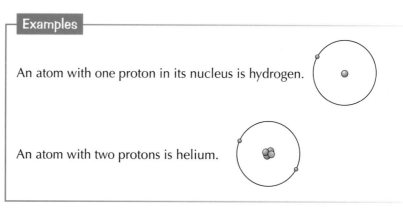

Examples

An atom with one proton in its nucleus is hydrogen.

An atom with two protons is helium.

If a substance only contains one type of atom it's called an **element**. The smallest part of an element is an atom.

Example

Lithium is an element. It's made up of lithium atoms only. Each lithium atom contains three protons.

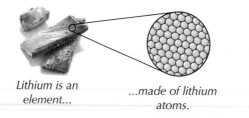

Lithium is an element...

...made of lithium atoms.

Each lithium atom has the same number of protons.

Atoms of each element can be represented by a one or two letter symbol — it's a type of shorthand that saves you the bother of having to write the full name of the element.

Examples

Some nuclear symbols make sense: B = boron, C = carbon and N = nitrogen. However, others are less obvious: Na = sodium, Fe = iron and Pb = lead.

There are about 100 different elements — quite a lot of everyday substances are elements. For example, copper, iron, aluminium, oxygen and nitrogen are all elements. The important things to remember are...

- All the atoms of a particular element (e.g. nitrogen) have the same number of protons.

- Different elements have atoms with different numbers of protons.

Tip: Atoms of an element will also have the same number of electrons as each other, but it's the number of <u>protons</u> that's important — that's what determines what the element is.

Nuclear symbols

A nuclear symbol of an atom is the chemical symbol for the element with two numbers by it. The smaller (bottom) number is the **atomic number**. This is the number of protons, which conveniently also tells you the number of electrons. The larger (top) number is the **mass number**. This is the total number of protons and neutrons.

Tip: All the known elements are shown in the periodic table (see the inside of the back cover for a periodic table).

Example

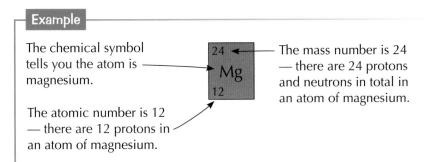

The chemical symbol tells you the atom is magnesium.

The mass number is 24 — there are 24 protons and neutrons in total in an atom of magnesium.

The atomic number is 12 — there are 12 protons in an atom of magnesium.

Tip: The atomic number is sometimes called the <u>proton number</u>.

You can use the mass number and atomic number to work out the number of neutrons in an atom of an element. All you have to do is subtract the atomic number from the mass number.

Example

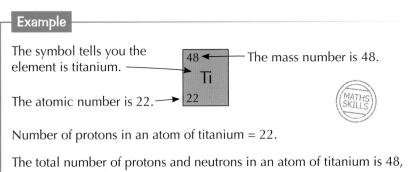

The symbol tells you the element is titanium.

The mass number is 48.

The atomic number is 22.

Number of protons in an atom of titanium = 22.

The total number of protons and neutrons in an atom of titanium is 48, so the number of neutrons = 48 − 22 = 26.

The number of electrons in an atom is equal to the number of protons, so the number of electrons in an atom of titanium is 22.

Exam Tip
You could be asked to calculate the number of protons, neutrons or electrons in an atom from its atomic number and mass number. So make sure you know how to do it.

Practice Questions — Fact Recall

Q1 What is an element?

Q2 a) What does the atomic number tell you about an atom?

b) What does the mass number tell you about an atom?

Q3 How would you find the number of neutrons in an atom from the mass number and the atomic number?

Q4 Is the following statement true or false?
All atoms of an element have the same number of protons.

Practice Questions — Application

Q1 An atom of copper (chemical symbol, Cu) has 29 protons and 34 neutrons. Give the nuclear symbol for this atom.

Q2 An atom of arsenic has a mass number of 75 and an atomic number of 33. How many neutrons does the atom contain?

Q3 Write down how many protons and neutrons each of the following atoms have:

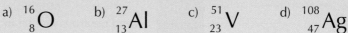

a) $^{16}_{8}O$ b) $^{27}_{13}Al$ c) $^{51}_{23}V$ d) $^{108}_{47}Ag$

3. Isotopes

Atoms of the same element always have the same number of protons, but the number of neutrons can change. And that's where isotopes come in.

What are isotopes?

Isotopes are different forms of the same element, which have the same number of protons but a different number of neutrons. This means they have the same atomic number but a different mass number.

Example

Carbon-12 and carbon-13 are a well known pair of isotopes. They each have 6 protons (and so an atomic number of 6). But carbon-12 has 6 neutrons (giving it a mass number of 12), while carbon-13 has 7 neutrons (giving it a mass number of 13).

$^{12}_{6}C$ 6 Protons
6 Electrons
6 Neutrons

$^{13}_{6}C$ 6 Protons
6 Electrons
7 Neutrons

Relative atomic mass

Many elements have more than one isotope. This means when referring to the masses of elements, **relative atomic mass** (A_r) is used. This is an average mass taking into account the different masses of isotopes that make up the element, and how abundant each isotope is (how much there is of it). This means it's not always a whole number.

You can use this formula to work out the relative atomic mass of an element:

$$\text{relative atomic mass } (A_r) = \frac{\text{sum of (isotope abundance} \times \text{isotope mass number)}}{\text{sum of abundances of all the isotopes}}$$

Example 1

Copper has two stable isotopes. Cu-63 has an abundance of 69.2% and Cu-65 has an abundance of 30.8%.

$$\text{Relative atomic mass} = \frac{\text{sum of (isotope abundance} \times \text{isotope mass number)}}{\text{sum of abundances of all the isotopes}}$$

$$= \frac{(69.2 \times 63) + (30.8 \times 65)}{69.2 + 30.8} = \frac{4359.6 + 2002}{100}$$

$$= \frac{6361.6}{100} = 63.616 = \textbf{63.6}$$

Learning Objectives:

- Know that isotopes of an element have the same number of protons but different numbers of neutrons.
- Be able to describe the relative atomic mass of an element as the average mass of its isotopes, taking their relative abundances into account.
- Be able to use the percentage abundances of isotopes to calculate the relative atomic mass of an element.

Specification References
5.1.1.5, 5.1.1.6

Exam Tip
Examiners love to ask you about isotopes, so make sure you know what isotopes are and how to spot them.

Tip: The mass numbers of elements that are given on the periodic table are actually relative atomic masses.

Tip: If you're given the abundances as percentages, the sum of the abundances should always be 100.

Example 2

Magnesium has three stable isotopes, as shown in the table below.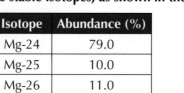

Isotope	Abundance (%)
Mg-24	79.0
Mg-25	10.0
Mg-26	11.0

Tip: You might see the isotopes of an element represented by the chemical symbol followed by the mass number (e.g. Mg-24), or by the chemical symbol with the mass number as a superscript before it (e.g. ^{24}Mg). Don't worry — both versions mean the same thing.

$$\text{Relative atomic mass} = \frac{\text{sum of (isotope abundance} \times \text{isotope mass number)}}{\text{sum of abundances of all the isotopes}}$$

$$= \frac{(79.0 \times 24) + (10.0 \times 25) + (11.0 \times 26)}{79.0 + 10.0 + 11.0}$$

$$= \frac{1896 + 250 + 286}{100} = \frac{2432}{100} = 24.32 = \mathbf{24.3}$$

Practice Questions — Fact Recall

Q1 What are isotopes?

Q2 What is relative atomic mass?

Practice Questions — Application

Q1 Which of these is the chemical symbol of an isotope of $^{35}_{17}$Cl?

A: $^{37}_{17}$Cl   B: $^{35}_{16}$Cl   C: $^{36}_{16}$Cl   D: $^{17}_{35}$Cl

Q2 The relative atomic mass of copper is 63.5.
Explain why this value is not a whole number.

Q3 92.5% of lithium atoms are Li-7 and the remaining 7.5% are Li-6.
Calculate the relative atomic mass of lithium to 1 decimal place.

Q4 Boron has two stable isotopes — ^{10}B and ^{11}B. ^{10}B has an abundance of 19.9%. Calculate the relative atomic mass of boron to 1 decimal place.

4. Compounds

*Elements are substances that are made up of just one type of atom.
If a substance is made up of more than one type of atom then it might be a
compound — and that's what these pages are about.*

What are compounds?

When elements react, atoms combine with other atoms to form **compounds**.
Compounds are substances formed from two or more elements. The atoms of
the elements are in fixed proportions throughout the compound, and they're
held together by **chemical bonds**. Making bonds involves atoms giving away,
taking or sharing electrons. If the different atoms aren't bonded together then
it's not a compound — it's a mixture (see Figure 1).

An element.

A compound.

A mixture.

Figure 1: *Diagrams to represent the atoms in
an element, a compound and a mixture.*

How do compounds form?

Metals and non-metals react to from compounds made of **ions**. The metal
atoms lose electrons to form positive ions and the non-metal atoms gain
electrons to form negative ions. The opposite charges (positive and negative)
of the ions mean that they're strongly attracted to each other. This is called
ionic bonding (there's more on this on page 72). Examples of compounds
which are bonded ionically include sodium chloride, magnesium oxide and
calcium oxide.

A compound formed from non-metals usually consists of **molecules**.
Atoms share electrons with other atoms — this is called **covalent bonding**
(there's more on page 78). Examples of compounds that are bonded
covalently include hydrogen chloride, carbon monoxide, and water.

Formulas

Just as elements can be represented by symbols, compounds can be
represented by formulas. The formulas are made up of elemental symbols in
the same proportions that the elements can be found in the compound.

Examples

Carbon dioxide is a compound formed from a chemical
reaction between carbon and oxygen. It contains one carbon
atom and two oxygen atoms, so the formula is CO_2.

The formula of sulfuric acid is H_2SO_4. So, each molecule contains two
hydrogen atoms, one sulfur atom and four oxygen atoms.

There might be brackets in a formula. For example, calcium
hydroxide is $Ca(OH)_2$. The little number outside the brackets
applies to everything inside the brackets. So in $Ca(OH)_2$ there is one
calcium atom, two oxygen atoms and two hydrogen atoms.

Learning Objectives:
- Know that elements can react to form compounds.
- Know that compounds contain two or more elements in fixed proportions held together by chemical bonds.
- Understand that compounds can be shown by formulas, which use the symbols of the elements that they were formed from.
- Know that to separate compounds back into elements a chemical reaction must take place.

**Specification Reference
5.1.1.1**

Tip: You can work out whether an element is a metal or a non-metal by its position in the periodic table (see page 54 for more on how to work out if an element is a metal or a non-metal).

Tip: 'Formulas' is just the plural of 'formula'. You may sometimes see it written as 'formulae'.

Properties of compounds

The properties of a compound are totally different from the properties of the original elements.

> **Example**
>
> If iron (a lustrous magnetic metal) and sulfur (a nice yellow powder) react, the compound formed (iron sulfide) is a dull grey solid lump, and doesn't behave anything like either iron or sulfur.
>
>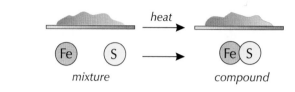
>
> mixture   compound

Compounds can be small molecules or great big structures called lattices (when I say big I'm talking in atomic terms).

> **Example**
>
>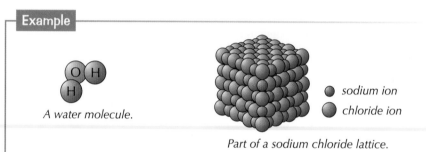
>
> A water molecule.
>
> sodium ion
> chloride ion
>
> Part of a sodium chloride lattice.

Once a compound has been formed the elements can't be separated by physical processes. The only way to reform the elements is by more chemical reactions.

Figure 2: *Iron sulfide (bottom) is a compound of iron and sulfur (top).*

Tip: A physical process is one that <u>doesn't</u> involve a chemical reaction.

Practice Questions — Fact Recall

Q1   What are compounds?

Q2   Do metal atoms form positive ions or negative ions when they form a compound?

Q3   What type of bonding holds the atoms in a molecule together?

Practice Questions — Application

Q1   The formula of carbon monoxide is CO.
What elements are in a molecule of carbon monoxide?

Q2   The formula of nitric acid is HNO_3.
How many atoms are in one molecule of nitric acid?

Q3   Look at diagrams A, B, C and D. Which one shows a compound?

A   B   C   D

5. Chemical Equations

Equations crop up again and again in chemistry. You need to know what they show and how to write them.

Chemical reactions

During a chemical reaction, bonds between atoms break and the atoms change places — the atoms from the substances you start off with (the reactants) rearrange themselves to form different chemicals. These new chemicals are called the products. You can show what happens in a chemical reaction using equations.

Word equations

Word equations show what happens in a chemical reaction using the full names of the substances involved. They show the **reactants** (the substances that react together) and the **products** (the substances that are made in a reaction).

> **Examples**
>
> Magnesium and oxygen react to form magnesium oxide. This can be represented by a word equation:
>
> magnesium + oxygen → magnesium oxide
>
> Magnesium and oxygen are the reactants in this reaction. Magnesium oxide is the product.
>
> Sodium and chlorine can react to form sodium chloride. The word equation for this reaction is below:
>
> sodium + chlorine → sodium chloride
>
> Sodium and chlorine are the reactants in this reaction. Sodium chloride is the product.

Symbol equations

Symbol equations show exactly the same as the word equation but using chemical symbols and formulas. However, when balanced correctly they also show the ratio of the amounts of substances involved in the reaction.

> **Examples**
>
> The balanced symbol equation for the reaction of magnesium (Mg) and oxygen (O_2) to form magnesium oxide (MgO) is:
>
> $$2Mg + O_2 \rightarrow 2MgO$$
>
> The balanced symbol equation for the reaction of sodium (Na) and chlorine (Cl_2) to form sodium chloride (NaCl) is:
>
> $$2Na + Cl_2 \rightarrow 2NaCl$$
>
> The '2's in front of Na, Mg, MgO and NaCl are there to balance the equations — there's more on this coming up.

Learning Objectives:
- Know that, when chemicals react, new substances are made.
- Know that word equations and symbol equations can be used to represent reactions.
- Understand and be able to write word equations.
- Understand and be able to write balanced symbol equations.

Specification Reference 5.1.1.1

Tip: When a chemical reaction takes place, you can usually measure a change in energy, such as a temperature change.

Tip: The reactants are on the <u>left-hand side</u> of an equation and the products are on the <u>right-hand side</u>.

Tip: Equations must be balanced because mass doesn't disappear during a reaction — there are always the same atoms present at the end of a reaction as there are at the start. This is known as the <u>law of conservation of mass</u> (there's more on this on page 108).

Balancing equations

There must always be the same number of atoms of each element on both sides of an equation — they can't just disappear. If there aren't the same number on each side then the equation isn't balanced.

Example

Sulfuric acid (H_2SO_4) reacts with sodium hydroxide (NaOH) to give sodium sulfate (Na_2SO_4) and water (H_2O). To write the symbol equation start by writing out the formulas in an equation:

$$H_2SO_4 \ + \ NaOH \ \rightarrow \ Na_2SO_4 \ + \ H_2O$$

The formulas are all correct but the numbers of some atoms don't match up on both sides (e.g. there are three Hs on the left, but only two on the right). So the equation isn't balanced.

Method for balancing equations

You balance the equation by putting numbers in front of the formulas where needed. All you do is this:

Exam Tip
If you're asked to write a symbol equation you <u>always</u> have to make sure it's balanced. If it's not balanced it's not a correct equation.

1. Find an element that doesn't balance and pencil in a number to try and sort it out.

2. See where it gets you. It may create another imbalance — if so, just pencil in another number and see where that gets you.

3. Carry on chasing unbalanced elements and it'll sort itself out pretty quickly.

Example 1

In this equation we're short of H atoms on the right-hand side — there are three H atoms on the left and only two on the right.

$$H_2SO_4 \ + \ NaOH \ \rightarrow \ Na_2SO_4 \ + \ H_2O$$

The only thing you can do about it is add more H_2O — let's try $2H_2O$.

$$H_2SO_4 \ + \ NaOH \ \rightarrow \ Na_2SO_4 \ + \ 2H_2O$$

Tip: You <u>can't</u> change the small numbers inside formulas (like changing H_2O to H_3O). You can only put numbers in front of formulas (like changing H_2O to $3H_2O$).

But now you have too many H atoms and O atoms on the right-hand side, so to balance that up you could try putting 2NaOH on the left-hand side.

$$H_2SO_4 \ + \ 2NaOH \ \rightarrow \ Na_2SO_4 \ + \ 2H_2O$$

And suddenly there it is! Everything balances. There are four H, one S, six O and two Na on each side of the equation.

Example 2

In this equation we're short of Cl atoms on the left-hand side.

$$Al + Cl_2 \rightarrow AlCl_3$$

Try making it $3Cl_2$ instead of just Cl_2.

$$Al + 3Cl_2 \rightarrow AlCl_3$$

That causes too many Cl atoms on the left-hand side, so balance up the Cls by putting 2 before the $AlCl_3$.

$$Al + 3Cl_2 \rightarrow 2AlCl_3$$

Now you can balance the Al atoms by adding a 2 in front of the Al.

$$2Al + 3Cl_2 \rightarrow 2AlCl_3$$

Everything is now balanced. There are two Al atoms on each side and six Cl atoms on each side.

Tip: If you made it '$2Cl_2$', you'd have four Cl on the left-hand side. There isn't a whole number that you could put in front of $AlCl_3$ to also give you four Cl on the right-hand side. So it's best to try $3Cl_2$.

Symbol equations show how many atoms of one element there are compared to the number of atoms of other elements. So it's fine to double, or triple, or quadruple the number of atoms in a balanced equation, as long as you do the same to every term in the equation.

Example

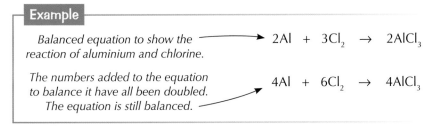

Balanced equation to show the reaction of aluminium and chlorine. → $2Al + 3Cl_2 \rightarrow 2AlCl_3$

The numbers added to the equation to balance it have all been doubled. The equation is still balanced. → $4Al + 6Cl_2 \rightarrow 4AlCl_3$

Tip: You don't <u>have</u> to use whole numbers to balance an equation. For example: $2Mg + O_2 \rightarrow 2MgO$ can also be shown as $Mg + \frac{1}{2}O_2 \rightarrow MgO$. However, it's usually easiest to use whole numbers.

Practice Questions — Application

Q1 Copper sulfate and iron react to form iron sulfate and copper.

a) What substances are the products in this reaction?

b) What substances are the reactants in this reaction?

c) Write a word equation for the reaction of copper sulfate and iron.

Q2 Sodium hydroxide reacts with hydrochloric acid to give sodium chloride and water. Write a word equation for this reaction.

Q3 Balance the following equations:

a) $Cl_2 + KBr \rightarrow Br_2 + KCl$

b) $HCl + Mg \rightarrow MgCl_2 + H_2$

c) $C_3H_8 + O_2 \rightarrow CO_2 + H_2O$

d) $Fe_2O_3 + CO \rightarrow Fe + CO_2$

Tip: The more you practise balancing equations, the quicker you'll get...

- Know that a mixture is made up of more than one element or compound that aren't chemically combined.

- Understand that adding a substance to a mixture doesn't alter the properties of the substance.

- Recognise that physical methods can be used to separate mixtures.

Specification Reference 5.1.1.2

6. Mixtures

The different substances in mixtures aren't bound together like the substances in compounds. So they can be separated by physical methods. Here's what you need to know...

What is a mixture?

A **mixture** is made up of separate substances which, unlike in a compound, aren't joined together with chemical bonds. The parts of a mixture can be either elements or compounds, and they can be easily separated out by physical methods.

> **Example**
>
> Air is a mixture of gases consisting mainly of nitrogen, oxygen, argon and carbon dioxide. These gases can be separated out fairly easily by physical methods.
>
>

Figure 1: *Iron filings (left) and silica (right) can be combined to form a mixture.*

The properties of mixtures

The properties of a mixture are just a mixture of the properties of the separate parts — the chemical properties of a substance aren't affected by it being part of a mixture.

> **Example**
>
> A mixture of iron powder and sulfur powder will show the properties of both iron and sulfur.
>
> It will contain grey, magnetic bits of iron and bright yellow bits of sulfur.
>
>

Separating mixtures

Because the components of mixtures aren't chemically combined they can be separated using physical methods. Physical methods of separation include **chromatography**, **filtration**, **crystallisation**, **simple distillation** and **fractional distillation**. All of these methods rely on the different physical properties of each component of a mixture to separate them.

Tip: There's more on chromatography, filtration, crystallisation, simple distillation and fractional distillation on pages 35-41.

Practice Questions — Fact Recall

Q1 What is a mixture?

Q2 Describe the properties of a mixture compared to the properties of its components.

Q3 List three physical methods that can be used to separate mixtures.

7. Paper Chromatography REQUIRED PRACTICAL 12

Paper chromatography is often used in labs to separate a mixture.

How to carry out paper chromatography

Chromatography can be used to separate mixtures made up of liquids of different colours. An example of this is the use of paper chromatography to separate different dyes in an ink. Here's how you can do it:

1. Draw a line near the bottom of a sheet of filter paper. (Use a pencil to do this — pencil marks are **insoluble** and won't dissolve in the solvent.)

2. Spot the ink by placing a small amount on the line in a single place. Then put the sheet upright in a beaker of **solvent**, e.g. water. The solvent used depends on what's being tested. Some compounds dissolve well in water, but sometimes other solvents, like ethanol, are needed. Make sure the ink isn't touching the solvent initially — you don't want it to be washed away.

3. Place a lid on top of the container to stop the solvent evaporating.

4. The solvent will seep up the paper, carrying the ink with it.

5. The different dyes in the ink will move up the paper at different rates, so the dyes will separate out and form spots in different places. If any of the dyes in the ink are insoluble (won't dissolve) in the solvent you've used, they'll stay on the baseline.

6. The point the solvent has reached as it moves up the paper is known as the **solvent front**. When the solvent front has nearly reached the top of the paper, take the paper out of the beaker, draw a line with a pencil along the solvent front and leave to dry.

7. The end result is a pattern of spots called a **chromatogram**.

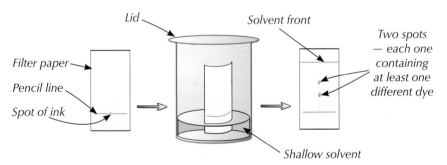

Figure 1: *A diagram showing the stages of carrying out paper chromatography.*

You can use chromatography to separate out more than one ink at a time. Figure 2 shows a chromatogram with four mixtures separated out. Follow the same steps as above, but instead of adding a spot of just one mixture to the pencil line, spot all the inks you want to separate in different places along the line. Make sure they're far enough apart that they won't run into each other.

Learning Objectives:

- Be able to describe how paper chromatography works.

- Be able to use paper chromatography to separate coloured substances (Required Practical 12).

Specification Reference 5.1.1.2

Tip: As part of Required Practical 12 you need to be able to <u>identify</u> substances using a chromatogram. This is covered in Topic 8.

Tip: 'Spot' or 'spotting' inks is just a technical term for placing a dot of the ink on the pencil line.

Figure 2: *A finished chromatogram, showing the different dyes in 4 different samples of ink.*

Tip: There's more on the theory behind chromatography on page 200.

Interpreting chromatograms

On some chromatograms, the number of spots you end up with tells you the number of different substances there were in the mixture. For example, if you end up with two spots, that might mean the ink contains two dyes.

This isn't always the case though — sometimes the number of visible spots on the chromatogram doesn't match the number of dyes in the ink. For example, two dyes could travel the same distance up the filter paper so would only show one spot.

So all we can say is there are at least as many substances in the mixture as there are spots on the chromatogram.

Tip: The reason two dyes may travel the same distance is to do with how they interact with the solvent and the paper. For more, turn to page 200.

Practice Questions — Fact Recall

Q1 During paper chromatography, why must you make sure the ink spot doesn't touch the solvent when you place the filter paper into the solvent?

Q2 Why do you place a lid on top of the container whilst carrying out paper chromatography?

Q3 What is the pattern of spots produced by paper chromatography known as?

Q4 How could you use paper chromatography to separate more than one ink at a time on a single piece of filter paper?

Practice Questions — Application

Q1 A student tries to carry out paper chromatography using water as a solvent on two different inks. Both inks are mixtures of dyes. One of the inks produces a number of spots going up the filter paper. The other ink does not produce any spots. Suggest why this is and what the student could do differently to separate both inks.

Q2 Paper chromatography was used to analyse the dyes in some food colouring. The result is shown on the right. How many dyes does this colouring contain? Explain your answer

A: Three or less.   B: Exactly three.   C: Three or more

8. More Separating Techniques

Learning Objectives:
- Be able to describe and explain how to carry out filtration.
- Be able to describe and explain how to carry out evaporation and crystallisation.
- Be able to suggest a suitable separation technique to separate a given mixture.

Specification Reference 5.1.1.2

Filtration and crystallisation are two more physical processes that are used to separate mixtures. They can be used to separate solids from liquids.

Separating an insoluble solid and a liquid

Filtration is often used if your desired product is an **insoluble** solid that needs to be separated from a liquid reaction mixture. It's also a useful technique for purification. For example, solid impurities in a reaction mixture can be removed using filtration. Here's how it's done:

1. Fold a piece of filter paper into a cone. You can do this by folding the paper in half and then in half again, and then gently separating one leaf of paper from the rest so that you've got a cone shape.

2. Place the filter paper point down into a filter funnel that's sitting in the neck of a container such as a conical flask — see Figure 2.

3. Pour the mixture containing the insoluble solid into the funnel lined by the filter paper. Make sure that none of the mixture goes over the top or down the side of the filter paper.

4. The liquid will pass through the filter paper but the solid won't — it will be left behind in the funnel.

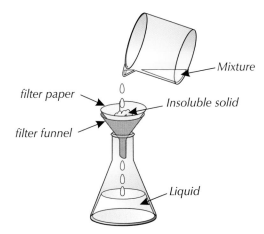

Figure 2: *Filtering out an insoluble solid from a mixture using filter paper and a filter funnel.*

Tip: An insoluble solid is one that can't be dissolved in the liquid.

Figure 1: *Filtering a copper sulfate ($CuSO_4$) solution to remove any undissolved copper sulfate crystals.*

Tip: The laboratory techniques, evaporation and crystallisation, are very similar. This often means the terms are used interchangeably.

Separating a soluble solid and a solution

If a solid can be dissolved it is said to be **soluble**. There are two methods commonly used to remove a soluble product from a solution — **evaporation** and **crystallisation**.

Tip: If the solvent is flammable you shouldn't use a Bunsen burner to heat it, as it may catch fire. You'd need to use a different heating method, such as using a hot plate. See pages 239-240 for more on different heating methods.

Tip: Whenever you carry out an experiment it is vital to take safety precautions such as wearing goggles, a lab coat and heating substances on a heatproof mat. You should also carry out a risk assessment before attempting to carry out any practical work.

Evaporation

Evaporation is a really quick way of separating a soluble salt from a solution, but you can only use it if the salt doesn't decompose (break down) when it's heated. Otherwise, you'll have to use crystallisation. All you have to do is:

1. Pour the solution into an evaporating dish.

2. Place the evaporating dish on top of a tripod and gauze and place a Bunsen burner underneath — see Figure 3.

3. Slowly heat the solution. The solvent will evaporate and the solution will get more concentrated. Eventually, the solid will start to form.

4. Keep heating the evaporating dish until all you have left is dry solid.

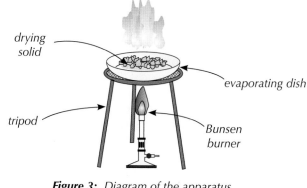

Figure 3: *Diagram of the apparatus required to carry out evaporation.*

Figure 4: *Hydrated copper sulfate crystals can be obtained from an aqueous copper sulfate solution using crystallisation.*

Tip: Make sure you use <u>tongs</u> to move very hot evaporating dishes.

Tip: The longer the solution is left to cool following heating, the larger the crystals will be.

Crystallisation

Crystallisation takes more time than evaporation, however it can produce nice crystals, that would decompose if heated. You can crystallise soluble solids using this method:

1. Place an evaporating dish on top of a tripod with a gauze mat. Place a Bunsen burner underneath the tripod.

2. Pour the solution into the evaporating dish and gently heat it. Some of the solvent will evaporate and the solution will get more concentrated.

3. Once some of the solvent has evaporated, or when you see crystals start to form (the point of crystallisation), remove the dish from the heat and leave the solution to cool.

4. The salt should start to form crystals as it becomes insoluble in the cold, highly concentrated solution.

5. Filter the crystals out of the solution, and leave them in a warm place to dry. You could also use a drying oven or a desiccator.

Figure 5: *Salt crystallising out of a solvent in an evaporating dish.*

Combining practical techniques

Chemists don't usually use one of these techniques in isolation, but will often use two or more in order to separate a mixture.

Exam Tip
You may be asked to suggest what technique could be used to separate a certain mixture, so you need to know which techniques separate what.

> **Example**
>
> Rock salt is mainly found as a mixture of salt and sand. Salt and sand are both compounds, but salt dissolves in water and sand doesn't. This vital difference in their physical properties means they can be easily separated.
>
> Here's how you do it:
>
> 1. Grind the mixture to make sure the salt crystals are small, so will dissolve easily.
>
> 2. Put the mixture in water and stir. The salt will dissolve, but the sand won't. Heating the mixture will help to dissolve the salt.
>
> 3. Filter the mixture. The grains of sand won't fit through the tiny holes in the filter paper, so they collect on the paper instead. The salt passes through the filter paper as it's part of the solution.
>
> 4. Evaporate the water from the salt so that it forms dry salt.

Tip: You can use crystallisation <u>instead</u> of evaporation to form salt crystals. This is useful if you want to form large crystals.

Practice Questions — Fact Recall

Q1 Give one technique that can be used to separate an insoluble solid from a liquid.

Q2 List the equipment you could use to carry out evaporation.

Q3 What is the final stage in crystallisation?

Practice Questions — Application

Q1 Silver bromide is insoluble in water. A student needs to separate a mixture containing water and silver bromide. Describe a method to remove the silver bromide from water.

Q2 Sodium nitrate is highly soluble in water but will decompose on excessive heating. Suggest a technique to remove the sodium nitrate from solution and give reasons why this technique would be suitable.

Q3 A student separated a mixture of lead bromide and sodium sulfate solution by filtration followed by crystallisation.
Lead bromide is insoluble in water whereas sodium sulfate is soluble. Which component of the mixture was separated out at:

a) filtration?

b) crystallisation?

- Understand when simple distillation can be used to separate mixtures.
- Be able to describe and explain simple distillation.
- Understand when fractional distillation can be used to separate mixtures.
- Be able to describe and explain fractional distillation.

Specification Reference 5.1.1.2

Tip: Make sure that the water goes in at the bottom of the condenser and out at the top so that the condenser fills fully.

Tip: You'll need to be able to carry out simple distillation for Required Practical 13. See Topic 10 for more on Required Practical 13.

9. Distillation

Distillation is used to separate mixtures that include a liquid. There are two kinds you need to know about — simple and fractional distillation.

Simple distillation

Simple distillation is used to separate out a liquid from a mixture. It's used in industry to get pure water from sea water (see p.227). This is the method used in the lab:

1. The equipment is set up as in Figure 1 and the mixture is heated. The component of the mixture that has the lowest boiling point evaporates.

2. As the vapour rises it passes into the condenser, where it is cooled, condenses (turns back into liquid) and is collected in a container below the condenser.

3. Components of the mixture with higher boiling points are left behind in the flask.

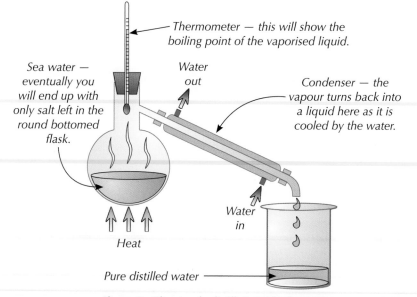

Thermometer — this will show the boiling point of the vaporised liquid.

Sea water — eventually you will end up with only salt left in the round bottomed flask.

Water out

Condenser — the vapour turns back into a liquid here as it is cooled by the water.

Water in

Heat

Pure distilled water

Figure 1: *The simple distillation of salt water.*

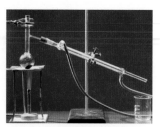

Figure 2: *Simple distillation apparatus being used to separate ink from water.*

Simple distillation can be used to separate substances with **boiling points** significantly apart from one another. But if the boiling points of the substances are close to each other simple distillation doesn't work. The temperature may rise above the boiling point of more than one of the substances, and they'll end up mixing again.

Fractional distillation

Fractional distillation can be used for separating a mixture of different liquids and is especially useful when the boiling points of the liquids are close together.

Although fractional distillation is a technique commonly used in industry to separate liquid mixtures, for example separating crude oil into different groups (see p.191-192), it is also used in the lab.

1. Figure 4 shows the set up of equipment that you need. You place the mixture in a flask, attach a fractionating column on top and heat it.

2. The different liquids will all have different boiling points — so they will evaporate at different temperatures.

3. The liquid with the lowest boiling point evaporates first. When the temperature on the thermometer matches the boiling point of this liquid, its vapour has reached the top of the column and passed into the condenser. It will then cool and condense and run out of the end. The pure liquid can then be collected.

4. Liquids with higher boiling points might also start to evaporate. But the column is cooler towards the top. So they will only get part of the way up before condensing and running back down towards the flask.

5. When the first liquid has been collected, you raise the temperature to the next lowest boiling point of the liquids in the mixture.

Figure 3: *A fractionating column containing glass beads. The beads act as a surface for the vapour to condense on as it makes its way up the column.*

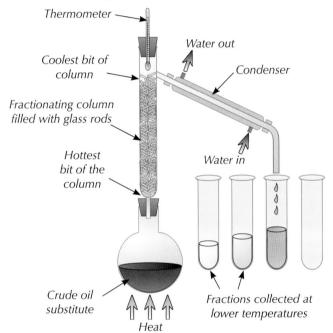

Figure 4: *Fractional distillation of a crude oil substitute.*

Exam Tip
You need to be able to describe how to carry out simple distillation and fractional distillation and know when you would use each technique.

Practice Questions — Application

Q1 A student tries to separate a mixture of ethanol, boiling point 78 °C, and propanol, boiling point 97 °C, using simple distillation.

a) Suggest a reason why she was not successful.

b) Suggest another method of separation that would be successful.

Q2 Butanoic acid and propanoic acid have boiling points of 164 °C and 141 °C respectively. During fractional distillation of a mixture containing both acids only, which liquid would be collected in the first fraction?

Q3 A mixture contains methanol, ethanol and propanol. The boiling points of the components are 65 °C, 78 °C and 97 °C respectively. Describe a process that could be used to separate the mixture.

Learning Objectives:

- Know what atoms were thought to be before the discovery of the electron.
- Be able to describe the plum pudding model and why it was developed.
- Understand and be able to describe the role of Rutherford in the development of the nuclear model of the atom.
- Understand how and why Bohr adapted the nuclear model of the atom.
- Know that later experiments led to the discovery of the proton and neutron.
- Be able to describe the differences between different atomic models.

Specification Reference 5.1.1.3

Our current idea of the structure of the atom didn't just materialise out of thin air — theories have been built upon over time to get to where we are now.

The plum pudding model

At the start of the 19th century John Dalton described atoms as solid spheres, and said that different spheres made up the different elements.

In 1897, J J Thomson concluded from his experiments that atoms weren't solid spheres. His measurements of charge and mass showed that an atom must contain even smaller, negatively charged particles — **electrons**. The 'solid sphere' idea of atomic structure had to be changed. The new theory was known as the '**plum pudding model**'. The plum pudding model showed the atom as a ball of positive charge with electrons stuck in it — see Figure 1.

Figure 1: *The plum pudding model showing electrons within a sphere of positive charge.*

The nuclear model

In 1909 Ernest Rutherford and his student Ernest Marsden conducted the famous alpha particle scattering experiments. They fired positively charged alpha particles at an extremely thin sheet of gold.

From the plum pudding model, they were expecting the particles to pass straight through the sheet or be slightly deflected at most. This was because the positive charge of each atom was thought to be very spread out through the 'pudding' of the atom. But, whilst most of the particles did go straight through the gold sheet, some were deflected more than expected, and a small number were deflected backwards. So the plum pudding model couldn't be right.

Rutherford came up with an idea that could explain this new evidence — the nuclear model of the atom. In this, there's a tiny, positively charged **nucleus** at the centre, where most of the mass is concentrated. A 'cloud' of negative electrons surrounds this nucleus — most of the atom is empty space.

Tip: <u>Models</u> are used to predict the outcome of experiments. If the prediction is proved wrong the model may need to change.

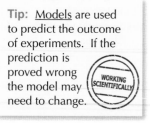

Exam Tip
Questions on these pages may focus on the development of scientific models and theories over time. Remember, theories are built upon previous work and new evidence which has come to light.

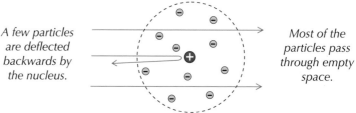

A few particles are deflected backwards by the nucleus.

Most of the particles pass through empty space.

Figure 2: *Alpha particle scattering experiments by Rutherford and Marsden showed that the atom was mainly empty space with a positively charged nucleus.*

Bohr's nuclear model

Scientists realised that electrons in a 'cloud' around the nucleus of an atom, as Rutherford described, would be attracted to the nucleus, causing the atom to collapse. Niels Bohr's nuclear model of the atom suggested that all the electrons were contained in **shells**. Bohr proposed that electrons orbit the nucleus in fixed shells and aren't anywhere in between. Each shell is a fixed distance from the nucleus. Bohr's theory of atomic structure was supported by many experiments and it helped to explain lots of other scientists' observations at the time.

Tip: For a theory to be accepted there must be experimental evidence to support it.

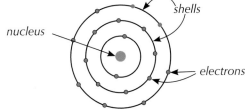

Figure 3: Bohr's model of the atom proposes that electrons orbit the nucleus at fixed distances.

The discovery of protons and neutrons

Further experimentation by Rutherford and others gave the conclusion that the nucleus could be divided into smaller particles, each of which has the same charge as a hydrogen nuclei. By the late 1920's, scientists were referring to these hydrogen nuclei as **protons**.

About 20 years after scientists had accepted that atoms have nuclei, James Chadwick carried out an experiment which provided evidence for neutral particles in the nucleus. These became known as **neutrons**. The discovery of neutrons resulted in a model of the atom which was pretty close to the modern day accepted version, known as the nuclear model (see p.22).

Figure 4: Niels Bohr (1885-1962) discovered that electrons were contained in shells of fixed energies.

Practice Questions — Fact Recall

Q1 Who described atoms as solid spheres in the early 19th century?

Q2 Whose experiments provided evidence of the neutron?

Practice Questions — Application

Q1 Rutherford and Marsden developed a new model of the atom based on their alpha particle experiments.

a) Describe the alpha particle experiments and their results.

b) Suggest why evidence from this experiment disproved the plum pudding model.

Q2 Bohr built upon the work by Ernest Rutherford in developing the nuclear model further.

a) What did Bohr suggest about the arrangement of the electrons within the atom?

b) Why was Bohr's proposal taken seriously?

Tip: The nuclear model can refer to both Rutherford's and Bohr's model as they both include a positively charged nucleus surrounded by electrons. But Bohr's model has the electrons in <u>fixed shells</u> and is closer to the modern day accepted version.

Exam Tip
You don't need to know details of the experiments of Bohr and Chadwick for your exam, but you do need to know the theories they came up with.

11. Electronic Structure

Learning Objectives:

- Know that electrons fill the shells closest to the nucleus first.
- Know how many electrons each shell can hold.
- Be able to draw and write out the electronic structures of the first 20 elements of the periodic table.

Specification Reference
5.1.1.7

So, you know that electrons are found in shells around the nucleus. The next thing you need to know is how they're arranged in these shells. Read on...

How are the electrons arranged in atoms?

Electrons always occupy **shells** (sometimes called **energy levels**). The electron shells with the lowest energy are always filled first — these are the ones closest to the nucleus. Only a certain number of electrons are allowed in each shell — see Figure 1.

Shell	Maximum number of electrons
1st	2
2nd	8
3rd	8

Figure 1: *Table showing how many electrons each electron shell can hold.*

Tip: There's more on noble gases (Group 0) elements) on p.64-65.

Atoms are much happier when they have full electron shells — like the **noble gases** in Group 0. In most atoms the outer shell is not full and this makes the atom react to fill it.

Electronic structures

Tip: Sometimes you'll see electrons drawn as dots (like on page 72), other times you'll see them drawn as crosses. For these diagrams, it doesn't matter which is used — they all represent electrons.

The **electronic structure** of an element is how the electrons are arranged in an atom of that element. You need to know the electronic structures for the first 20 elements (things get a bit more complicated after that). But they're not hard to work out. You just need to follow these steps:

1. Find the number of electrons in an atom of the element (you can find this from the atomic number of the element, which is on the periodic table).

2. Draw the first electron shell and add up to two electrons to it.

3. Draw the second electron shell and add up to eight electrons to it.

4. If you need to, draw the third electron shell and add up to eight electrons.

5. As soon as you've added enough electrons, stop.

Tip: You'd usually draw the first four electrons in each shell spread out around the shell. Then the next four electrons are drawn next to them to make pairs of electrons. But you don't need to worry about this for GCSE — just make sure you've got the right number of electrons in each shell.

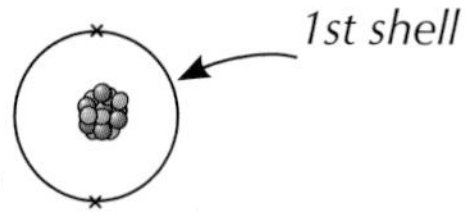

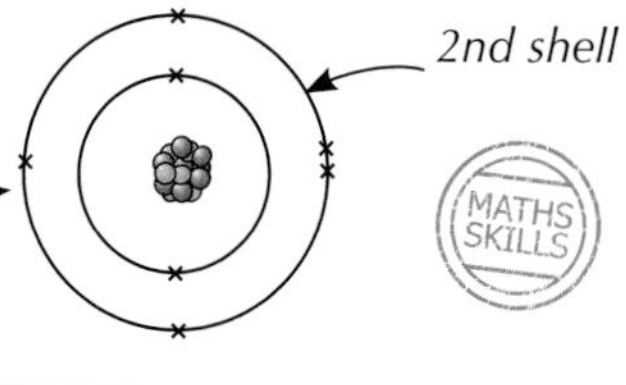

Tip: Representing 3D objects, such as atoms, by 2D diagrams is an important maths skill.

Example

Draw the electronic structure of nitrogen.

1. The atomic number of nitrogen is seven, so it has seven protons and therefore seven electrons.

2. Draw the first electron shell and add 2 electrons.

3. Draw the second shell and add the remaining five electrons.

4. Nitrogen only has seven electrons so you don't need to draw a third shell.

Drawing an atom is one way of showing its electronic structure, but you can also write out the electronic structure using numbers.

Examples

1. You can show the electronic structure of nitrogen using a diagram like this...   ...or you can write it out like this.

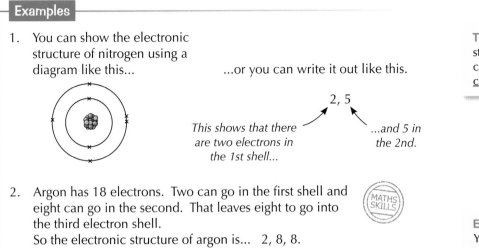

2, 5

This shows that there are two electrons in the 1st shell...   *...and 5 in the 2nd.*

2. Argon has 18 electrons. Two can go in the first shell and eight can go in the second. That leaves eight to go into the third electron shell.
    So the electronic structure of argon is...   2, 8, 8.

After the 3rd shell is filled things get more complicated. Luckily, the only electronic structures with electrons in the 4th shell that you need to know are potassium (2,8,8,1) and calcium (2,8,8,2).

Tip: An electronic structure is sometimes called an <u>electron configuration</u>.

Exam Tip
You need to be able to <u>draw</u> and <u>write</u> electronic structures for the first 20 elements of the periodic table. So make sure you know how to do it both ways.

Practice Questions — Fact Recall

Q1 What is another name for an electron shell?

Q2 What is the maximum number of electrons that can go in the first electron shell?

Q3 What is the maximum number of electrons that can go in the second electron shell?

Q4 What is the maximum number of electrons that can go in the third electron shell?

Q5 Which shell fills with electrons first?

Tip: You'll need a periodic table to answer some of these questions so that you can find the atomic numbers of the elements. You'll find one on the back cover of the book.

Practice Questions — Application

Q1 This diagram shows the electronic structure of an element. Which element is it?

Q2 Which element has the electronic structure 2, 4?

Q3 Which element has the electronic structure 2, 8, 6?

Q4 Draw the electronic structure of oxygen.

Q5 Draw the electronic structure of boron.

Q6 Write out the electronic structure of phosphorus.

Q7 Write out the electronic structure of magnesium.

Tip: You don't need to draw all the protons and neutrons out when you're drawing the electronic structure of an element. You can just draw a circle to represent the nucleus instead (as in Q1).

Topic Checklist — Make sure you know...

Atoms

- ☐ That everything is made up of tiny particles called atoms.
- ☐ The structure of the atom, including the arrangement of protons, neutrons and electrons.
- ☐ That the radius of an atom is very small (around 0.1 nm) and the nucleus' radius is even smaller at around 1/10 000 the size.
- ☐ The relative masses and charges of protons, neutrons and electrons.
- ☐ That atoms are neutral (have no overall charge) as they have equal numbers of protons and electrons.

Elements

- ☐ That an element is a substance made of one type of atom and there are about 100 different elements.
- ☐ That atoms of an element have the same number of protons and atoms of different elements have a different number of protons.
- ☐ What nuclear symbols show.

Isotopes

- ☐ That isotopes are atoms with the same number of protons but a different number of neutrons.
- ☐ That the relative atomic mass of an element is the average mass of all the isotopes of the element.
- ☐ How to calculate the relative atomic mass of an element using the mass numbers of its isotopes and their percentage abundances.

Compounds

- ☐ That a compound is made of atoms of different elements, chemically bonded together.
- ☐ That compounds can be shown by formulas made of chemical symbols representing the elements.
- ☐ That chemical reactions are needed to separate compounds back into elements.

Chemical Equations

- ☐ Know that new substances are made during chemical reactions.
- ☐ That word and symbol equations are used to show the reactants and products of a chemical reaction.
- ☐ How to write word equations and balanced symbol equations for reactions.

Mixtures

- ☐ That mixtures are made of compounds and/or elements that aren't held together by chemical bonds.

cont...

☐ That the properties of the individual substances don't alter when they become part of a mixture.

☐ That mixtures can be separated by physical methods such as chromatography, filtration, crystallisation, evaporation, simple distillation and fractional distillation.

Paper Chromatography

☐ How to carry out paper chromatography to separate mixtures containing coloured liquids.

More Separating Techniques

☐ How filtration is used to separate an insoluble solid from a solution and how to carry out filtration.

☐ How evaporation and crystallisation can be used to separate a soluble solid from a solution.

☐ How to carry out evaporation and crystallisation.

Distillation

☐ That simple distillation can be used to separate a liquid from a mixture where the components have large differences in boiling point.

☐ That fractional distillation can be used to separate a mixture of liquids with similar boiling points.

☐ How simple distillation and fractional distillation are carried out.

The History of The Atom

☐ That scientists thought that atoms were solid spheres before the discovery of the electron.

☐ What the plum pudding model is and why this model was proposed.

☐ Why the work of Rutherford and Marsden disproved the plum pudding model.

☐ What Bohr proposed about the arrangement of the electrons in the atom and how the nuclear model was adapted as a result of this.

☐ How the discovery of protons and neutrons changed the accepted model of the atom.

☐ The differences between the nuclear model and the plum pudding model.

Electronic Structure

☐ That electrons will fill shells closest to the nucleus first.

☐ How to work out and show the electronic structures of the first 20 elements of the periodic table.

Exam-style Questions

1   Carbon monoxide (CO) and carbon dioxide (CO_2) both contain carbon atoms and oxygen atoms.

1.1   Which term below best describes carbon and oxygen? Tick **one** box.

    ☐ Elements   ☐ Mixtures   ☐ Compounds   ☐ Isotopes

(1 mark)

1.2   Which term below best describes carbon monoxide and carbon dioxide? Tick **one** box.

    ☐ Elements   ☐ Mixtures   ☐ Compounds   ☐ Isotopes

(1 mark)

1.3   Carbon monoxide and oxygen can react to form carbon dioxide.
Write a word equation for the reaction of carbon monoxide with oxygen.

(1 mark)

1.4   Balance the symbol equation for this reaction.

$$......CO \ + \ ......O_2 \ \rightarrow \ ......CO_2$$

(1 mark)

1.5   Using your balanced symbol equation, describe the reaction of carbon monoxide and oxygen in terms of the number of molecules of each substance involved.

(3 marks)

1.6   Complete this diagram so that it shows the electronic structure of carbon.

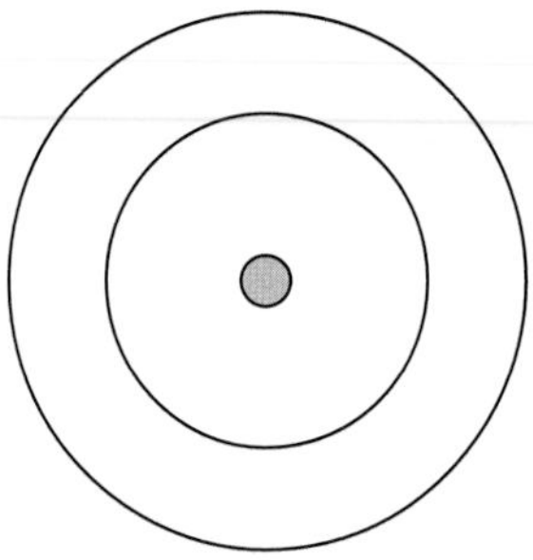

(2 marks)

1.7   What is the charge of the nucleus of an atom of carbon? Explain your answer.

(2 marks)

2   Chlorine is a non-metallic element.
A particular atom of chlorine has the nuclear symbol $^{37}_{17}$Cl.

2.1   Complete **Table 1** by filling in the missing information about
the atomic structure of the atom of chlorine.

Table 1

Atomic number	
Mass number	37
Number of protons	17
Number of electrons	
Number of neutrons	

(3 marks)

2.2   A separate atom of chlorine has a mass number of 35.
Suggest how the two atoms are related.

(1 mark)

2.3   Chlorine can bond with the metal sodium to form sodium chloride (NaCl).
Sodium chloride dissolves easily in water. Explain whether an aqueous
solution of sodium chloride is a mixture or a compound.

(1 mark)

2.4   Give the electronic structure of chlorine in number form.

(1 mark)

2.5   An atom of sodium has the nuclear symbol $^{23}_{11}$Na.
Complete the diagram below to show the electronic structure of sodium.

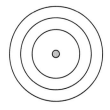

(2 marks)

2.6   A student needs to separate a mixture of sodium chloride and water.
Suggest **two** methods that could be used separate the mixture.

(4 marks)

3   Through their experiments using alpha particles Rutherford and Marsden
proposed a new structure for the atom known as the nuclear model.

3.1   Describe Rutherford's nuclear model of the atom.

(3 marks)

3.2   How is the plum pudding model of the atom different to the nuclear model?

(2 marks)

3.3   Following experimental work by Bohr, how did the accepted
view of the electronic structure of the atom change?

(2 marks)

1. Development of the Periodic Table

Learning Objectives:
- Know that elements were classified by atomic weight before the discovery of sub-atomic particles.
- Know that the first periodic tables were incomplete and elements were often placed in the wrong group if placed in order of atomic weight.
- Be able to describe what Mendeleev did to solve some of the problems of early periodic tables.
- Know that the discovery of isotopes supported Mendeleev's periodic table.

Specification Reference 5.1.2.2

As we discovered more elements, early chemists looked to try and understand patterns in their properties.

Early periodic tables

Until recently, there were two obvious ways to classify elements:

1. Their physical and chemical properties.

2. Their **relative atomic mass**.

To begin with, scientists had no idea of atomic structure or of protons, neutrons and electrons, so there was no such thing as atomic number to them. It was only after protons and electrons were discovered that it was realised the elements were best arranged in order of atomic number.

Before the 20th century, the only thing that scientists could measure was relative atomic mass, and so the known elements were arranged in order of relative atomic mass. When this was done, a periodic pattern was noticed in the properties of the elements — the properties repeated at regular intervals. This is where the name '**periodic table**' comes from.

Tip: Atomic number is the number of protons an atom has in its nucleus.

When they were arranged, not all elements had been discovered, so early periodic tables were not complete. In addition, those elements that had been discovered were placed in order of relative atomic mass, so some ended up in the wrong group (column) with elements that didn't have similar properties.

Mendeleev's periodic table

In 1869, Dmitri Mendeleev overcame some of the problems of early periodic tables by taking 57 known elements and arranging them into his Table of Elements — with various gaps as shown in Figure 1.

Tip: The relative atomic mass is the average mass of one atom of an element. This was first introduced on page 27. There's more about using relative atomic masses on page 104.

<u>Mendeleev's Table of Elements</u>

H																	
Li	Be											B	C	N	O	F	
Na	Mg											Al	Si	P	S	Cl	
K	Ca	*	Ti	V	Cr	Mn	Fe	Co	Ni	Cu	Zn	*	*	As	Se	Br	
Rb	Sr	Y	Zr	Nb	Mo	*	Ru	Rh	Pd	Ag	Cd	In	Sn	Sb	Te	I	
Cs	Ba	*	*	Ta	W	*	Os	Ir	Pt	Au	Hg	Tl	Pb	Bi			

Figure 1: *Mendeleev's periodic table.*

Mendeleev put the elements mainly in order of atomic mass but did switch the order of some elements if the properties meant it should be changed. An example of this can been seen with tellurium (Te) and iodine (I) — iodine actually has a smaller relative atomic mass but is placed after tellurium as it has similar properties to the elements in that group.

Gaps were left in the table to make sure that elements with similar properties stayed in the same groups. Some of these gaps indicated the existence of undiscovered elements and allowed Mendeleev to predict what their properties might be. When these elements were found and their properties fitted with Mendeleev's predictions, it helped confirm his ideas. For example, Mendeleev made really good predictions about the chemical and physical properties of an element he called ekasilicon, which we know today as germanium.

The discovery of isotopes

The discovery of isotopes (see page 27) in the early 20th century confirmed that Mendeleev was correct not to place elements in a strict order of atomic mass but to also take account of their properties. This is because isotopes of the same element have different atomic masses but have the same chemical properties so occupy the same position on the periodic table.

Figure 2: *Dmitri Mendeleev (1834-1907)*

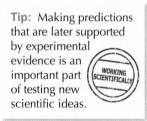

Tip: Making predictions that are later supported by experimental evidence is an important part of testing new scientific ideas.

Practice Questions — Fact Recall

Q1 Before Mendeleev's table, how were the elements arranged in order to classify them?

Q2 State one problem associated with early periodic tables that came before Mendeleev's table.

Q3 How did Mendeleev overcome some of the early problems of periodic tables?

Q4 Give one piece of evidence that strongly suggested Mendeleev's system of ordering elements was correct.

- Know that elements in the periodic table are arranged by increasing atomic number and so that elements with similar properties are in the same group.
- Know that elements in a group have the same number of electrons in their outer shell.
- Be able to explain how the atomic structure of an element can be found from its position in the periodic table.
- Be able to explain why elements in a group have similar properties.
- Be able to predict reactions based on the position of elements in the periodic table.

Specification Reference
5.1.2.1

Tip: See page 27 for more on how relative atomic masses are calculated.

Tip: There's a larger version of a periodic table on the inside of the back cover if you need to look anything up.

Exam Tip
You'll be given a copy of the periodic table on the data sheet in the exam.

2. The Modern Periodic Table

The periodic table is a chemist's best friend. At first glance it might seem a bit intimidating but it's got loads of useful information in it.

What is the periodic table?

The **periodic table** is a table that contains all the known elements (about 100). The table is laid out in order of increasing atomic number so that elements with similar properties form columns. These vertical columns are called **groups**. The rows are called **periods**. The periodic table is a useful tool for working out which elements are metals and which are non-metals. Metals are generally found to the left and non-metals to the right.

In the periodic table, the elements are represented by their symbols. As many elements can have several isotopes, relative atomic mass (A_r) is used when referring to the elements as a whole on the periodic table. This leads to some mass numbers not being whole numbers. E.g. the A_r of chlorine is 35.5.

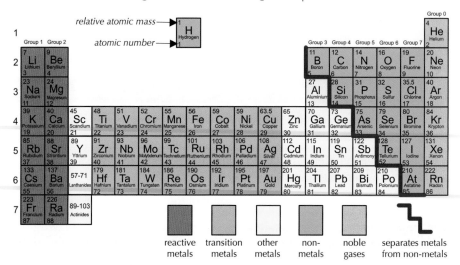

Figure 1: The periodic table of the elements.

Electronic structure and the periodic table

The number of the period that an element's in tells you how many electron shells it has. Meanwhile, the group number of an element tells you how many electrons there are in its outer shell. For example, Group 1 elements all have one electron in their outer shell and Group 7 elements all have seven electrons in their outer shell. The exception to the rule is Group 0. These elements all have a full outer shell of electrons, but as you saw on page 44, the number of electrons needed to fill each shell is different. So helium has two electrons in its outer shell, while neon has eight.

If you know the position of an element in the periodic table, you can work out its electronic structure, and so how many electrons it has when neutral, which is the same as its atomic number.

> **Example**
>
> Carbon is in Period 2 and Group 4 so has 1 full inner shell of two electrons and four electrons in its outer shell. 2 + 4 = 6 electrons.

Predicting reactivity

The way atoms react depends upon the number of electrons in their outer shell. So all elements in the same group are likely to react in a similar way. This means that if you know the properties of one element, you can predict properties of other elements in that group.

> **Example**
>
> The Group 1 elements are Li, Na, K, Rb, Cs and Fr.
>
> They all have one electron in their outer shell.
>
> They're all metals and they react the same way. For example:
>
> - They all react with water to form an alkaline solution and hydrogen gas.
> - They all react with oxygen to form an oxide.

You can also make predictions about trends in reactivity.

> **Examples**
>
> In Group 1, the elements react more vigorously as you go down the group. This means you can predict that potassium will react more vigorously than lithium, as it's further down the group.
>
> In Group 7, reactivity decreases as you go down the group. This means you can predict that bromine will react less vigorously than fluorine as it's further down the group.

Figure 2: *Lithium, sodium and potassium are all in the same group so have similar properties. For example, they are all metals that are shiny when cut.*

Tip: There's more on trends of reactivity of Group 1 and Group 7 on p.56 and p.61.

Practice Questions — Fact Recall

Q1 Describe how elements are arranged in the periodic table.

Q2 What do the following features tell you about the electron configuration of an element?

　　a) The period number.

　　b) The group number.

Q3 How many electrons do Group 1 elements have in their outer shell?

Q4 Why do elements in the same group of the periodic table have similar chemical properties?

Practice Questions — Application

Q1 Using a periodic table, state how many electrons boron has in its outer shell.

Q2 Calcium readily forms 2+ ions. What ions is magnesium likely to form? Give a reason for your answer.

- Know that elements that form positive ions when they react are metals.

- Know that elements that don't form positive ions when they react are non-metals.

- Know where metals and non-metals are found in the periodic table.

- Understand that most elements are metals.

- Be able to explain the relationship between the electronic structure of metals and non-metals, and their positions in the periodic table.

- Understand how the electronic structure of metals and non-metals affects how they react and their properties.

- Be able to compare the differences in properties between metals and non-metals.

Specification Reference
5.1.2.3

Tip: Ions are atoms or molecules which have either gained or lost electrons. This means the number of electrons doesn't equal the number of protons leading to ions having an overall charge.

Tip: Positive ions are often called <u>cations</u> and negative ions are called <u>anions</u>.

Tip: Hydrogen is an exception. It's a non-metal that forms positive ions.

3. Metals and Non-metals

The majority of elements in the periodic table can be classed as metals or non-metals. Here's why they are interesting...

What are metals and non-metals?

Metals are elements which can form positive ions when they react. Most metals are found further down the periodic table and to the left-hand side. The elements in the centre of the periodic table are known as the transition metals.

Non-metals are elements which don't form positive ions when they react. They either form negative ions in ionic compounds or bond covalently with other non-metals (see page 78).

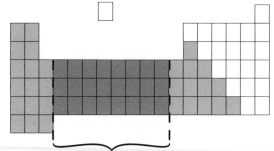

Transition Metals

Figure 1: *The position of metals (coloured) and non-metals (in white) on the periodic table.*

As is shown in Figure 1, the majority of elements in the periodic table are metals, with only those to the right-hand side and top being classed as non-metals.

Electronic structure of metals and non-metals

Atoms generally react to form a full outer shell. They do this by either losing, gaining or sharing electrons. The electronic structure of metals and non-metals explains why they react the way they do.

Metals to the left of the periodic table don't have many electrons to remove from their outer shells and metals towards the bottom of the periodic table have outer electrons which are a long way from the nucleus so feel a weaker attraction. Both these effects mean that not much energy is needed to remove the electrons from the outer shell so it's feasible for the elements to react to form positive ions with a full outer shell.

For non-metals, forming positive ions is much more difficult. This is because they are found to the right of the periodic table — where they have lots of electrons to remove to get a full outer shell, or towards the top — where the outer electrons are close to the nucleus so feel a strong attraction. It's far more feasible for them to either share or gain electrons to get a full outer shell.

Physical properties of metals and non-metals

All metals have metallic bonding (take a look at page 90 for more on this) and therefore have similar physical properties:

1. They're strong (hard to break) but can be bent or hammered into different shapes (malleable).

2. They're great at conducting heat and electricity.

3. They generally have high boiling and melting points, so tend to be solids at room temperature.

Non-metals don't have metallic bonding, so they don't tend to exhibit the same properties as metals:

1. They tend to be dull looking and more brittle than metals.

2. They generally have lower boiling and melting points than metals, so aren't always solids at room temperature.

3. They don't generally conduct electricity.

4. They often have a lower density than metals.

Tip: There's more on why metals have these properties on p.90-91.

Tip: Non-metals form a wide variety of different structures so have a large range of chemical properties.

Practice Questions — Fact Recall

Q1 What kind of ions do metals form when they react?

Q2 What kind of ions do non-metals form in ionic compounds?

Q3 Are the majority of elements in the periodic table metals or non-metals?

Q4 Using your knowledge of their electronic structure, explain the relative ease of forming positive ions for:

a) Metals.

b) Non-metals.

Q5 Compare the general physical properties of metals and non-metals.

Figure 2: *Copper (top) is a metal and sulfur (bottom) is a non-metal.*

- Know that the elements in Group 1 of the periodic table are called the alkali metals.
- Know that the alkali metals have characteristic properties.
- Know that the reactivity of the alkali metals increases down the group.
- Be able to explain how the outer shell of electrons determines the properties of the Group 1 elements.
- Be able to use trends in Group 1 to predict certain properties of Group 1 elements.
- Be able to describe the reactions of lithium, sodium and potassium with water, chlorine and oxygen.

Specification Reference
5.1.2.5

4. Group 1 — The Alkali Metals

The elements in Group 1 are commonly known as the alkali metals. The next few pages are all about these metals and their properties.

Properties of the alkali metals

The **alkali metals** are the elements in Group 1 of the periodic table — they are lithium, sodium, potassium, rubidium, caesium and francium (see Figure 1).

They're all silvery solids that have to be stored in oil and handled with forceps (they can cause chemical burns on the skin).

The alkali metals all have one electron in their outer shell. This makes them very reactive and means they react in similar ways. The alkali metals all have similar properties. For example, all the alkali metals have low density. In fact, the first three in the group are less dense than water.

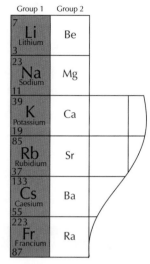

Figure 1: Group 1 of the periodic table.

Trends down Group 1

There are a couple of trends within the Group 1 elements that you need to know about.

Reactivity

Reactivity increases down the group, so elements at the bottom of the group are more reactive than elements at the top of the group — see Figure 2.

This is because Group 1 metals react by losing the single electron in their outer energy level. As you move down the group, the outer electron gets further away from the nucleus. This means the attraction between the nucleus and the outer electron decreases and so the outer electron is more easily lost. As a result, elements further down the group are more reactive.

Melting and boiling points

The melting and boiling points of the Group 1 metals decrease down the group, so elements at the bottom of the group have lower melting points and lower boiling points than the elements at the top of the group — see Figure 2.

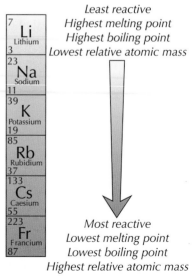

Least reactive
Highest melting point
Highest boiling point
Lowest relative atomic mass

Most reactive
Lowest melting point
Lowest boiling point
Highest relative atomic mass

Figure 2: Trends in Group 1.

Relative atomic mass

The relative atomic mass of Group 1 elements increases as you go down the group — see Figure 2.

Reaction with non-metals

The alkali metals react with non-metals, such as water, oxygen or chlorine, to form **ionic compounds**. This is because the alkali metals have only one electron in their outer shell, so it's easy for them to lose it to form a 1+ ion. In fact, it's so favourable for them to lose the outer electron that they never share electrons to form covalent bonds. Instead, they always form ionic bonds.

Tip: An ionic compound is a compound that contains oppositely charged ions held together by ionic bonds — see pages 75-77 for more.

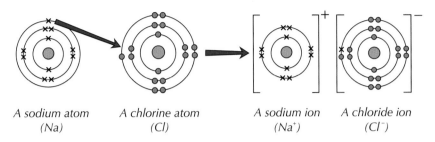

| A sodium atom (Na) | A chlorine atom (Cl) | A sodium ion (Na^+) | A chloride ion (Cl^-) |

Figure 3: *The alkali metal sodium (Na) reacts with the non-metal chlorine (Cl) to form the ionic compound sodium chloride (NaCl).*

The compounds that are produced when alkali metals react with non-metals are usually white solids that dissolve in water to form colourless solutions.

> ## Example
>
> The alkali metal sodium (Na) reacts with chlorine (Cl) to form sodium chloride (NaCl) — see Figure 3. Sodium chloride is a white solid (see Figure 4) that will dissolve in water to form a colourless solution.

Figure 4: *Sodium chloride in a salt shaker.*

Reaction with water

The alkali metals react with water to form a metal hydroxide and hydrogen gas. The general equation for this reaction is:

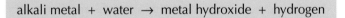

alkali metal + water → metal hydroxide + hydrogen

> ## Examples
>
> - Sodium reacts with water to form sodium hydroxide and hydrogen:
>
> $$2Na_{(s)} + 2H_2O_{(l)} \rightarrow 2NaOH_{(aq)} + H_{2(g)}$$
>
> - Potassium reacts with water to form potassium hydroxide and hydrogen:
>
> $$2K_{(s)} + 2H_2O_{(l)} \rightarrow 2KOH_{(aq)} + H_{2(g)}$$

Tip: You can test for the production of hydrogen in these reactions using a burning splint. A lighted splint will indicate hydrogen by producing the notorious "squeaky pop" as the H_2 ignites. See page 203 for more about this.

Because the alkali metals are so reactive, they react with water very vigorously. The more reactive (lower down in the group) an alkali metal is, the more violent the reaction. When lithium, sodium or potassium are put in water, they float and move around the surface, fizzing furiously as the hydrogen gas is produced — see Figure 6 on the next page. In some cases, the reaction can get hot enough to ignite the hydrogen. Elements below potassium in Group 1 react explosively with water.

Metal hydroxide solutions

The hydroxides that are formed when the alkali metals react with water will dissolve in water to give alkaline solutions. This is where the name 'alkali metals' comes from. The reaction of sodium with water is illustrated in Figure 6. The reaction is similar for the other alkali metals but becoming more vigorous as you go down the group.

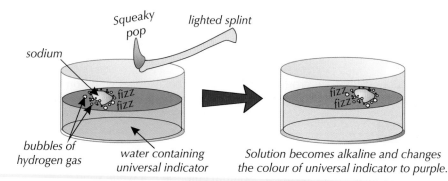

Figure 5: Sodium reacting with water.

Figure 6: The reaction of sodium with water.

Reaction with chlorine

Group 1 metals react vigorously when heated in chlorine gas to form white metal chloride salts. The general equation for this reaction is:

Tip: The alkali metals also react with the other halogens in similar reactions.

alkali metal + chlorine → metal chloride

As you go down the group, reactivity increases so the reaction with chlorine gets more vigorous.

> **Examples**
>
> ▪ Lithium reacts with chlorine to form lithium chloride:
>
> $$2Li_{(s)} + Cl_{2(g)} \rightarrow 2LiCl_{(s)}$$
>
> ▪ Rubidium reacts with chlorine to form rubidium chloride:
>
> $$2Rb_{(s)} + Cl_{2(g)} \rightarrow 2RbCl_{(s)}$$

Reaction with oxygen

The Group 1 metals can react with oxygen to form a metal oxide. Different types of oxide will form depending on the Group 1 metal.

Examples

- Lithium reacts to form lithium oxide (Li_2O).

  The equation for this reaction is: $4Li_{(s)} + O_{2\,(g)} \rightarrow 2Li_2O_{(s)}$

- Sodium reacts to form a mixture of sodium oxide (Na_2O) and sodium peroxide (Na_2O_2).

  The equation for the reaction to form sodium oxide is:
  $$4Na_{(s)} + O_{2\,(g)} \rightarrow 2Na_2O_{(s)}$$
  The equation for the reaction to form sodium peroxide is:
  $$2Na_{(s)} + O_{2\,(g)} \rightarrow Na_2O_{2\,(s)}$$

- Potassium reacts to form a mixture of potassium peroxide (K_2O_2) and potassium superoxide (KO_2).

  The equation for the reaction to form potassium peroxide is:
  $$2K_{(s)} + O_{2\,(g)} \rightarrow K_2O_{2\,(s)}$$
  The equation for the reaction to form potassium superoxide is:
  $$K_{(s)} + O_{2\,(g)} \rightarrow KO_{2\,(s)}$$

Tip: The reactions with oxygen are why Group 1 metals tarnish in the air — the metal reacts with oxygen in the air to form a dull metal oxide layer.

Practice Questions — Fact Recall

Q1 Which group in the periodic table are the alkali metals?

Q2 Do the alkali metals have low density or high density?

Q3 State the trend in reactivity as you go down Group 1.

Q4 Alkali metals can react with non-metals.

   a) What type of bonds do alkali metals form during these reactions?

   b) Give two properties of the compounds that are produced during these reactions.

Q5 a) Write down the general word equation for the reaction of an alkali metal with water.

   b) Will the solution formed when a Group 1 metal reacts with water be acidic, neutral or alkaline?

Q6 Write the general word equation for the reaction of an alkali metal with chlorine gas.

Q7 Name the compounds that form when potassium reacts with oxygen.

Practice Questions — Application

Tip: You might need to have a peek back at the order of the elements in Group 1 at the top of page 56 to help you answer these questions.

Q1 Which is more reactive:

   a) sodium or potassium?

   b) lithium or rubidium?

Q2 The boiling points of Group 1 metals decrease as you go down the group. State which has the higher melting point:

   a) lithium or potassium?

   b) caesium or potassium?

Q3 Is potassium oxide a covalent compound or an ionic compound?

Q4 Write a balanced symbol equation, including state symbols, for each of the following reactions:

   a) Lithium and water.

   b) Sodium and chlorine.

   c) Rubidium and oxygen to form rubidium superoxide (RbO_2).

5. Group 7 — The Halogens

The halogens are the Group 7 elements. If you want to know more about their properties and trends, have a look at the next few pages...

Properties of the halogens

The **halogens** are the elements in Group 7 of the periodic table — they include fluorine, chlorine, bromine and iodine (see Figure 1) and exist as molecules which are pairs of atoms.
For example, F_2, Cl_2 Br_2 or I_2. The halogens are all non-metals that have coloured vapours:

- Fluorine is a poisonous, yellow gas.

- Chlorine is a poisonous, dense, green gas.

- Bromine is a dense, poisonous, red-brown volatile liquid or an orange vapour.

- Iodine is a poisonous dark grey, crystalline solid or a purple vapour.

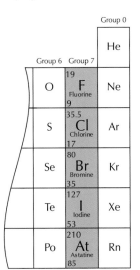

Figure 1: *Group 7 of the periodic table.*

Trends down Group 7

There are a couple of trends in the Group 7 elements that you need to know about.

Reactivity

All the Group 7 elements react in similar ways. This is because they all have seven electrons in their outer shell. Reactivity decreases down the group, so elements at the bottom of the group are less reactive than elements at the top of the group — see Figure 2.

This is because Group 7 elements react by gaining an electron in their outer electron shell. As you move down the group, the increased distance between the outer electron shell and the nucleus means that the outer electron shell is less likely to gain an electron — there's less attraction from the nucleus pulling electrons into the atom. So elements further down the group are less reactive.

Melting and boiling point

The melting and boiling points of the halogens increase down the group, so elements at the bottom of the group have higher melting points and higher boiling points than the elements at the top of the group — see Figure 2.

Relative atomic mass

The relative atomic mass of Group 7 elements increases as you go down the group — see Figure 2.

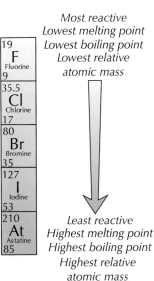

Most reactive
Lowest melting point
Lowest boiling point
Lowest relative atomic mass

Least reactive
Highest melting point
Highest boiling point
Highest relative atomic mass

Figure 2: *Trends in Group 7.*

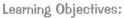

Learning Objectives:

- Know that the Group 7 elements are called the halogens and are non-metals that exist as molecules containing pairs of atoms.

- Be able to explain why Group 7 elements react similarly.

- Know that the reactivity of the halogens decreases down the group.

- Be able to explain how the outer shell of electrons determines the properties of the halogens.

- Know that the melting points, boiling points and relative atomic masses of the halogens increase down the group.

- Be able to use trends in the properties of the halogens to predict the properties of certain elements in the group.

- Know that halogens react with other non-metals to form molecular compounds and that they react with metals to form ionic compounds.

- Understand that a more reactive halogen will displace a less reactive halogen from a solution of its salt.

Specification Reference
5.1.2.6

Tip: These trends can be used to predict properties of halogens. For example, you know that bromine will have a higher boiling point than chlorine as it's further down the group.

Reactions with non-metals

Halogen atoms can share electrons via covalent bonding with other non-metals so as to achieve a full outer shell. For example HCl, PCl_5, HF and CCl_4 contain covalent bonds. The compounds that form when halogens react with non-metals all have simple molecular structures.

Tip: See pages 78-80 for more on covalent bonding and pages 81-84 for more on simple molecular structures.

Reaction with metals

The halogens have seven electrons in their outer shells, so it is easy to gain one extra electron and fill up their outer shell. When the halogens gain an electron they form 1– ions, known as **halide ions**.

Examples

- When a chlorine atom gains an electron it forms a chloride ion (Cl^-).

- When a bromine atom gains an electron it forms a bromide ion (Br^-).

Tip: See pages 72-74 for lots more about ionic bonding.

The halogens can gain electrons by reacting with metals. When this happens, an **ionic compound** is formed, which is held together by ionic bonding.

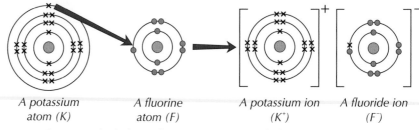

| A potassium atom (K) | A fluorine atom (F) | A potassium ion (K^+) | A fluoride ion (F^-) |

Figure 3: *The halogen fluorine (F) reacts with the metal potassium (K) to form the ionic compound potassium fluoride (KF).*

Displacement reactions

A more reactive halogen can displace (kick out) a less reactive halogen from an aqueous solution of its salt.

Figure 4: *Chlorine water being added to potassium bromide. The chlorine displaces the bromide ions and bromine (orange) is formed.*

Examples

- Chlorine is more reactive than bromine, so chlorine will displace bromine from an aqueous solution of its salt (a bromide). For example:

  chlorine + potassium bromide → bromine + potassium chloride

  $Cl_{2(g)}$ + $2KBr_{(aq)}$ → $Br_{2(aq)}$ + $2KCl_{(aq)}$

- Chlorine is more reactive than iodine, so chlorine will displace iodine from an aqueous solution of its salt (an iodide). For example:

  chlorine + sodium iodide → iodine + sodium chloride

  $Cl_{2(g)}$ + $2NaI_{(aq)}$ → $I_{2(aq)}$ + $2NaCl_{(aq)}$

- Bromine is more reactive than iodine, so bromine will displace iodine from an aqueous solution of its salt (an iodide). For example:

  bromine + lithium iodide → iodine + lithium bromide

  $Br_{2(g)}$ + $2LiI_{(aq)}$ → $I_{2(aq)}$ + $2LiBr_{(aq)}$

A less reactive halogen will not displace a more reactive halogen from the aqueous solution of the more reactive halogen's salt.

Example

If you mixed bromine with sodium chloride, nothing would happen — there wouldn't be any reaction. This is because chlorine is more reactive than bromine, so the bromine cannot displace the chlorine from the chloride salt.

Astatine is the least reactive halogen so it can't displace any other halogen.

Practice Questions — Fact Recall

Q1 How many atoms are in the molecules of halogens in their elemental form?

Q2 Where are the most reactive halogens found — at the top of Group 7 or at the bottom of Group 7?

Q3 Explain the trend in reactivity going down Group 7.

Q4 State the trend in melting points as you go down Group 7.

Q5 What is the charge on a halide ion?

Q6 Halogens can react with metals. What type of bonding exists in the compounds that are formed during these reactions?

Figure 5: *Some of the elements in Group 7 — chlorine, bromine and iodine.*

Practice Questions — Application

Q1 Which is more reactive:

a) chlorine or iodine?   b) bromine or fluorine?

Q2 Which has the higher boiling point:

a) fluorine or iodine?   b) chlorine or bromine?

Q3 Would a displacement reaction occur between the following reactants?

a) Chlorine and sodium bromide solution.

b) Bromine and magnesium chloride solution.

c) Iodine and lithium chloride solution.

d) Chlorine and calcium iodide.

Q4 Write a balanced symbol equation, including state symbols, for the reaction that would occur between:

a) Chlorine (Cl_2) and potassium iodide (KI).

b) Bromine (Br_2) and sodium iodide (NaI).

Tip: Have a look back at the order of Group 7 at the top of page 61 to help you answer these questions.

Learning Objectives:
- Know that elements in Group 0 are known as the noble gases.
- Be able to explain that Group 0 elements are unreactive because they have a full outer shell of electrons.
- Know that the boiling points of the elements in Group 0 increase down the group.
- Be able to use trends in Group 0 to predict certain properties of Group 0 elements.

Specification Reference
5.1.2.4

6. Group 0 — The Noble Gases

Group 0 elements aren't very reactive at all. This is because they have a stable arrangement of electrons in their outer shell.

Properties of the Group 0 elements

Group 0 elements are called the **noble gases** and include the elements helium, neon and argon (plus a few others).

They all have a full outer shell of electrons. For most of the noble gases, this means there are eight outer electrons. Helium, however, only has electrons in the first shell, which only needs two electrons to be filled. As their outer shell is energetically stable they don't need to give up or gain electrons to become more stable. This means they are more or less **inert** — they don't react with much at all. As they are inert they're non-flammable (they won't set on fire).

At room temperature they all exist as colourless monatomic gases — single atoms not bonded to anything else.

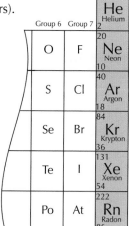

Figure 1: Group 0 of the periodic table.

Figure 2: Group 0 elements are all unreactive. This property means that neon is safe to use in neon signs.

Trends down Group 0

The boiling points of the noble gases increase as you move down the group along with increasing relative atomic mass.

Going down the group the atomic number increases and so the number of electrons increases. This causes the intermolecular forces between the atoms to increase, so more energy is needed to break them and so the boiling points increase.

Tip: There's more on intermolecular forces for small molecules on page 83.

Predicting properties of elements in groups

The trends in properties within groups means that you can use information about some elements to predict the properties of other elements in the same group. For example, you can use information about the boiling points of some of the Group 0 elements to predict what the boiling points of other Group 0 elements will be.

Tip: The actual boiling point of xenon is −108 °C as predicted.

Example 1

The boiling points of radon and krypton are −62 °C and −153 °C respectively. As xenon comes in between radon and krypton in the group you can estimate that its boiling point will be around halfway between the boiling points of radon and krypton:

$(-153) + (-62) = -215$
$-215 \div 2 = -107.5 \approx -108 \; °C$

So, xenon should have a boiling point of about −108 °C.

Example 2

The boiling points of neon, argon and krypton are –246 °C, –186 °C and –153 °C respectively. Using this information, you can calculate the average gap between boiling points and therefore estimate the boiling point of xenon.

Gap between neon and argon: $(-186) - (-246) = 60$ °C
Gap between argon and krypton: $(-153) - (-186) = 33$ °C
Average gap: $(60 + 33) \div 2 = 46.5$ °C

As you know from the trend that xenon will have a higher boiling point than neon, argon and krypton you can predict its boiling point by adding 46.5 to the boiling point of krypton.

Estimated boiling point of xenon: $(-153) + 46.5 = -106.5$ °C

You can also use trends to predict the state of elements at a particular temperature.

Example

Argon has a boiling point of –186 °C. As the trend is increasing boiling point as you go down the group, at –186 °C we can say that both neon and helium will be gases.

Exam Tip
In the exam you may be given the boiling point of one noble gas and asked to estimate the value for another one. So make sure you know the pattern.

Exam Tip
You could also use these methods to predict the properties of elements in other groups from the trends within their group, e.g. Group 1 and Group 7 elements.

Tip: There's more about predicting what state a substance will be in at a certain temperature on page 101.

Practice Questions — Fact Recall

Q1 What are the elements in Group 0 of the periodic table commonly known as?

Q2 What happens to the boiling points of the Group 0 elements as you go down the group?

Practice Questions — Application

Q1 Argon is an inert gas.

   a) How many electrons does argon have in its outer shell?

   b) Explain how the electron arrangement of argon affects its reactivity.

Q2 The boiling point of xenon is –108 °C. Predict with reasoning whether krypton will be a solid, liquid or gas at this temperature.

Topic Checklist — Make sure you know...

Development of the Periodic Table

☐ That early versions of the periodic table had the elements arranged in order of relative atomic mass.

☐ That the first periodic tables put some elements in the wrong order as they were based entirely on relative atomic mass and did not take account of properties.

☐ How Mendeleev's table solved some of the problems of early periodic tables.

☐ That the discovery of elements that fitted into the gaps in Mendeleev's table provided evidence that Mendeleev's system of ordering elements was a good one.

☐ That the discovery of isotopes showed that ordering elements by atomic weight only was incorrect.

The Modern Periodic Table

☐ That in the modern periodic table, elements are arranged by atomic (proton) number, and placed into suitable groups.

☐ How the position of an element in the periodic table relates to its electronic structure.

☐ That the chemical properties of an element can be predicted by its position in the periodic table.

Metals and Non-metals

☐ That when they react, metals form positive ions but non-metals don't.

☐ That most elements are metals and can be found towards the bottom and left of the periodic table and that non-metals can be found towards the top and right of the periodic table.

☐ How the electronic structure of both metals and non-metals affects how they react.

☐ The differences between the physical properties of metals and non-metals.

Group 1 — The Alkali Metals

☐ That the elements in Group 1 are known as the alkali metals.

☐ That the alkali metals all have low densities.

☐ That reactivity increases down Group 1 and both melting and boiling points decrease down Group 1.

☐ How the outer shell of electrons determines the properties of the Group 1 elements.

☐ How to predict properties of the Group 1 metals from the trends.

☐ That the alkali metals lose electrons and form 1+ ions when they react to form ionic compounds. These compounds are usually white solids that dissolve in water to form colourless solutions.

☐ That the alkali metals react with water to form hydrogen and metal hydroxides. These hydroxides form alkaline solutions when dissolved in water.

☐ That the alkali metals react with chlorine to form metal chlorides.

☐ That the alkali metals react with oxygen, and that the products depend on the metal that reacts.

cont...

Group 7 — The Halogens

☐ That the elements in Group 7, known as the halogens, are non-metals which exist as molecules made up of pairs of atoms.

☐ The trends in reactivity, melting point, boiling point and relative atomic mass in Group 7.

☐ How the outer shell of electrons determines the properties and reactions of the Group 7 elements.

☐ That the halogens gain electrons and form 1– ions when they react with metals to form ionic compounds.

☐ That halogens react with non-metals to form molecules which are held together by covalent bonds.

☐ That a less reactive halogen will be displaced from an aqueous solution of its salt when reacted with a more reactive halogen.

Group 0 — The Noble Gases

☐ That the elements in Group 0 are known as the noble gases.

☐ How the outer shell of electrons determines the properties of the Group 0 elements.

☐ That the Group 0 elements are unreactive because they have a full outer shell of electrons.

☐ That the boiling points of noble gases increase as you go down the group.

☐ How to predict the properties of noble gases from the trends in the group.

Exam-style Questions

1   This question is on the periodic table.

    1.1   Early periodic tables placed elements in relative atomic mass order.
Mendeleev developed his periodic table of elements in 1869. State **one**
difference that Mendeleev made in the order of elements in his periodic table.

(1 mark)

    1.2   The modern periodic table was a development of Mendeleev's table
and looks very similar to it. However, they are different in the way that
the elements are arranged. What is this difference?

(1 mark)

2   The modern periodic table can tell you a lot about the properties of an element.
Use the periodic table on the inside of the back cover to help you answer
the following questions.

    2.1   How many electrons does an atom of selenium (Se) have in its highest occupied
energy level?

(1 mark)

    2.2   How many electron shells are occupied in an atom of selenium?

(1 mark)

    2.3   Explain why selenium and sulfur both react in similar ways.

(2 marks)

3   Copper(II) chloride ($CuCl_2$) is an ionic compound formed from the reaction
of copper with chlorine.

    3.1   Copper is a metal, whilst chlorine is a non-metal. Describe one difference
in the typical reactivities of metals and non-metals.

(2 marks)

    3.2   Name an element of Group 7 which has a lower boiling point than chlorine.

(1 mark)

    3.3   Would a displacement reaction occur if bromine gas was bubbled through a solution
of aqueous copper(II) chloride? Explain your answer.

(2 marks)

4 The elements in Group 1 of the periodic table are commonly known as the alkali metals. The alkali metals show trends in their reactivities and their physical properties.

4.1 State whether lithium or potassium will be more reactive. Explain your answer.

(4 marks)

4.2 The alkali metals react vigorously with water. When sodium is added to water, the metal fizzes and bubbles of gas can be seen. What gas is produced when sodium reacts with water?

(1 mark)

4.3 If Universal indicator was added to the solution at the end of the reaction between sodium and water, the solution would turn purple, showing that it was alkaline. Explain why the solution is alkaline.

(2 marks)

4.4 Alkali metals can also react with non-metals. When sodium reacts with bromine, sodium bromide is formed. What is the charge on the sodium ion in sodium bromide?

(1 mark)

4.5 The table below shows the melting points and boiling points of some Group 1 metals.

Group 1 Metal	Boiling Point (°C)	Melting Point (°C)
Sodium	883	98
Potassium		63
Rubidium	688	
Caesium	671	28

Use the information in the table to predict the boiling point of potassium and the melting point of rubidium.

(2 marks)

5 Magnesium generally reacts to form ionic compounds containing magnesium ions with a 2+ charge. For example, magnesium chloride can be formed by reacting magnesium with chlorine.

5.1 What group of the periodic table is chlorine in?

(1 mark)

5.2 The reaction of magnesium and bromine is similar to the reaction of aluminium and chlorine. Explain why.

(1 mark)

5.3 Describe a reaction that could be used to make magnesium chloride from magnesium bromide.

(2 marks)

5.4 Aluminium does not react with argon. Explain why not.

(2 marks)

Learning Objectives:
- Know that metal atoms become positive ions when they lose electrons.
- Know that non-metal atoms become negative ions when they gain electrons.
- Know that the electronic structure of ions formed by elements in Groups 1, 2, 6 and 7 is the same as that of a noble gas.
- Be able to work out the charge on ions formed by elements in Groups 1, 2, 6 and 7 using their group number.

Specification Reference
5.2.1.2

1. Ions

Ions are rather important. These pages explain what they are and why they're formed, as well as telling you how to predict the charges on some simple ones.

What are ions?

Ions are charged particles. They can be single atoms (e.g. Cl^-) or groups of atoms (e.g. NO_3^-). They are made when electrons are lost or gained. Metal atoms lose electrons to form positive ions and non-metal atoms gain electrons to form negative ions. The number of electrons lost or gained is the same as the charge on the ion — so chlorine atoms gain one electron to form Cl^- ions, whereas oxygen atoms gain two electrons to form O^{2-} ions.

Example 1

Metal atoms form positive ions (cations)

A sodium atom has 11 protons and 11 electrons. Protons have a relative charge of +1 and electrons have a relative charge of −1, so the atom has no overall charge.

$$\text{total charge of protons} \rightarrow 11 - 11 = 0 \leftarrow \text{overall charge}$$
$$\text{total charge of electrons}$$

If a sodium atom loses an electron it will only have 10 electrons, but it will still have 11 protons. So the sodium will have an overall charge of +1, and is said to be a positively charged ion.

$$\text{total charge of protons} \rightarrow 11 - 10 = +1 \leftarrow \text{overall charge}$$
$$\text{total charge of electrons}$$

Tip: Ions can be represented using chemical symbols, but the charge on the ion needs to be shown as well. For example, a chloride ion is written as Cl^- and a sodium ion is written as Na^+.

Example 2

Non-metal atoms form negative ions (anions)

A chlorine atom has 17 protons and 17 electrons, so has no overall charge.

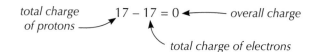

$$\text{total charge of protons} \rightarrow 17 - 17 = 0 \leftarrow \text{overall charge}$$
$$\text{total charge of electrons}$$

If a chlorine atom gains an electron it will have 18 electrons, but it will still only have 17 protons. So it will have an overall charge of −1, and is said to be a negatively charged ion.

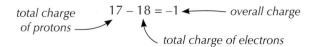

$$\text{total charge of protons} \rightarrow 17 - 18 = -1 \leftarrow \text{overall charge}$$
$$\text{total charge of electrons}$$

Why are ions formed?

When atoms lose or gain electrons to form ions, all they're trying to do is get a full outer shell like a **noble gas** (also called a "stable electronic structure"). Atoms with full outer shells are very stable.

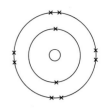

Figure 1: *The electronic structure of neon. Neon is a noble gas so has a full outer shell of electrons.*

Example 1

A potassium atom's electronic structure is 2, 8, 8, 1.
It gets rid of its single outer electron so it has a full outer shell: $K \rightarrow K^+ + e^-$
It now has the same electronic structure as argon: 2, 8, 8, and is stable.

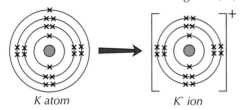

K atom ⟶ K⁺ ion

Tip: There's more on electronic structures on pages 44-45.

Example 2

An oxygen atom has six electrons in its outer shell — its electronic structure is 2, 6. It gains two electrons to fill its outer shell: $O + 2e^- \rightarrow O^{2-}$
It now has the same electronic structure as neon: 2, 8, so is stable.

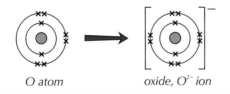

O atom ⟶ oxide, O^{2-} ion

Tip: Negatively charged ions have the end of their element name replaced with -ide, e.g. oxide, sulfide, fluoride, bromide.

Ionic charge and group number

You don't have to remember what ions most elements form — you can just look at the periodic table. Elements in the same **group** all have the same number of outer electrons. So they have to lose or gain the same number to get a full outer shell. And this means that they form ions with the same charges.

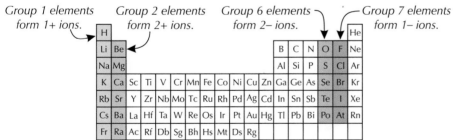

Figure 2: Periodic table group number and ionic charge.

Exam Tip
You'll be given a periodic table in the exam so don't worry about trying to memorise it.

Practice Questions — Fact Recall

Q1   What are ions?

Q2   What type of ions do metals form? What type do non-metals form?

Q3   What charge do the ions of Group 2 elements have?

- Know that ionic bonding takes place between ions with opposite charges.
- Know that metals and non-metals form ionic bonds when they react together to form compounds.
- Know that electrostatic forces hold ions together in ionic compounds.
- Know that ionic bonding involves the transfer of electrons from the outer shell of a metal to the outer shell of a non-metal atom.
- Be able to draw dot and cross diagrams to show electron transfer when metals in Groups 1 or 2 react with non-metals in Groups 6 or 7.

Specification References
5.2.1.1, 5.2.1.2

2. Ionic Bonding

There's loads to know about ionic bonding — what it is, how it works, how to represent it, working out formulas... So best crack on...

What is ionic bonding?

When metals react with non-metals, electrons are transferred from the metal atoms to the non-metal atoms. The metal atoms lose electrons to become positively charged ions with a full outer shell of electrons. The non-metal atoms gain electrons and become negatively charged ions with a full outer shell of electrons.

The oppositely charged ions are strongly attracted to each other, and this strong electrostatic attraction holds the ions together in the ionic compound. This is known as **ionic bonding**.

Representing ionic bonding

Dot and cross diagrams are used to show what happens during ionic bonding. The electrons in one type of atom are represented by dots, and the electrons in the other type of atom are represented by crosses. This means you can tell which atom the electrons in an ion originally came from. To show the charge on each ion, you use a big square bracket and a + or −.

Tip: Being able to interpret and draw diagrams to represent scientific ideas and models is an important skill.

WORKING SCIENTIFICALLY

Tip: Metals just have a few electrons in their outer shell. It's easier for them to lose these to get a full outer shell than to gain electrons to fill their outer shell up. The opposite is true for non-metals. It's easier for them to gain the few electrons they need to fill their outer shell up than to lose all their outer shell electrons.

Example

- A potassium atom has one electron in its outer shell.
- A chlorine atom has seven electrons in its outer shell.
- Potassium and chlorine react to form the compound potassium chloride, which is held together by ionic bonding.
- The potassium ion and the chloride ion both have full outer shells.

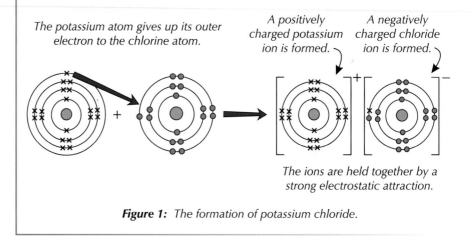

The potassium atom gives up its outer electron to the chlorine atom.

A positively charged potassium ion is formed.

A negatively charged chloride ion is formed.

The ions are held together by a strong electrostatic attraction.

***Figure 1:** The formation of potassium chloride.*

More dot and cross diagrams of ionic structures

You need to be able to draw dot and cross diagrams for all the ionic compounds formed between a Group 1 or 2 metal and a Group 6 or 7 non-metal.
The potassium chloride example on page 72 showed the bonding between a Group 1 metal and a Group 7 non-metal.
The examples below show the bonding in the other combinations.

Example 1

A Group 2 metal and a Group 6 non-metal — magnesium oxide
The magnesium atom gives up its two outer electrons, becoming an Mg^{2+} ion. The oxygen atom picks up the electrons, becoming an O^{2-} (oxide) ion.

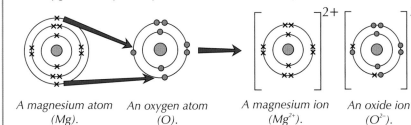

| A magnesium atom (Mg). | An oxygen atom (O). | A magnesium ion (Mg^{2+}). | An oxide ion (O^{2-}). |

Figure 2: *A representation of the electronic structures of the ions in magnesium oxide.*

Tip: Remember, you can work out how many electrons an atom will gain or lose from its group number. See page 71.

Example 2

A Group 2 metal and a Group 7 non-metal — calcium chloride
The calcium atom gives up its two outer electrons, becoming a Ca^{2+} ion. The two chlorine atoms pick up one electron each, becoming two Cl^- (chloride) ions.

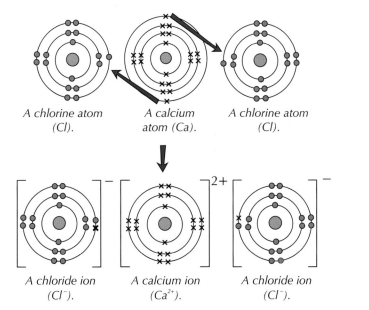

A chlorine atom (Cl).   A calcium atom (Ca).   A chlorine atom (Cl).

A chloride ion (Cl^-).   A calcium ion (Ca^{2+}).   A chloride ion (Cl^-).

Figure 3: *A representation of the electronic structures of the ions in calcium chloride.*

Tip: In reality, all electrons are identical. It's just for clarity that different representations are used.

Exam Tip
Don't forget to include the charge when you're drawing the electronic structures of ions — you won't get all the marks without it.

Tip: Sometimes only the outer, incomplete electron shells are shown in dot and cross diagrams. This can make it clearer to see what's going on. So, for example, a sodium atom could be shown as:

and a sodium ion as:

Example 3

A Group 1 metal and a Group 6 non-metal — sodium oxide
Two sodium atoms each give up their single outer electron, becoming two Na^+ ions. The oxygen atom picks up the two electrons, becoming an O^{2-} ion.

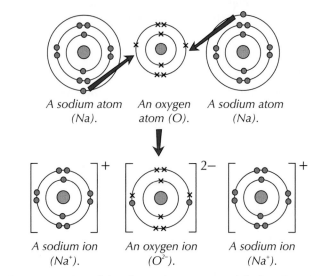

A sodium atom (Na).   An oxygen atom (O).   A sodium atom (Na).

A sodium ion (Na^+).   An oxygen ion (O^{2-}).   A sodium ion (Na^+).

Figure 4: *A representation of the electronic structures of the ions in sodium oxide.*

Practice Questions — Fact Recall

Q1   What is ionic bonding?

Q2   What types of elements do ionic bonds form between?

Q3   Draw dot and cross diagrams to show the electron transfer when the following compounds are formed:

a) potassium chloride

b) magnesium oxide

c) sodium oxide

Practice Questions — Application

Q1   Potassium reacts with iodine to form potassium iodide.

a) Describe, in terms of electrons and electron transfer, the reaction between potassium and iodine.

b) Explain why the electron transfer will be the same in the reaction in which potassium fluoride is formed.

Q2   Draw a dot and cross diagram to show the formation of lithium oxide from lithium and oxygen.

Q3   Which of the compounds below are held together by ionic bonds?

A: Hydrogen fluoride   B: Methane   C: Potassium chloride

Exam Tip
You may be asked to complete a dot and cross diagram that only shows the outer shell. Just do exactly the same as usual but ignore the electrons in inner energy levels.

3. Ionic Compounds

Ionic compounds actually form giant structures containing many, many ions. Of course, in the world of chemistry, a grain of salt counts as 'giant'...

The structure of ionic compounds

Ionic compounds have a structure called a giant ionic **lattice** (a closely-packed regular arrangement). There are very strong **electrostatic forces** of attraction between oppositely charged ions which act in all directions. Ionic compounds can be represented in different ways:

1. Dot and cross diagrams

These were covered on pages 72-73. They are useful for showing how ionic compounds are formed, but they don't show the structure of the compound, the relative sizes of the ions or how they're arranged.

2. 3D models

3D models show the relative sizes of the ions, as well as the regular pattern in an ionic crystal. However, they only let you see the outer layer of the compound.

> **Example**
>
> Here's a representation of a 3D model of a tiny part of a sodium chloride (salt) crystal. A whole crystal (see Figure 1) would actually consist of billions of ions. The Na^+ and Cl^- ions are held together in a regular, cuboid-shaped lattice.
>
>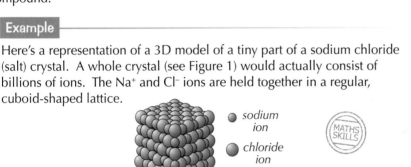
>
> ● sodium ion
> ● chloride ion

3. Ball and stick models

Like 3D models, ball and stick models show the regular pattern in an ionic lattice, as well as how all the ions are arranged. In addition, they suggest that the crystal extends beyond what is shown in the diagram. They may show the relative sizes of the ions (see Figure 2), but sometimes the ions are not shown to scale. Another disadvantage of them is that they suggest that there are gaps between the ions, when in reality there aren't.

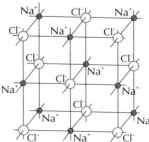

Figure 2: *Ball and stick model of the sodium chloride lattice showing relative ion sizes.*

Learning Objectives:

- Know that ionic compounds are giant structures of ions, held together in a lattice by electrostatic forces known as ionic bonds.

- Know that ionic compounds can be represented by different types of models and diagrams and that each type has its limitations.

- Be able to identify that a structure is ionic from a diagram of it.

- Know the structure of sodium chloride.

- Be able to work out the empirical formula of an ionic compound from a diagram showing the types of ions it contains.

- Know why ionic compounds have high melting and boiling points and why they conduct electricity when they are melted or dissolved in water.

Specification References
5.2.1.3, 5.2.2.3

Tip: The ability to use 2D representations of 3D objects is an important maths skill.

Figure 1: *Crystals of salt.*

Exam Tip
You need to know the structure of sodium chloride for the exam.

Tip: $MgCl_2$ is an empirical formula — the simplest whole number ratio of atoms in a compound. In reality you'd never get just one magnesium ion and two chloride ions stuck together. They form a giant lattice with twice as many chloride ions as magnesium ions.

Working out the formula of an ionic compound

You need to be able to find the **empirical formula** of an ionic compound from a diagram of it.

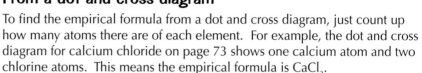

From a dot and cross diagram

To find the empirical formula from a dot and cross diagram, just count up how many atoms there are of each element. For example, the dot and cross diagram for calcium chloride on page 73 shows one calcium atom and two chlorine atoms. This means the empirical formula is $CaCl_2$.

From a 3D model or a ball and stick model

This is slightly trickier. You need to use the diagram to work out what ions are in the ionic compound. You then have to balance the charges of the ions so that the overall charge on the compound is zero.

Tip: When writing formulas, it's convention to put the metal first. So, MgO, not OMg.

Example 1

This ball and stick model shows that sodium chloride contains sodium (Na^+) and chloride (Cl^-) ions.

Because a sodium ion has a 1+ charge and a chloride ion has a 1– charge only one of each ion is needed to balance out the charges.

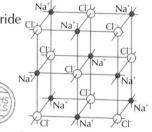

$$(+1) + (-1) = 0$$

So the empirical formula for sodium chloride is NaCl.

Tip: See page 71 for how to use group numbers to work out the charges on ions.

Example 2

This 3D model shows that the compound contains potassium and oxide ions.

Potassium is in Group 1 so forms 1+ ions. Oxygen is in Group 6 so forms 2– ions.

A potassium ion only has a 1+ charge, so you'll need two of them to balance out the 2– charge of an oxide ion.

○ = Potassium ion
● = Oxide ion

$$(+1) + (+1) + (-2) = 0$$

The empirical formula is K_2O.

Properties of ionic compounds

The bonding in ionic compounds affects their properties.

Tip: It might seem odd that ionic compounds require a lot of energy to melt, but dissolve so easily in water. This is because parts of water molecules are slightly charged and so can pull the ions away from the lattice.

Melting and boiling point

Ionic compounds all have high melting points and high boiling points due to the strong electrostatic attraction between the ions. It takes a large amount of energy to overcome this attraction and break the many strong bonds.

Solubility

Most ionic compounds dissolve easily in water.

Electrical conductivity

Ionic compounds don't conduct electricity when solid because the ions are all held in fixed positions. However, when they're melted or dissolved, the ions are free to move and they'll carry electric charge.

Tip: An electric current is a flow of charged particles, which can either be ions or free electrons.

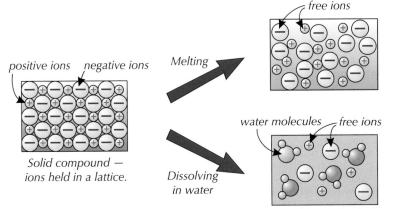

Figure 3: Particle diagrams of an ionic compound when solid, melted and dissolved.

Figure 4: The ionic compound potassium chloride conducts electricity when it's dissolved in water. It completes the circuit so the bulb lights up.

Practice Questions — Fact Recall

Q1   What type of structure do ionic compounds have?

Q2   Give one advantage and one disadvantage of using each of the following representations to show ionic bonding:

   a) dot and cross diagrams

   b) 3D models

   c) ball and stick models

Q3   Sketch a ball and stick model of part of a sodium chloride lattice.

Q4   Explain how you work out the empirical formula of an ionic compound from a 3D diagram of it.

Q5   Describe the properties of ionic compounds including melting point, solubility and conductivity.

Exam Tip
If you're asked to describe the electrical conductivity of a substance, make sure you consider its conductivity in different states, including what happens when the substance is in solution.

Practice Questions — Application

Q1   Magnesium reacts with iodine to form magnesium iodide.

   a) What type of structure does magnesium iodide have?

   b) What is the formula of magnesium iodide?

Q2   Use the diagram on the right to work out the empirical formula of the compound.

$\bigcirc$ = Cs^+ ion
$\bigcirc$ = Cl^- ion

Q3   Which of these substances is most likely to be potassium chloride?

Substance	Melting point	Soluble in water	Conducts electricity when solid
A	-39	Yes	Yes
B	770	Yes	No

Tip: Before working out the formula of a compound, you need to find the charge on each of the ions in the compound using their group numbers — see page 71.

- Know that covalent bonding takes place between atoms that share pairs of electrons.

- Know that a covalent bond is a strong electrostatic force between the positive nuclei of the atoms and the pair of electrons they share.

- Know that covalent bonds are formed between atoms of non-metallic elements.

- Know that covalent molecules can be represented in several ways and that each representation has advantages and disadvantages.

- Be able to find the molecular formula of a compound from a diagram of it.

Specification References
5.2.1.1, 5.2.1.4

4. Covalent Bonding

Ionic bonding — done. Next up is covalent bonding, which is all about atoms sharing their electrons.

What is covalent bonding?

A **covalent bond** is formed when a pair of electrons is shared between two atoms. Atoms share electrons with each other to get full outer shells (highest energy levels). They only share electrons in their outer shells and both atoms involved in the bond end up with one extra electron in their outer shell. The positively charged nuclei of the bonded atoms are attracted to the shared pair of electrons by electrostatic forces, making covalent bonds very strong.

Each single covalent bond provides one extra shared electron for each atom. Each atom involved has to make enough covalent bonds to fill up its outer shell so they have the electronic structure of a noble gas (which is very stable). See Figure 1 for a reminder of how many electrons the first three shells can hold.

Covalent bonds occur between non-metal atoms. This can either be in non-metallic elements, e.g. Cl_2 or O_2, or in compounds of non-metals, e.g. H_2O or CH_4.

Representing covalent bonding

There are a few different ways of representing covalent bonding. They each have their advantages and disadvantages.

Shell	Max. number of electrons
1st	2
2nd	8
3rd	8

Figure 1: *Table showing the number of electrons each shell (energy level) can hold.*

Tip: Just the outer electron shells are shown in these diagrams.

1. Dot and cross diagrams

In dot and cross diagrams, the shared electrons can be drawn in the overlap between the outer orbitals of the two atoms.

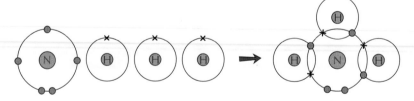

Figure 2: *Dot and cross diagrams showing covalent bonding in ammonia.*

Sometimes the orbitals aren't shown.

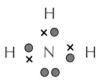

Figure 3: *Dot and cross diagram without orbitals.*

Dot and cross diagrams can also represent **double covalent bonds**, such as those formed by the oxygen atoms in oxygen gas. To get full outer shells, each oxygen atom has to share two electrons with another oxygen atom, meaning two pairs of electrons are shared between each pair of oxygen atoms.

Tip: If an atom shares one pair of electrons with one atom and another pair of electrons with another atom then there are two single bonds. You get <u>double bonds</u> when two atoms share two pairs of electrons with each other.

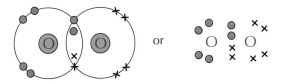

Figure 4: *Dot and cross diagrams showing the double covalent bond in oxygen.*

Dot and cross diagrams are useful for showing which atoms the electrons in a covalent bond come from, but they don't show the relative sizes of the atoms, or how the atoms are arranged in space.

2. Displayed formulas

A displayed formula shows the covalent bonds as single lines between atoms.

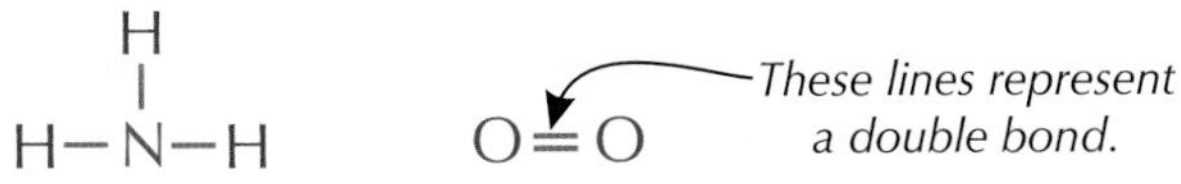

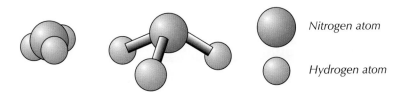

Figure 5: *Displayed formulas of ammonia and oxygen.*

This is a great way of showing how atoms are connected in large molecules. However, they don't show the 3D structure of the molecule, or which atoms the electrons in the covalent bond have come from.

Exam Tip
When drawing displayed formulas make sure you show every bond in the molecule.

3. 3D models and ball and stick models

A 3D model shows the atoms and their arrangement in space. Ball and stick models show the bonds, whereas other 3D models don't.

Nitrogen atom

Hydrogen atom

Figure 6: *3D models of ammonia. The second is a ball and stick model showing the bonds.*

Ball and stick models can show double bonds clearly too.

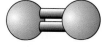

Figure 8: *Ball and stick model showing an oxygen molecule.*

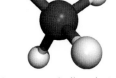

Figure 7: *A ball and stick model of methane.*

A disadvantage of 3D models is that they can quickly get confusing for large molecules where there are lots of atoms to include. They don't show where the electrons in the bonds have come from, either.

Finding molecular formulas

You can find the **molecular formula** of a simple molecular compound by counting up how many atoms of each element there are in a diagram of the molecule.

Example 1

In ammonia, there is one nitrogen atom and three hydrogen atoms, so the molecular formula is NH_3.

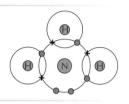

Example 2

The displayed formula of ethane is shown on the right.

There are two carbons and six hydrogen atoms. So the molecular formula is C_2H_6.

$$H-\overset{\displaystyle H}{\underset{\displaystyle H}{C}}-\overset{\displaystyle H}{\underset{\displaystyle H}{C}}-H$$

Practice Questions — Fact Recall

Q1 What types of atoms form covalent bonds?

Q2 What is a double covalent bond?

Q3 Draw dot and cross diagrams to represent the following molecules.

a) ammonia   b) oxygen

Q4 How are covalent bonds shown in displayed formulas?

Q5 Give one advantage and one disadvantage of the following representations of covalent molecules.

a) dot and cross diagrams   b) 3D models

Practice Questions — Application

Q1 Draw the displayed formulas of Molecules A, B and C.

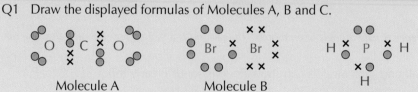

Q2 Lithium reacts with hydrogen to form lithium hydride, LiH. Would you expect the bond between lithium and hydrogen to be covalent? Explain your answer.

Q3 Write down the molecular formulas of the compounds below:

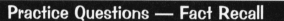

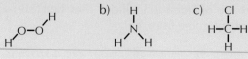

5. Simple Molecular Substances

Learning Objectives:
- Know that small molecules contain covalent bonds.
- Be able to represent the bonding in the simple molecules H_2, Cl_2, HCl, CH_4, NH_3, H_2O, O_2 and N_2.
- Be able to explain why simple molecular substances do not conduct electricity.
- Know that intermolecular forces exist between simple molecules and that the intermolecular forces are much weaker than the covalent bonds inside the molecules.
- Be able to explain, in terms of intermolecular forces, why simple molecular substances have low melting and boiling points and are usually gases or liquids at room temperature.
- Be able to explain why larger molecules have higher melting and boiling points.

Specification References
5.2.1.4, 5.2.2.4

There are two very different types of covalent substances — simple molecules and macromolecules. First, the simple molecules...

Simple molecules

Simple molecules are made up of only a few atoms joined by **covalent bonds**. Hydrogen, chlorine, hydrogen chloride, methane, ammonia, water, nitrogen and oxygen are all examples of simple molecules, and you need to know the bonding in them all. Ammonia and oxygen were covered on pages 78-79, and here are the other six.

1. Hydrogen (H_2)

Hydrogen atoms have just one electron. They only need one more to complete the first shell, so they often form **single covalent bonds** to achieve this (see Figure 1).

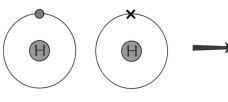

Two hydrogen atoms.

The hydrogen atoms share one pair of electrons to form one covalent bond. Both atoms now have full outer shells.

Figure 1: *The formation of a covalent bond between hydrogen atoms.*

As mentioned on pages 78-79, you can also represent the bonding as a dot and cross diagram without the orbitals, or as a displayed formula.

In this representation, only the electrons are shown.

Here, the line represents the covalent bond.

WORKING SCIENTIFICALLY

Figure 2: *Alternative representations of the bonding in hydrogen molecules.*

2. Chlorine (Cl_2)

Chlorine atoms need one more electron to gain a stable electronic structure. So, two chlorine atoms each share one of their electrons to form a chlorine molecule containing one shared pair of electrons — a single covalent bond.

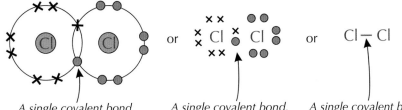

A single covalent bond.   *A single covalent bond.*   *A single covalent bond.*

Figure 3: *Representations of covalent bonding in chlorine.*

Figure 4: *Chlorine is a yellow-green gas at room temperature.*

Tip: Hydrogen chloride dissolves in water to form hydrochloric acid.

3. Hydrogen chloride (HCl)

The bonding in hydrogen chloride is very similar to the bonding in H_2 and Cl_2. Again, both atoms only need one more electron to complete their outer shells, so they share one pair of electrons and one single covalent bond is formed.

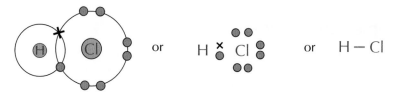

Figure 5: Representations of covalent bonding in hydrogen chloride.

4. Methane (CH₄)

Carbon has four outer electrons, which is half a full shell. So it forms four covalent bonds to make up its outer shell. Hydrogen atoms only need to form one covalent bond to achieve a full outer shell. So a carbon atom will form covalent bonds with four hydrogen atoms to form a CH_4 molecule (methane).

Tip: It's easy to think that methane molecules are flat when you see diagrams like this. They're actually tetrahedral shapes (imagine one hydrogen at each corner of a triangular-based pyramid and the carbon atom in the centre of it). This is one of the disadvantages of dot and cross diagrams and displayed formulas — you can't see the shape of the molecule.

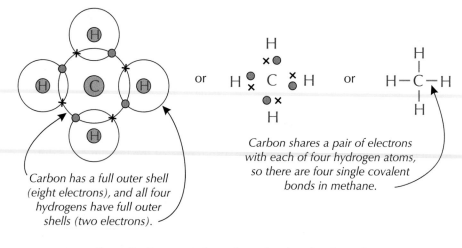

Carbon has a full outer shell (eight electrons), and all four hydrogens have full outer shells (two electrons).

Carbon shares a pair of electrons with each of four hydrogen atoms, so there are four single covalent bonds in methane.

Figure 6: Representations of covalent bonding in methane.

5. Water (H₂O)

Oxygen atoms have six outer electrons. They sometimes form ionic bonds by taking two electrons from other atoms to complete their outer shell (see page 73). However they'll also form covalent bonds and share two electrons instead. In water molecules, the oxygen shares electrons with two hydrogen atoms to form two single covalent bonds.

Exam Tip
Always check you've got the bonding right by counting the number of electrons each atom has in its outer shell. If it's not got a full outer shell you've gone wrong somewhere.

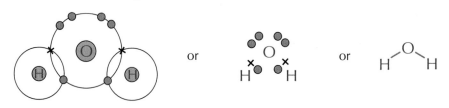

Figure 7: Representations of covalent bonding in water.

6. Nitrogen (N₂)

A nitrogen atom has five electrons in its outer shell, so it needs three more to fill it. Two nitrogen atoms can each fill their shells by sharing three pairs of electrons. This creates a **triple bond**.

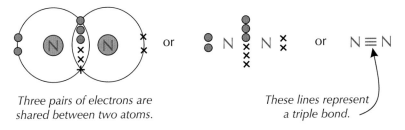

Three pairs of electrons are shared between two atoms.

These lines represent a triple bond.

Tip: The triple bond is really strong. That's why nitrogen gas is so unreactive.

Figure 8: *Representations of covalent bonding in nitrogen.*

Properties of simple molecules

All simple molecular substances have similar properties.

Electrical conductivity

Covalent substances made up of simple molecules don't conduct electricity in any state — there are no ions or free electrons so there's nothing to carry an electrical charge.

Melting and boiling points

Covalent substances, made up of simple molecules, have low melting and boiling points, so they are mostly gases or liquids at room temperature, but they can be solids.

The reason for the low melting and boiling points is that, although the atoms within the small molecules form very strong covalent bonds with each other, the forces of attraction between the molecules (**intermolecular forces**) are very weak (see Figure 10). It's the intermolecular forces that must be overcome in order to melt or boil a simple molecular substances — not the much stronger covalent bonds. Overcoming these weak intermolecular forces doesn't take much energy, so the melting and boiling points are low.

Tip: Substances made of larger molecules are more likely to be solid at room temperature — more on page 85.

Figure 9: *Water is a simple molecular compound. Not much energy is needed to break the intermolecular forces and melt it so it's a liquid at room temperature.*

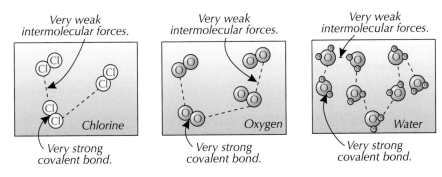

Very weak intermolecular forces.

Very weak intermolecular forces.

Very weak intermolecular forces.

Chlorine

Oxygen

Water

Very strong covalent bond.

Very strong covalent bond.

Very strong covalent bond.

Figure 10: *The bonding within and between simple molecules.*

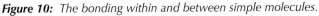

Trends in melting and boiling points

Exam Tip
If you're asked to compare or explain boiling or melting points of molecular compounds, make sure you look at the number of electron shells the atoms have. The more electron shells, the larger the atom and the greater the strength of the intermolecular forces.

As molecules get bigger, the strength of the intermolecular forces increases, so more energy is needed to break them, and the melting and boiling points increase.

Example

- The Group 7 halogens all form simple covalent molecules.

- The molecules increase in size down the group because the atoms have extra electron shells.

- This means the intermolecular forces increase and so the melting and boiling points do too.

Element	Melting point (°C)	Boiling point (°C)
Fluorine, F_2	−220	−188
Chlorine, Cl_2	−101	−34
Bromine, Br_2	−7	59
Iodine, I_2	114	184

Increasing size

Figure 11: *Iodine is a solid at room temperature, whilst all the halogens above it in the group are liquids or gases.*

Practice Questions — Fact Recall

Q1 What is a simple molecule?

Q2 Name the molecules shown by the dot and cross diagrams below.

a) 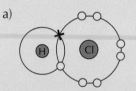 b)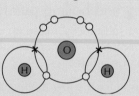

Q3 Draw dot and cross diagrams to represent the following molecules.

a) hydrogen b) chlorine c) methane

Q4 Draw the displayed formula of a nitrogen gas molecule.

Q5 Simple molecular substances have low melting points. Explain why.

Q6 Do simple molecules conduct electricity? Give a reason for this.

Practice Questions — Application

Tip: Each atom wants to end up with a full outer shell of electrons, so work out how many extra electrons each needs.

Q1 An element, 'A', has 3 shells of electrons. Its 3rd shell contains seven electrons. 'A' covalently bonds to hydrogen. Describe and explain the bonding in the molecule that is formed.

Q2 Under normal conditions, sulfur exists as S_8 molecules and phosphorus exists as P_4 molecules.

Use this information to predict which element will have the highest melting point. Give a reason for your answer.

6. Larger Covalent Substances

The previous pages have looked at simple covalent molecules. Now it's time for the larger ones — those in polymers and giant covalent structures.

Polymers

A **polymer** consists of lots of long molecules made up of repeating sections. All the atoms in a polymer molecule are joined by strong covalent bonds. Polymer molecules are formed when lots of small units link together.

> ### Example
>
> Many ethene molecules can be joined up to produce poly(ethene) or "polythene".
>
>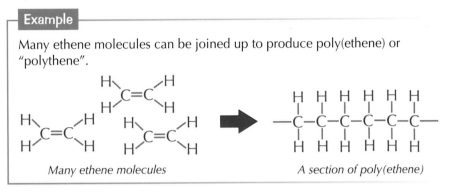
>
> Many ethene molecules   A section of poly(ethene)

A polymer molecule can contain thousands or even millions of atoms, so it would be pretty difficult to draw in full. Instead you can draw the shortest repeating section, called the **repeating unit**, put it in large brackets and put an *n* after the brackets to show it's repeated many times.

> ### Example
>
> Here's the short way of drawing a poly(ethene) molecule.
>
>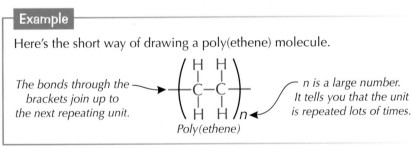
>
> The bonds through the brackets join up to the next repeating unit.   *n is a large number. It tells you that the unit is repeated lots of times.*
>
> *Poly(ethene)*

Writing the molecular formula of a polymer

To write the **molecular formula** of a polymer, write down the molecular formula of the repeating unit by counting the number of atoms of each element it contains, put brackets around it and put an 'n' after the brackets.

> ### Example
>
> So the molecular formula of a poly(ethene) molecule is $(C_2H_4)_n$.

Melting and boiling points of polymers

Polymers have higher melting and boiling points than simple covalent molecules. This is because the **intermolecular forces** between the larger polymer molecules are stronger, so more energy is needed to break them. This means most polymers are solid at room temperature. However, the intermolecular forces in polymers are still weaker than ionic or covalent bonds, so they generally have lower boiling points than ionic or giant covalent compounds (see next page).

Learning Objectives:

- Know that polymers have large molecules made up of atoms joined by covalent bonds.
- Be able to interpret and draw diagrams to represent polymers.
- Be able to work out the molecular formulas of polymers.
- Be able to explain why polymers are solids at room temperature.
- Know that diamond, graphite and silicon dioxide are giant covalent structures (macromolecules).
- Understand why giant covalent substances have high melting and boiling points.

Specification References 5.2.1.4, 5.2.2.5, 5.2.2.6

Tip: It's only the intermolecular forces that need to be overcome in order to melt a polymer. The covalent bonds inside the molecules don't need to be broken.

Giant covalent structures

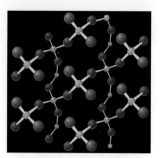

Figure 1: *The structure of silicon dioxide. Silicon dioxide, sometimes called silica, is what sand is made of. Each grain of sand is one giant structure of silicon and oxygen.*

Giant covalent structures (**macromolecules**) are similar to giant ionic structures (**lattices**) but there are no charged ions. Instead, all the atoms are bonded to each other by strong covalent bonds. Common examples are diamond and graphite, which are both made only from carbon atoms, and silicon dioxide (silica) — see Figure 1.

To melt or boil a giant covalent molecule you need to overcome the strong covalent bonds between the atoms. This takes a lot of energy, so giant molecules have very high melting and boiling points.

Tip: Diamond and graphite are allotropes of carbon — different structural forms of the same element. There's more on them on the next page.

Example

In diamond, each carbon atom forms four covalent bonds with other carbon atoms. The diagram shows just a tiny part of the macromolecule — in reality it contains many more atoms.

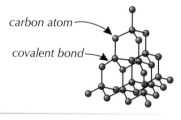

carbon atom

covalent bond

Practice Questions — Fact Recall

Q1 What is a polymer?

Q2 a) Put the following in order of melting point, starting with the lowest melting point.

    A: Giant covalent substance
    B: Simple molecular substance
    C: Polymer

    b) Explain the reasons for this order.

Practice Questions — Application

Q1 The diagram shows the structure of the repeating unit of a polymer. Draw a representation of the polymer and give its molecular formula.

Q2 The table below shows the melting points of poly(ethene), oxygen and diamond (under certain conditions).

Substance	Melting Point
A	110 °C
B	3500 °C
C	−218 °C

Match the letters A, B and C to the substance they represent.

Q3 The diagram shows a representation of a molecule of poly(propene). Give the molecular formula of the polymer.

7. Allotropes of Carbon

Allotropes are just different structural forms of the same element in the same physical state, e.g. they're all solids. Carbon has four allotropes you need to know about — diamond, graphite, graphene and fullerenes.

Diamond

In diamond, each carbon atom forms four covalent bonds with other carbon atoms. This forms a very rigid structure, which is why diamond is so hard. Diamond also has a very high melting point because the strong covalent bonds take a lot of energy to overcome. It doesn't conduct electricity because it has no free electrons or ions.

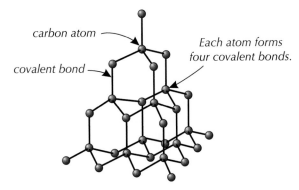

carbon atom

Each atom forms four covalent bonds.

covalent bond

Figure 1: The structure of diamond.

Graphite

In graphite, each carbon atom only forms three covalent bonds. This creates sheets of carbon atoms arranged in hexagons. There aren't any covalent bonds between the layers — they're only held together by weak **intermolecular forces**, so they're free to move over each other. This makes graphite soft and slippery, so it's ideal as a lubricating material.

Graphite has a high melting point because the covalent bonds in the layers need a lot of energy to break. Only three out of each carbon's four outer electrons are used in bonds, so each carbon atom has one electron that's delocalised (free) and can move. This means that graphite conducts electricity and thermal energy.

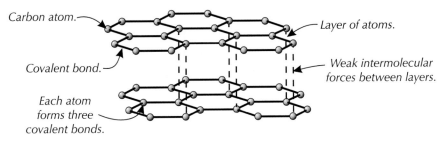

Carbon atom.

Layer of atoms.

Covalent bond.

Weak intermolecular forces between layers.

Each atom forms three covalent bonds.

Figure 3: The structure of graphite.

Learning Objectives:

- Know the structures of diamond, graphite and graphene and be able to explain their properties in terms of their structures.

- Know that graphene has properties that make it useful in composite materials and in electronics.

- Know that fullerenes are hollow molecules made of carbon atoms arranged in rings.

- Know the structure of Buckminsterfullerene, the first fullerene that was discovered.

- Know what nanotubes are and their main properties.

- Know some uses of fullerenes.

- Be able to explain how the properties of nanotubes make them suitable for its uses.

Specification References
5.2.3.1, 5.2.3.2,
5.2.3.3

Figure 2: A cut, polished and sparkly diamond.

Tip: A substance needs charged particles (ions or electrons) which are free to move in order to conduct electricity.

Figure 4: Graphite. Not as nice as diamond. :(

Graphene

Graphene is a sheet of carbon atoms joined together in hexagons. It's basically a single layer of graphite. The sheet is just one atom thick, making it a two-dimensional substance.

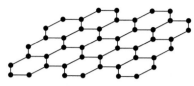

Figure 5: *The structure of graphene.*

The network of covalent bonds makes graphene very strong. It's also incredibly light, so can be added to composite materials to improve their strength without adding much weight. Like graphite, it contains delocalised electrons so can conduct electricity through the whole structure. This means it has the potential to be used in electronics.

Fullerenes

Fullerenes are hollow molecules of carbon, shaped like tubes or balls. They're mainly made up of carbon atoms arranged in hexagons, but can also contain pentagons (rings of five carbon atoms) or heptagons (rings of seven carbon atoms).

Tip: Other balls of carbon atoms have since been made, e.g. C_{70}.

Examples

- Buckminsterfullerene was the first fullerene to be discovered. It's got the molecular formula C_{60} and forms a hollow sphere containing 20 hexagons and 12 pentagons.

Tip: This is the basic nanotube structure, but there are loads of interesting variations, such as tubes within tubes.

- Nanotubes are fullerenes which are tiny carbon cylinders. The ratio between the length and the diameter of nanotubes is very high. They're good conductors of heat and electricity.

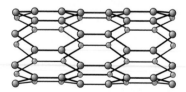

Tip: Science isn't just about facts in a book. You need to be able to explain the applications and uses of some areas of chemistry, such as fullerenes.

Uses of fullerenes

1. In medicine
Fullerenes can be used to 'cage' other molecules. The fullerene structure forms around another atom or molecule, which is then trapped inside. This could be used to deliver a drug to where it is needed in the body in a highly controlled way.

Tip: Catalysts speed up the rates of chemical reactions without being used up themselves (see p.166-167)

2. As catalysts
Fullerenes have a huge surface area, so they could help make great industrial catalysts — individual catalyst molecules could be attached to the fullerenes (the bigger the surface area the better).

3. As lubricants

Coating moving machine parts in fullerenes dramatically reduces friction. They could one day also be used to reduce friction in artificial joints.

4. Strengthening materials

Nanotubes have a high tensile strength (they don't break when stretched) so can be used to strengthen materials without adding much weight, such as in tennis racket frames.

5. In electronics

Nanotubes can conduct electricity, and they're very small, so they can be used in very small electrical circuits, for example in the microchips found in computers and phones.

Tip: Technology that uses small particles such as nanotubes is called nanotechnology.

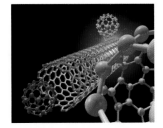

Figure 6: *Computer artwork of buckyballs (buckminsterfullerene) and nanotubes.*

Practice Questions — Fact Recall

Q1 Which statement(s) below describe(s) the structure of graphite?

   A Each carbon atom is covalently bonded to four other atoms.

   B The layers are held together by weak intermolecular forces.

   C Electrons not involved in covalent bonding are delocalised.

Q2 Which allotrope of carbon doesn't conduct electricity? Explain why this is.

Q3 What is graphene?

Q4 Which of the diagrams below shows the arrangement of carbon atoms found in graphene?

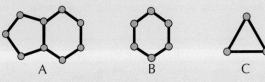

   A   B   C

Q5 What are fullerenes?

Q6 What is the molecular formula of buckminsterfullerene?

Q7 Give two properties of nanotubes.

Q8 Describe three uses of fullerenes.

Practice Question — Application

Q1 Match the properties listed below with the correct substance.

Substance   Properties

Ammonia

Graphite

Diamond

Conducts electricity.
Melting point = 3500 °C

Doesn't conduct electricity.
Melting point = 3500 °C

Doesn't conduct electricity.
Melting point = −78 °C

- Know that metals are giant structures in which the atoms have regular arrangements.
- Know that electrons from the outer shells of metal atoms are delocalised.
- Understand how strong electrostatic attraction between the delocalised electrons and the positively charged metal ions holds the metal together.
- Be able to draw diagrams to represent the bonding in metals.
- Know the properties of metals and be able to explain them in terms of metallic structure and bonding.
- Know what an alloy is and why alloys are harder than pure metals.

Specification References
5.2.1.1, 5.2.1.5
5.2.2.7, 5.2.2.8

8. Metallic Bonding

Metallic bonding is the final type of bonding in this section. There's no complicated transferring or sharing of electrons between specific atoms, so it's probably the most straightforward type of bonding.

The structure of metals

Metals consist of a giant structure. The atoms in a metal are arranged in a regular pattern (see Figure 1). Metals are said to have giant structures because they have lots of atoms. Exactly how many depends on how big the piece of metal is.

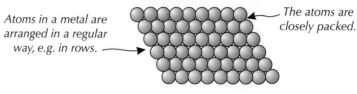

Atoms in a metal are arranged in a regular way, e.g. in rows.

The atoms are closely packed.

Figure 1: *The structure of a metal.*

Bonding in metals

In metals, the electrons in the outer shells of the atoms are **delocalised**. This means that they aren't associated with a particular atom or bond — they're free to move through the whole structure (see Figure 2). There are strong forces of electrostatic attraction between the positive metal ions and the negative electrons and these forces, known as metallic bonding, hold the metal structure together.

Metal atoms become positively charged when they lose electrons.

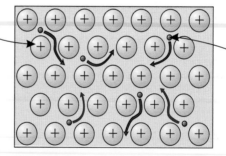

Free electrons move throughout the structure.

Figure 2: *Delocalised electrons within a giant metallic structure.*

Properties of metals

High melting and boiling points

The electrostatic forces between the metal atoms and the delocalised sea of electrons are very strong, so need lots of energy to be broken. This means that most compounds with metallic bonds have very high melting and boiling points, so they're generally solid at room temperature.

Conductivity

Metals have delocalised electrons that are free to move through the whole structure. Because of this, they are good conductors of thermal energy and electricity. The electrons carry the charge or the thermal energy through the structure.

Malleability

Metals consist of atoms held together in a regular structure. The atoms form layers that are able to slide over each other — see Figure 3. This means they are malleable — they can be bent and shaped, as well as hammered or rolled into shapes.

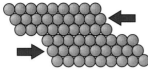

Figure 3: Layers of atoms in a metal sliding over each other.

Figure 4: Lead lining on a roof pressed into shape.

Alloys

Pure metals often aren't quite right for certain jobs — they're often too soft when they're pure so are mixed with other metals to make them harder. Most of the metals we use everyday are alloys — a mixture of two or more metals or a metal and another element. Alloys are harder and so more useful than pure metals.

Examples

- Pure gold is mixed with copper and silver to make it harder.

- Copper is alloyed with zinc to make brass, e.g. for pipes or musical instruments. Another alloy of copper is bronze which contains tin. It's used in sculptures and electrical connectors.

Different elements have different sized atoms. So when another element is mixed with a pure metal, the new element atoms will distort the layers of metal atoms, making it more difficult for them to slide over each other (see Figure 5). This is why alloys are harder than pure metals.

Tip: The exact properties of alloys can be adjusted by varying the proportion of each metal. E.g. the higher the copper content in a gold alloy, the redder it will be.

Practice Questions — Fact Recall

Q1 Describe the structure of a metal.

Q2 What type of forces hold the particles in a metal together?

Q3 Explain why metals can be easily bent.

Q4 Metals are good conductors of heat. Explain why.

Q5 Why are alloys harder than pure metals?

Figure 5: Distorted layers of atoms in an alloy.

Topic Checklist — Make sure you know...

Ions

☐ That metals lose electrons to form positive ions and non-metals gain electrons to form negative ions.

☐ That ions formed by Group 1, 2, 6 and 7 elements have the stable electronic structure of a noble gas.

☐ That the charge on an ion is related to the element's group number in the periodic table.

Ionic Bonding

☐ That ionic bonding occurs between metals and non-metals.

☐ That ionic bonding involves the transfer of electrons to form ions with full outer shells of electrons.

☐ How to represent the electron transfer in ionic bonding using dot and cross diagrams.

Ionic Compounds

☐ That ions in ionic compounds are held together in a giant lattice by electrostatic forces.

☐ The different ways of representing ionic compounds, and the pros and cons of each representation.

☐ The structure of sodium chloride.

☐ How to work out the empirical formula of an ionic compound from a diagram showing its structure.

☐ That a lot of energy is needed to overcome the electrostatic forces and melt or boil the compound.

☐ That melted or dissolved ionic compounds can conduct electricity because the ions are free to move.

Covalent Bonding

☐ That non-metal atoms form covalent bonds by sharing electrons to fill their outer shells of electrons.

☐ The different ways of representing simple molecules, and the pros and cons of each representation.

☐ How to work out the molecular formula of a simple molecule from a diagram of it.

Simple Molecular Substances

☐ How to represent the bonding in simple molecules using dot and cross diagrams.

☐ That the intermolecular forces in simple covalent substances are very weak and not much energy is needed to overcome them, so simple covalent substances have low melting and boiling points.

☐ That bigger molecules have stronger intermolecular forces and so higher melting and boiling points.

☐ That simple molecules have no free ions or electrons so don't conduct electricity.

cont...

Larger Covalent Substances

☐ That polymers contain large covalent molecules made up of repeating units.

☐ How to draw diagrams and write formulas to represent polymer molecules.

☐ That polymers are mostly solid at room temperature due to their strong intermolecular forces.

☐ That diamond, graphite and silicon dioxide have giant covalent structures.

☐ That all the atoms in macromolecules are joined by strong covalent bonds and large amounts of energy are needed to break these bonds, so macromolecules have very high melting points.

Allotropes of Carbon

☐ The structure of diamond and how this explains why it is so hard and doesn't conduct electricity.

☐ The structure of graphite and how this explains why it is soft and slippery and a good conductor.

☐ What graphene is and why it is used in electronics and composites.

☐ What fullerenes are (including Buckminsterfullerene and nanotubes).

☐ Some uses of fullerenes, e.g. in drug delivery and in strengthening materials.

Metallic Bonding

☐ That metals consist of giant structures in which the atoms are held together by delocalised electrons.

☐ That the strong electrostatic forces between the metal atoms and the delocalised electrons take a lot of energy to break so the melting and boiling points of metals are generally high.

☐ That the delocalised electrons mean that metals conduct electricity and heat.

☐ That metals can be bent and shaped because the layers of metal atoms can slide over each other.

☐ That alloys are harder than pure metals because atoms of another element are added, disrupting the layers and stopping them from sliding over each other.

1   Different substances have different structures.

1.1   Draw a straight line from each structure listed below to the name of the substance that has that structure.

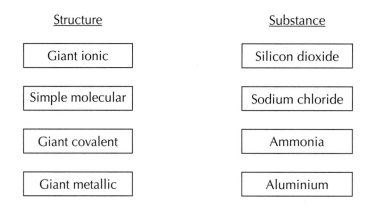

Structure	Substance
Giant ionic	Silicon dioxide
Simple molecular	Sodium chloride
Giant covalent	Ammonia
Giant metallic	Aluminium

(4 marks)

1.2   The structure of a substance affects its properties. The melting point, boiling point and electrical conductivity of four substances were tested. The results are shown in the table below.

Substance	Melting point (°C)	Boiling point (°C)	Good electrical conductor?
A	−218.4	−182.96	No
B	1535	2750	Yes
C	1410	2355	No
D	801	1413	When molten

Use the words in the box to complete the sentences below.
You can use each structure once, more than once or not at all.

giant ionic   simple molecular   giant covalent   giant metallic

Substance A has a .... structure.

Substance B has a .... structure.

Substance C has a .... structure.

Substance D has a .... structure.

(4 marks)

2 Lithium chloride is formed from lithium and chlorine. The diagrams below show the electronic structures of the outer shells of lithium and chlorine atoms.

Lithium atom   Chlorine atom

2.1 Name the type of bonding found in chlorine gas.

(1 mark)

2.2 Explain, as fully as you can, why chlorine is a gas at room temperature.

(3 marks)

2.3 The electronic structures of lithium and chlorine change when they react together.
Describe the changes in the electronic structures of lithium and chlorine when they react.

(3 marks)

2.4 Complete the diagram below to show the electronic structures of the particles formed during the reaction of lithium and chlorine.

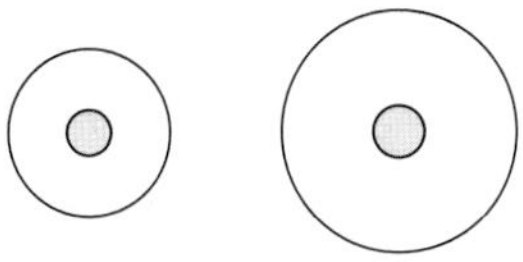

(3 marks)

2.5 Give the chemical formula of lithium chloride.

(1 mark)

2.6 Lithium chloride has a high melting point. Explain why.

(2 marks)

3 A section of a molecule of the polymer polychlorotrifluoroethene is shown below.

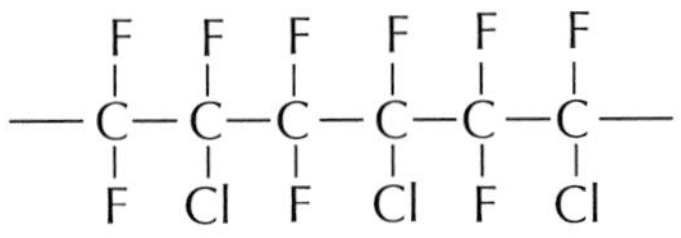

3.1 The atoms in a polymer chain are held together by covalent bonds.
Explain what happens when a covalent bond is formed.

(1 mark)

3.2 Each carbon atom in the chain forms four covalent bonds. Explain why this is.

(2 marks)

3.3 Covalent bonds are very strong but polychlorotrifluoroethene has a relatively low melting point of about 212 °C. Explain why.

(2 marks)

3.4 The structure of polychlorotrifluoroethene is represented above using a displayed formula. Give one advantage and one disadvantage of this type of representation of a covalent molecule.

(2 marks)

4   Carbon can exist in different forms. How the atoms are arranged and the bonding
between the atoms determines which form of carbon is made.

4.1   Diamond and graphite are macromolecular forms of carbon.
Why are their melting and boiling points so much higher than those of simple
molecular substances?

Tick **one** box.

They contain covalent bonds. ☐

Their intermolecular forces are so strong. ☐

Their strong covalent bonds must be broken for the substance to melt. ☐

There are no delocalised electrons. ☐

(1 mark)

4.2* Diamond is very hard, but graphite is soft and slippery. Explain why this is.
Your answer should include details of the arrangements of atoms and the bonding in
the structures.

(6 marks)

4.3   Name the two-dimensional form of carbon shown below.

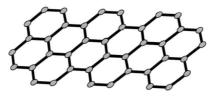

(1 mark)

4.4   Give **two** uses of fullerenes.

(2 marks)

5   Sterling silver is a silver alloy.

5.1   Sterling silver and silver are both good conductors of electricity. Explain why.

(2 marks)

The diagrams below show the arrangement of atoms in a sample of pure silver
and in a sample of sterling silver.

Diagram A   Diagram B

5.2   Which diagram shows the atoms in sterling silver? Explain your answer.

(1 mark)

5.3   Which substance is harder, pure silver or sterling silver? Explain your answer.

(2 marks)

1. States of Matter

You've probably learnt about solids, liquids and gases many times before. But make sure you know how the particle theory model can be used to explain the different states.

The three states of matter

Materials come in three different forms — **solid**, **liquid** and **gas**. These are three states of matter. Which state a material is in depends on how strong the forces of attraction are between the particles of the material (the atoms, ions or molecules). The strength of forces between particles is determined by:

- the material (the structure of the substance and the type of bonds holding the particles together),

- the temperature,

- the pressure.

You can use a model called particle theory to explain how the particles in a material behave in each of the three states of matter. In particle theory, each particle is considered to be a small, solid, inelastic sphere.

Solids

In solids, there are strong forces of attraction between particles. These forces hold the particles close together in fixed positions to form a very regular lattice arrangement. The particles don't move from their positions, so all solids keep a definite shape and volume, and don't flow like liquids. The particles vibrate about their positions, and as the temperature increases, the particles vibrate more. This is why solids expand slightly when heated.

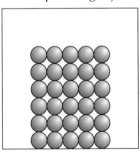

Figure 1: *Particle theory model of a solid.*

Liquids

In liquids, there are weak forces of attraction between the particles. The particles are randomly arranged and are free to move past each other, but they tend to stick closely together. Liquids have a definite volume but don't keep a definite shape, and will flow to fill the bottom of a container — see Figure 3. The particles are constantly moving with random motion. The hotter the liquid gets, the faster the particles move. This causes liquids to expand slightly when heated.

Learning Objectives:

- Know that there are three states of matter — solid, liquid and gas.

- Know how to use the particle theory model to represent the three states of matter.

- **H** Know the limitations of the particle theory model.

- Know that the bulk properties of a material aren't possessed by the particles of that material.

- Know the state symbols (s), (l), (g) and (aq) and be able to use them correctly in chemical equations.

Specification References
5.2.2.1, 5.2.2.2

Tip: A model is a representation of a theory which can be used to explain observations from experiments. See p.3-4 for more on models.

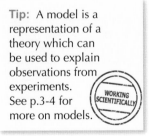

Figure 2: *Various elements in different states of matter.*

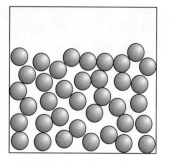

Figure 3: *Particle theory model of a liquid.*

Tip: Gases will expand to fill any container they're in. This means that, if they're in an unsealed flask, they'll escape out into the atmosphere. There's more on this on page 110.

Gases

In gases, the forces of attraction between the particles are very weak. The gas particles are free to move, and do so constantly with random motion. They travel in straight lines, until they collide with another particle or with the walls of the container. The particles are very far apart, so much so that most of a gas is actually empty space. Gases don't keep a definite shape or volume and will always fill any container. The hotter a gas gets, the faster the particles move and the harder and more frequently they hit the walls of the container. This causes the pressure of the gas to increase, or, if the container isn't sealed the volume of the gas will increase.

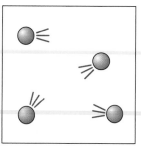

Figure 4: *Particle theory model of a gas.*

Tip: The limitations of a model are the aspects of it that don't match how things are in reality. Recognising them is an important part of working scientifically.

WORKING SCIENTIFICALLY

Limitations of particle theory `Higher`

Particle theory is a great model for explaining solids, liquids and gases but it isn't perfect. In reality, the particles aren't solid or inelastic and they aren't spheres — they're atoms, ions or molecules. Also, the model doesn't show the forces between the particles, so there's no way of knowing how strong they are. Also, the size of the particles and the distances between them aren't necessarily shown to scale.

Atomic properties and bulk properties

If you have a sample of a substance, it will contain billions of atoms or molecules. It has 'bulk properties', such as density and melting point, which stay the same, regardless of how many atoms or molecules you have in the sample. These properties depend on how the particles interact with each other, so a single atom or molecule would behave differently.

State symbols

A chemical reaction can be shown using a word equation or a symbol equation — see page 31. Symbol equations can also include state symbols next to each substance — they tell you what physical state the reactants and products are in:

see page 31

Tip: If a compound is said to be aqueous it means it's dissolved in water.

(s) — solid	(l) — liquid	(g) — gas	(aq) — aqueous

Example

Aqueous hydrochloric acid reacts with solid calcium carbonate to form aqueous calcium chloride, liquid water and carbon dioxide gas:

$$2HCl_{(aq)} + CaCO_{3(s)} \rightarrow CaCl_{2(aq)} + H_2O_{(l)} + CO_{2(g)}$$

Example

Ions are often in water when they react. E.g. aqueous calcium ions will react with aqueous hydroxide ions to form a white precipitate of calcium hydroxide.

$$Ca^{2+}_{(aq)} + 2OH^-_{(aq)} \rightarrow Ca(OH)_{2(s)}$$

Exam Tip
When you learn an equation for a reaction, make sure you learn the state symbols as well. Most are common sense, e.g. oxygen is pretty much always a gas, but it can be tricky to know if something is aqueous or not.

Practice Questions — Fact Recall

Q1 Name the three states of matter.

Q2 In which state(s) do substances have a:

a) definite volume?

b) definite shape?

Q3 Explain why a solid expands when it is heated.

Q4 Use the particle theory model to explain how the particles in a gas behave in a container.

Q5 Give three limitations of the particle theory model.

Q6 List the four state symbols and what they stand for.

Practice Question — Application

Q1 Iron is a solid at room temperature. Iron reacts with dilute hydrochloric acid to form iron(II) chloride, which is soluble in water, and hydrogen gas. Rewrite the equation for this reaction, shown below, so that it includes the missing state symbols to the equation. One state symbol is given for you.

$$Fe + 2HCl \rightarrow FeCl_{2(aq)} + H_2$$

Learning Objectives:
- Be able to use the particle theory model to explain changes of state.
- Know that substances melt and freeze at the melting point and boil and condense at the boiling point.
- Know that the strength of the forces between the particles of a substance determines how much energy it takes for the substance to melt or boil. This affects the temperatures at which the changes of state take place.
- Know that the strength of the forces between the particles depends on the structure and type of bonding of the substance.
- Be able to use data to predict the state of a substance at a particular temperature.

Specification Reference
5.2.2.1

Tip: Evaporation is also a change of state from liquid to gas. It can happen a long way below the boiling point though. The particles in a liquid have a variety of energies, so some of more energetic ones at the surface can have enough energy from the surroundings to escape the pull of their neighbours.

Figure 2: Ice melting to turn into liquid water.

2. Changing State

Substances aren't stuck in one state forever. Heating them up or cooling them down changes them from one state to another.

What happens when a substance changes state?

Changes of state are physical changes — only the arrangement or the energy of the particles changes, not the particles themselves. These changes of state can be explained using the particle model.

From solid to liquid — melting

When a solid is heated, its particles gain more energy. This makes them vibrate more, which weakens the forces that hold the solid together. At a certain temperature, called the **melting point** the particles have enough energy to break free from their positions. This is called **melting** and the solid turns into a liquid.

From liquid to gas — boiling

When a liquid is heated, the particles again get more energy. This energy makes them move faster, which weakens the attractive forces holding the liquid together. At a certain temperature, called the **boiling point**, the particles have enough energy to overcome the forces between them. This is **boiling** and the liquid becomes a gas.

From gas to liquid — condensing

As a gas cools, the particles no longer have enough energy to overcome the forces of attraction between them. At the boiling point, the forces between the gas particles are strong enough that the gas becomes a liquid. This is called **condensing**.

From liquid to solid — freezing

When a liquid cools, the particles have less energy, so move around less. There's not enough energy to overcome the attraction between the particles, so the particles are less free to move. At the melting point, the forces between the particles become strong enough that the particles are held in place. The liquid becomes a solid. This is **freezing**.

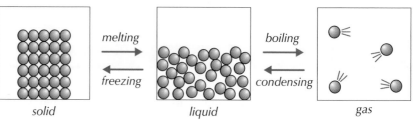

Figure 1: Particle theory model showing changes of state.

H Although the particle model is a really useful model, it does have some limitations — see page 98.

What do melting and boiling points depend on?

The amount of energy needed for a substance to change state depends on how strong the forces between the particles that need to be separated are. The stronger the forces, the more energy is needed to break them, and so the higher the melting and boiling points of the substance. The strength of the forces between the particles depends on the structure of the substance and the type of bonding in it.

Predicting the state of a substance

You might be asked to predict what state a substance is in at a certain temperature. If the temperature is below the melting point of substance, it'll be a solid. If it is above the boiling point, it'll be a gas. If it's in between the two points, then it's a liquid.

Tip: Simple molecular substances have weak forces between the particles (the molecules themselves), so often have low melting and boiling points. Ionic substances have strong electrostatic forces between the particles (the ions in the lattice), so have much higher melting and boiling points.

Example

Which of the molecular substances in the table is a liquid at room temperature (25 °C)?

	melting point	boiling point
oxygen	–219 °C	–183 °C
nitrogen	–210 °C	–196 °C
bromine	–7 °C	59 °C

Oxygen and nitrogen have boiling points below 25 °C, so will both be gases at room temperature.

Bromine melts at –7 °C and boils at 59 °C.
So, it's a liquid at room temperature.

Tip: The melting and boiling points of a material are bulk properties. They depend on how lots of particles interact together. A single particle, such as an atom, doesn't have a melting or a boiling point — see page 98.

Practice Questions — Fact Recall

Q1 What is it called when a substance changes from solid to liquid?

Q2 Use particle theory to describe the process of:

a) melting,

b) condensing.

Q3 Explain why some substances have higher melting and boiling points than others.

Practice Question — Application

Q1 Ethanol melts at –114 °C and boils at 78 ºC.
Predict the state of ethanol at:

a) –150 °C,   c) 0 °C,

b) 25 °C,   d) 100 °C.

Topic Checklist — Make sure you know...

States of Matter

☐ That there are three states of matter — solid, liquid and gas.

☐ How particle theory is used to represent each state.

☐ **H** The limitations of the particle model.

☐ That atoms of a material don't share the bulk properties of the material.

☐ What the state symbols (s), (l), (g) and (aq) mean and how to use them in equations.

Changing State

☐ How particle theory is used to explain changes of state and the limitations of the model

☐ That melting is a change from solid to liquid and freezing is a change from liquid to solid.

☐ That boiling is a change from liquid to gas and condensing is a change from gas to liquid.

☐ That the amount of energy a substance takes to melt or boil depends on the strength of the forces between the particles (which depends on the type of bonding and the structure of the substance).

☐ How to predict what state a substance will be in at a certain temperature using its melting and boiling points.

Exam-style Questions

1   A substance in two different states is represented in Figure 1 using the particle model.

Figure 1

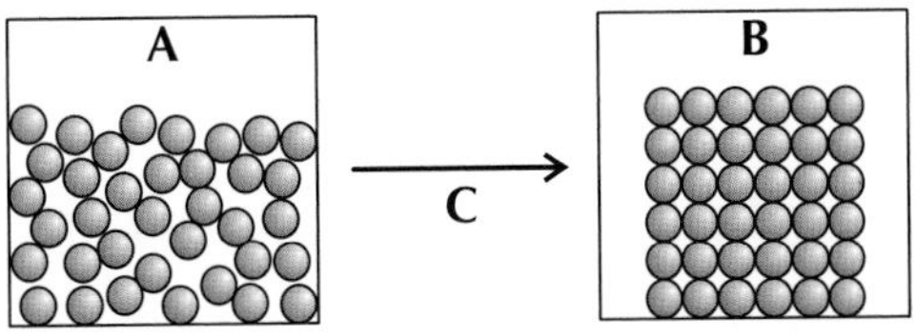

1.1   Which states are represented in boxes **A** and **B** of Figure 1?

(2 marks)

1.2   Give **one** factor that determines the strength of the forces between particles in a substance.

(1 mark)

1.3   Name the change of state represented by arrow **C** in Figure 1 and describe the changes that occur within the substance during it.

(3 marks)

1.4   Change of state **C** occurs in bromine at –7.2 °C.
Rewrite the equation below with state symbols to show change of state **C**.

$$Br_2 \rightarrow Br_2$$

(1 mark)

2   Table 1 shows the boiling and melting points of three substances.

Table 1

	melting point	boiling point
Chlorine	–102 °C	–34 °C
Fluorine	–220 °C	–188 °C
Sulfur	115 °C	445 °C

2.1   Which of the substances is a solid at room temperature (25 °C)?

(1 mark)

2.2   Use particle theory to describe the state of matter that chlorine is in at 0 °C.

(3 marks)

2.3   A chemist cools some chlorine gas from room temperature to below –102 °C.
Describe, using particle theory, what happens during this experiment, naming any changes of state that take place.

(5 marks)

Learning Objectives:

- Know how to calculate the relative formula mass, M_r of a compound from the relative atomic masses, A_r, of the atoms in the chemical formula.
- Be able to use M_r in chemical calculations.

Specification Reference 5.3.1.2

Tip: The relative atomic mass of chlorine is multiplied by 2 here because there are <u>two</u> chlorine atoms in $MgCl_2$.

Tip: Remember — relative atomic mass is the <u>average</u> mass of an element, taking into account the different masses of isotopes that make up the element (see p.27). You can find the relative atomic masses of elements in the periodic table.

Tip: Methane only contains carbon and hydrogen. So once you know that 75% of its mass is made up of carbon atoms, you can also say that 25% of its mass must be made up of hydrogen atoms.

1. Relative Formula Mass

Relative formula masses sound a lot scarier than they actually are. Give these pages a read and you should get to grips with them in no time...

Calculating relative formula mass

The **relative formula mass** (M_r) of a compound is just all the relative atomic masses (A_r) of the atoms in that compound added together.

> **Examples**
>
> - Magnesium chloride ($MgCl_2$) contains one atom of magnesium and two atoms of chlorine. Magnesium has a relative atomic mass of 24 and chlorine has a relative atomic mass of 35.5, so the relative formula mass of magnesium chloride is $24 + (2 \times 35.5) = 95$.
> - Iron oxide (Fe_2O_3) contains two atoms of iron and three atoms of oxygen. Iron has an A_r of 56 and oxygen has an A_r of 16, so the relative formula mass of iron oxide is $(2 \times 56) + (3 \times 16) = 160$.

Calculating percentage mass

The percentage mass of an element in a compound is a way of saying what proportion of the mass of the compound is due to atoms of that element.

> **Example**
>
> The percentage mass of carbon (C) in methane (CH_4) is 75%. This means that 75% of the mass of methane is made up of carbon atoms — so if you have 100 g of methane, it will contain 75 g of carbon.

If you know the molecular formula of a compound, you can work out the percentage mass of a particular element within that compound using this formula:

$$\text{Percentage mass of an element in a compound} = \frac{A_r \times \text{number of atoms of that element}}{M_r \text{ of the compound}} \times 100$$

> **Example**
>
> **Find the percentage mass of magnesium in magnesium oxide, MgO. Relative atomic masses (A_r): Mg = 24, O = 16**
>
> M_r of MgO = 24 + 16 = 40
>
> % mass of Mg $= \dfrac{A_r \text{ of Mg} \times \text{No. of Mg atoms}}{M_r \text{ of MgO}} \times 100 = \dfrac{24 \times 1}{40} \times 100 = 60\%$
>
> So magnesium makes up 60% of the mass of magnesium oxide.

You might also come across more complicated questions where you need to use the percentage mass of an element or compound in a mixture to do further calculations.

Example — Higher

A mixture contains 20% iron ions by mass. Given that the only compound in the mixture that contains iron is iron chloride ($FeCl_2$), calculate the mass of iron chloride in 50 g of the mixture.
Relative atomic masses (A_r): Fe = 56, Cl = 35.5.

1. Start by finding the mass of iron in the mixture:
   The mixture contains 20% iron by mass, so in 50 g there will be
   $50 \times \frac{20}{100} = 10$ g of iron.

Figure 1: Iron chloride crystals.

2. Then work out the relative formula mass of iron chloride, and use this to find the percentage mass of iron in iron chloride:
   M_r of iron chloride = A_r(Fe) + 2 × A_r(Cl) = 56 + (2 × 35.5) = 127
   Percentage mass of iron in iron chloride = $\frac{56 \times 1}{127} \times 100 = 44.09...$ %

3. Finally, calculate the mass of iron chloride that contains 10 g of iron:
   mass of iron chloride $\times \frac{44.09...}{100} = 10$ g
   So, mass of iron chloride $= 10$ g $\div \frac{44.09...}{100} = 23$ g

Exam Tip
When you're doing calculation questions, try not to round your intermediate answers — just round your final answer.

Practice Questions — Fact Recall

Q1 Describe how you would work out the relative formula mass (M_r) of a compound.

Q2 Write out the formula you could use to calculate the percentage mass of an element in a compound.

Practice Questions — Application

Use the periodic table on the back cover to answer these questions.

Q1 What is the relative formula mass of:

   a) oxygen (O_2)?   b) potassium hydroxide (KOH)?

   c) nitric acid (HNO_3)?   d) calcium carbonate ($CaCO_3$)?

Q2 Find the percentage mass of:

   a) hydrogen (H) in hydrochloric acid (HCl).

   b) aluminium (Al) in aluminium oxide (Al_2O_3).

   c) oxygen (O) in copper hydroxide ($Cu(OH)_2$).

Q3 A mixture contains 40% magnesium by mass. The only compound in the mixture that contains magnesium is magnesium oxide (MgO). Calculate the mass of magnesium oxide in 45 g of the mixture.

Exam Tip
The A_r for any elements you need might be given to you in the question. If not, you can look them up in the periodic table.

Learning Objectives:

- **H** Know that the Avogadro constant is equal to 6.02×10^{23}.
- **H** Know that amounts of substances are measured in moles.
- **H** Know that one mole of any substance contains 6.02×10^{23} particles.
- **H** Understand that moles can be used to describe many things, including atoms, molecules, ions, electrons and chemical formulas.
- **H** Be able to use the unit 'mol' to describe the amounts of substances.
- **H** Know that the mass in grams of one mole of any substance is the same as the value of its relative formula mass.
- **H** Know that one mole of any substance contains the same number of particles as one mole of any other substance.
- **H** Be able to calculate the number of moles of a substance in a given mass using its relative formula mass and vice versa.
- **H** Be able to rearrange a mathematical equation in order to change the subject.

Specification References
5.3.2.1, 5.3.2.3

2. The Mole `Higher`

Don't worry, you haven't accidentally opened a book about lawn maintenance. Moles are used in chemistry to measure amounts of substances.

The Avogadro constant

Just like 'a million' is this many: 1 000 000; or 'a billion' is this many: 1 000 000 000, so 'the **Avogadro constant**' is this many: 602 000 000 000 000 000 000 000 or 6.02×10^{23}. And that's all it is. Just a number.

What is a mole?

In chemistry, amounts of substances are measured in **moles**. One mole of any substance is just the amount of that substance that contains an Avogadro number of particles — so 6.02×10^{23} particles. The particles could be atoms, molecules, ions or electrons. And just like the units 'grams' are shortened to 'g', the units 'moles' are usually written as 'mol'.

The mass of one mole of atoms or molecules of any substance is exactly the same number of grams as the **relative atomic mass** (A_r) or **relative formula mass** (M_r) of the element or compound. In other words, one mole of atoms or molecules of any substance will have a mass in grams equal to the value of the relative formula mass (A_r or M_r) for that substance. Here are some examples:

Examples | **Higher**

- Iron (Fe) has an A_r of 56.
  So one mole of iron weighs exactly 56 g.

- Nitrogen gas (N_2) has an M_r of $2 \times 14 = 28$.
  So one mole of N_2 weighs exactly 28 g.

(MATHS SKILLS)

This means that 12 g of carbon, or 28 g of N_2, or 44 g of CO_2 all contain the same number of particles, namely one mole (6.02×10^{23}).

Calculating amounts of substances

You can find the number of moles in a given mass of a substance using this formula:

$$\text{Number of moles} = \frac{\text{Mass in g (of element or compound)}}{M_r \text{ (of element or compound) or } A_r \text{ (of element)}}$$

Example 1 | **Higher**

How many moles are there in 42 g of carbon?

The A_r of carbon is 12, so the number of moles in 42 g of carbon is:

$$\text{Moles} = \frac{\text{mass}}{A_r} = \frac{42}{12} = 3.5 \text{ moles}$$

Example 2 — Higher

How many moles are there in 66 g of carbon dioxide (CO_2)?

M_r of CO_2 = 12 + (16 × 2) = 44

No. of moles = $\dfrac{mass}{M_r}$ = $\dfrac{66}{44}$ = 1.5 mol

You can also rearrange the equation on the previous page to find the mass of a known number of moles of a substance, or to find the M_r of a substance from the mass and the number of moles.

Example — Higher

What is the mass in g of 0.80 moles of sulfuric acid (H_2SO_4)?

The M_r of sulfuric acid is (2 × 1) + 32 + (4 × 16) = 98.

Rearrange the formula to find mass (multiply both sides by M_r):

mass = moles × M_r = 0.80 × 98 = 78.4 g

So 0.80 moles of sulfuric acid would weigh 78 g.

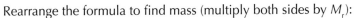

Practice Questions — Fact Recall

Q1 What is the value of the Avogadro constant?
Give your answer in standard form.

Q2 What is a mole?

Q3 What equation can you use to convert between moles and grams?

Practice Questions — Application

Use the periodic table on the back cover to answer the questions below.

Q1 What is the mass of one mole of each of the following?

    a) Sodium (Na)   b) Helium (He)

    c) Bromine (Br_2)   d) Potassium oxide (K_2O)

Q2 How many moles are there in each of the following?

    a) 19.5 g of potassium (K)

    b) 23.4 g of sodium chloride (NaCl)

    c) 76.8 g of sulfur dioxide (SO_2)

    d) 31.9 g of copper sulfate ($CuSO_4$)

Q3 How much would the following weigh in grams?

    a) 0.80 moles of nickel (Ni)

    b) 0.50 moles of magnesium oxide (MgO)

    c) 1.6 moles of ammonia (NH_3)

    d) 1.40 moles of calcium hydroxide (Ca(OH)$_2$)

Tip: An easy way to rearrange the equation is to use the formula triangle below — just cover up the thing you want to find with your finger and write down what's left showing.

```
        mass
   ────────────
   no. of  × M_r
   moles
```

Exam Tip
Unless told otherwise, the number of significant figures you give your answer to should be the same as the piece of data in the question with the smallest number of significant figures.

Tip: Standard form is where your number is written as '(a number between 1 and 10) × 10^x'. There's more about this on pages 242-243.

Exam Tip
You could be expected to rearrange equations in the exam. There's more on how to rearrange equations on pages 244-245.

Figure 1: *One mole of a variety of compounds.*

Learning Objectives:
- Know that, during a reaction, no atoms are created or destroyed, and that this is known as the law of conservation of mass.
- Know that the mass of the products in a reaction is the same as the mass of the reactants.
- Know that the law of conservation of mass is used to balance chemical equations so that the number of atoms of each element is the same on both sides of the equation.
- Know that the sum of the relative formula masses of the reactants in a balanced chemical equation is the same as the sum of the relative formula masses of the products.
- Be able to explain why some reactions seem to show a change in mass if one of the reactants or products is a gas.
- Be able to explain an apparent loss or gain in mass during a reaction in terms of the particle model.

Specification References
5.3.1.1-5.3.1.3

3. Conservation of Mass

Conservation of mass isn't too tricky to get your head round. You need to know how to use this idea to work out masses and balance equations.

Mass conservation in chemical reactions

During chemical reactions, things don't appear out of nowhere and things don't just disappear. You still have the same atoms at the end of a chemical reaction as you had at the start. They're just arranged in different ways. Because of this, no mass is lost or gained — we say that mass is conserved during a reaction. This is summarised by the law of conservation of mass:

> During a chemical reaction, no atoms are made or destroyed, so the mass of the products is the same as the mass of the reactants.

Balanced symbol equations show the atoms at the start (the reactant atoms) and the atoms at the end (the product atoms) and how they're arranged.

Example

Balanced symbol equation:

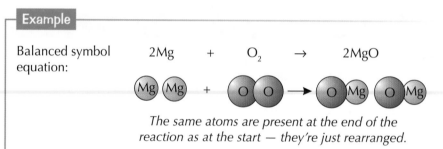

$$2Mg \quad + \quad O_2 \quad \rightarrow \quad 2MgO$$

The same atoms are present at the end of the reaction as at the start — they're just rearranged.

Conservation of mass and M_r

By adding up the relative formula masses of the substances on each side of a balanced symbol equation, you can see that mass is conserved. The total M_r of the reactants equals the total M_r of the products.

Example

The balanced equation for the reaction between lithium and fluorine is: $2Li + F_2 \rightarrow 2LiF$.
Relative atomic masses, A_r: Li = 7, F = 19

Total M_r of reactants = $(2 \times 7) + (2 \times 19) = 14 + 38 = 52$

Total M_r of products = $2 \times (7 + 19) = 2 \times 26 = 52$

The total M_r on the left-hand side of the equation is equal to the total M_r on the right-hand side, so mass is conserved.

Calculating reacting masses

You can use the idea of conservation of mass to work out the mass of individual reactants and products in a reaction.

Example 1

6 g of magnesium completely reacts with 4 g of oxygen. What mass of magnesium oxide is formed?

The total mass of the reactants is $4 + 6 = 10$ g, so the mass of the product (magnesium oxide) must be 10 g.

Example 2

30 g of magnesium oxide is formed from 18 g of magnesium. What mass of oxygen reacted?

The total mass of the product is 30 g, so the total mass of the reactants must be 30 g. The mass of the magnesium is 18 g, so the mass of the oxygen must be $30 - 18 = 12$ g.

Exam Tip
You could be asked to work out the mass of a product formed, or the mass of a reactant used. Just remember — the total mass of the products is exactly the same as the total mass of the reactants.

Reactions where mass seems to change

For many reactions, if you carry them out in a container that isn't sealed, the mass of the stuff inside the reaction container at the start of the reaction will be the same as at the end of the reaction. This is what you'd expect from the law of conservation of mass. But for some types of reaction, you might find that the mass of stuff inside the reaction container has either increased or decreased during the reaction. You can explain these changes in terms of the particle model.

Reactions where the mass seems to increase

If the mass increases, it's probably because one or more of the reactants is a gas that's found in air (e.g. oxygen) and all the products are solids, liquids or aqueous.

- The particles in a gas move around and fill the space they're in. So before the reaction, the gas is floating around in the air. It's there, but it's not contained in the reaction vessel, so you can't account for its mass.

- When the gas reacts to form part of the product, the particles become contained inside the reaction vessel — so the total mass of the stuff inside the reaction vessel increases.

Tip: If the reaction vessel is sealed, then no particles can get in or out, so the mass of the reaction vessel won't change.

Figure 1: When magnesium is heated in a crucible, it forms magnesium oxide. During the reaction, the mass of substance inside the crucible will increase.

Example

When a metal reacts with oxygen in an unsealed container, the mass in the container increases. This is because the mass of the metal oxide produced equals the total mass of the metal and the oxygen that reacted from the air, but the mass of the stuff inside the container at the beginning of the reaction was just the mass of the metal, and not the oxygen.

$$\text{metal}_{(s)} + \text{oxygen}_{(g)} \rightarrow \text{metal oxide}_{(s)}$$

Reactions where the mass seems to decrease

If the mass decreases, it's probably because one of the products is a gas and all the reactants are solids, liquids or aqueous.

Tip: If you need a reminder about the particle model, have a look back at page 97.

- Before the reaction, all the reactants are contained in the reaction vessel.

- If the vessel isn't enclosed, then the gas that's produced can escape from the reaction vessel as it's formed. This can be explained by the particle model, which states that a gas will expand to fill any container it's in. So if a reaction vessel isn't sealed, the gas expands out of the vessel and escapes into the air around. It's no longer contained in the reaction vessel, so you can't account for its mass — the total mass of the stuff inside the reaction vessel decreases.

Example

When a metal carbonate thermally decomposes to form a metal oxide and carbon dioxide gas, the mass in the reaction vessel will decrease if it isn't sealed, as the carbon dioxide will escape from the vessel and its mass won't be measured. But in reality, the mass of the metal oxide and the carbon dioxide produced will equal the mass of the metal carbonate that decomposed.

$$\text{metal carbonate}_{(s)} \rightarrow \text{metal oxide}_{(s)} + \text{carbon dioxide}_{(g)}$$

Figure 2: When copper carbonate (green) is heated, it thermally decomposes to form copper oxide (black) and carbon dioxide gas.

Practice Questions — Fact Recall

Q1 State the law of conservation of mass.

Q2 State the relationship between the sum of the relative formula masses of the products and the sum of the relative formula masses of the reactants in a reaction.

Q3 Give an example of a reaction where the mass of the products in the reaction container would be greater than the mass of the reactants.

Practice Questions — Application

Q1 Calculate the mass of copper oxide formed when 127 g of copper reacts with 32 g of oxygen to form copper oxide.

Q2 During a reaction, 56 g of nitrogen reacts with hydrogen to form 68 g of ammonia (NH_3). What is the mass of hydrogen that reacts?

Q3 Predict what will happen to the mass in an unsealed reaction vessel if zinc carbonate is heated inside it so that it thermally decomposes.

Q4 Chlorine reacts with sodium bromide according to the following equation: $Cl_2 + 2NaBr \rightarrow Br_2 + 2NaCl$.
Use the relative formula masses of the reactants and products to show that mass is conserved in this reaction.

Q5 A student heated 5 g of calcium in an unsealed test tube so that it reacted with oxygen. At the end of the reaction, the mass of the product inside the test tube was 7 g. Explain this observation.

Tip: For Q4, you can use the periodic table on the back cover to find the relative atomic masses of the elements.

4. The Mole and Equations Higher

You learnt how to balance equations back on page 32. But you also need to be able to write balanced equations from the masses of reactants and products involved in the reaction. And that's what these pages are all about.

Learning Objectives:
- **H** Be able to interpret chemical equations in terms of moles of reactants and products.
- **H** Be able to balance a symbol equation from the masses of reactants and products in a reaction.
Specification References
5.3.2.2, 5.3.2.3

Understanding chemical equations

In a balanced equation, the big numbers in front of the chemical formulas tell you the relative number of **moles** of each reactant that take part in the reaction, and the relative number of moles of each product that are formed. The little numbers within the chemical formulas tell you how many atoms of each element there are in the smallest unit of the substance.

Example — **Higher**

$$Mg_{(s)} + 2HCl_{(aq)} \rightarrow MgCl_{2(aq)} + H_{2(g)}$$

In this reaction, 1 mole of magnesium and 2 moles of hydrochloric acid react to form 1 mole of magnesium chloride and 1 mole of hydrogen gas.

The ratio of moles of reactants and products in a reaction always stays the same. You can use this fact to work out how many moles of a reactant or product is involved in a reaction, if you're given information about one of the other substances in the reaction.

Tip: H Remember that a mole is just the amount of a substance that contains 6.02×10^{23} particles. See page 106 for more.

Example 1 — **Higher**

How many moles of water are formed if 2 moles of methane combust completely in oxygen? The balanced equation for this reaction is: $CH_4 + 2O_2 \rightarrow CO_2 + 2H_2O$ (MATHS SKILLS)

From the balanced equation, you can see that 1 mole of methane reacts to form 2 moles of water, so the molar ratio is 1:2. So 2 moles of methane will react to form $(2 \times 2) = 4$ moles of water.

Example 2 — **Higher**

How many moles of oxygen will react if 3 moles of magnesium react completely to form magnesium oxide? The balanced equation for this reaction is: $2Mg + O_2 \rightarrow 2MgO$

From the balanced equation, you can see that 2 moles of magnesium react with 1 mole of oxygen, so the molar ratio is 2:1. So 3 moles of magnesium will react with $(3 \div 2) = 1.5$ moles of oxygen.

Tip: H You can also see from the reaction equation that the molar ratio of magnesium to magnesium oxide is 1:1, so in this experiment 3 moles of magnesium oxide will form.

Balancing equations using reacting masses

If you know the masses of the reactants and products that took part in a reaction, you can work out the balanced symbol equation for the reaction. Here are the steps you should take:

Tip: H The equation 'number of moles = mass ÷ M_r' will be really helpful in these calculations. Have a look back at page 106 for a reminder.

1. Divide the mass of each substance by its relative formula mass to find the number of moles.

2. Divide the number of moles of each substance by the smallest number of moles in the reaction.

3. If any of the numbers aren't whole numbers, multiply all the numbers by the same amount so that they all become whole numbers.

4. Write the balanced symbol equation for the reaction by putting these numbers in front of the chemical formulas.

Example 1 — Higher

Exam Tip
These calculations have several steps, so always write down your working to stop you getting in a muddle in the exam.

8.1 g of zinc oxide (ZnO) reacts completely with 0.60 g of carbon to form 2.2 g of carbon dioxide and 6.5 g of zinc. Write a balanced symbol equation for this reaction. Relative atomic masses, A_r: C = 12, O = 16, Zn = 65.

(MATHS SKILLS)

1. First work out M_r (or A_r) for each of the substances in the reaction:

$$ZnO: 65 + 16 = 81 \quad C: 12 \quad CO_2: 12 + (2 \times 16) = 44 \quad Zn: 65$$

Then divide the mass of each substance by its M_r to calculate how many moles of each substance reacted or were produced:

$$ZnO: \frac{8.1}{81} = 0.10 \text{ mol} \qquad C: \frac{0.60}{12} = 0.050 \text{ mol}$$

$$CO_2: \frac{2.2}{44} = 0.050 \text{ mol} \qquad Zn: \frac{6.5}{65} = 0.10 \text{ mol}$$

Tip: H Dividing by the smallest number of moles gives the ratio of the amounts of each substance in the reaction.

2. Divide by the smallest number of moles, which is 0.050:

$$ZnO: \frac{0.10}{0.050} = 2.0 \qquad C: \frac{0.050}{0.050} = 1.0$$

$$CO_2: \frac{0.050}{0.050} = 1.0 \qquad Zn: \frac{0.10}{0.050} = 2.0$$

3. The numbers are all whole numbers, so you can write out the balanced symbol equation straight away.

4. So the balanced equation is: $2ZnO + C \rightarrow CO_2 + 2Zn$

Example 2 — Higher

2.7 g of an element, X, reacts completely with 2.4 g of oxygen to form 5.1 g of an oxide, X oxide. Write a balanced symbol equation for this reaction.
$A_r(X) = 27$, $M_r(O_2) = 32$, $M_r(X \text{ oxide}) = 102$

1. First divide the mass of each substance by its M_r (or A_r) to find how many moles of each substance reacted or were produced:

   X: $\frac{2.7}{27} = 0.10$ mol O_2: $\frac{2.4}{32} = 0.075$ mol   X oxide: $\frac{5.1}{102} = 0.050$ mol

2. Divide by the smallest number of moles, which is 0.050:

   X: $\frac{0.10}{0.050} = 2.0$ O_2: $\frac{0.075}{0.050} = 1.5$ X oxide: $\frac{0.050}{0.050} = 1.0$

3. Multiply all the values by two so the number of moles of oxygen becomes a whole number:

   X: $2.0 \times 2 = 4$ O_2: $1.5 \times 2 = 3$ X oxide: $1.0 \times 2 = 2$

4. So the balanced equation is: $4X + 3O_2 \rightarrow 2(X \text{ oxide})$

   You can see from the reaction equation that 2 units of X oxide contain 4 atoms of X and 6 atoms of O. So one unit of X oxide contains 2 atoms of X and 3 atoms of O, making the formula of X oxide X_2O_3.

   So the balanced equation is: $4X + 3O_2 \rightarrow 2X_2O_3$

> **Exam Tip** H
> Always check that the final equation is <u>balanced</u>. If your answer is correct, the number of atoms of each element on the left-hand side should be the same as the number of atoms of each element on the right-hand side.

> **Tip:** H You should multiply all the values you get in step 2 by the smallest possible number that will make them all whole numbers.

Practice Questions — Application

Q1 What is the relative number of moles of water in each of the following reactions?

a) $Ca + 2H_2O \rightarrow Ca(OH_2) + H_2$ b) $HCl + NaOH \rightarrow NaCl + H_2O$

Q2 The balanced equation for the reaction between magnesium and oxygen is: $2Mg + O_2 \rightarrow 2MgO$.
How many moles of magnesium would react to form 3 moles of magnesium oxide?

Q3 The balanced equation for the reaction between chlorine and sodium bromide is: $Cl_2 + 2NaBr \rightarrow Br_2 + 2NaCl$.
How many moles of bromine (Br_2) would form from 0.4 moles of sodium bromide?

Q4 4.6 g of sodium reacted with 1.6 g of oxygen to form 6.2 g of sodium oxide (Na_2O). Use the reacting masses to write a balanced symbol equation for this reaction.
Relative atomic masses (A_r): O = 16, Na = 23

Q5 2.34 g of potassium reacted with 2.19 g of hydrochloric acid (HCl) to form 4.47 g of potassium chloride (KCl) and 0.06 g of hydrogen. Use the reacting masses to write a balanced symbol equation for this reaction. Relative atomic masses (A_r): H = 1, Cl = 35.5, K = 39

Q6 1.20 g of a hydrocarbon, Z, combusts completely in 4.48 g of oxygen to form 3.52 g of carbon dioxide (CO_2) and 2.16 g of water (H_2O). Write a balanced symbol equation for this reaction.
(A_r): Z = 30   (M_r): $O_2 = 32$, $H_2O = 18$, $CO_2 = 44$

> **Tip:** H For Q2 and Q3, start by using the reaction equation to work out the molar ratios of the substances you're interested in.

Learning Objectives:

- **H** Know that, during a chemical reaction, one of the reactants is often added in excess to make sure that the other reactant gets used up.

- **H** Know that a limiting reactant is one that gets completely used up during a reaction.

- **H** Know that the amount of product that forms is determined by the amount of the limiting reactant used.

- **H** Be able to explain how the amount of product formed will change if the amount of limiting reactant used is changed.

- **H** Be able to calculate the mass of substances in a reaction, given a balanced symbol equation and the mass of one of the reactants or products.

Specification References 5.3.2.2, 5.3.2.4

5. Limiting Reactants Higher

Knowing the limiting reactant in a reaction can help you work out the maximum amount of product that will be formed during a reaction. Handy.

What are limiting reactants?

When some magnesium carbonate ($MgCO_3$) is placed into a beaker of hydrochloric acid, you can tell a reaction is taking place because you see lots of bubbles of gas being given off. After a while, the amount of fizzing slows down and the reaction eventually stops...

The reaction stops when all of one of the reactants is used up. Any other reactants are **in excess**. They're usually added in excess to make sure that the other reactant is completely used up. The reactant that's used up in a reaction is called the **limiting reactant** (because it limits the amount of product that's formed).

The amount of product formed is directly proportional to the amount of limiting reactant. For example, if you halve the amount of limiting reactant the amount of product formed will also halve. If you double the amount of limiting reactant the amount of product will double (as long as the other reactants are still in excess). This is because if you add more of the limiting reactant there will be more reactant particles to take part in the reaction, which means more product particles can form.

> **Example** ⎯ **Higher**
>
> **When 2.24 g of iron were reacted with an excess of copper sulfate solution, 2.54 g of copper were produced. How much copper would be produced if 6.72 g of iron were reacted in an excess of copper sulfate solution?**
>
>
>
> $6.72 \div 2.24 = 3$, so three times as much iron was used in the second reaction. As iron is the limiting reactant, three times as much copper will be produced. $3 \times 2.54 = 7.62$ g.

Tip: Being able to use scientific vocabulary such as 'in excess' and 'limiting reactant' is an important part of working scientifically.

Calculating the mass of a product

You can calculate the mass of a product formed in a reaction by using the mass of the limiting reactant and the balanced reaction equation. Here are the steps you need to follow:

1. Write out the balanced equation.

2. Work out the relative formula masses (M_r) of the limiting reactant and the product you want to find the mass of.

3. Work out how many moles there are of the limiting reactant.

4. Use the balanced equation to work out how many moles there'll be of the product.

5. Use the number of moles, along with the relative formula mass of the product to calculate the mass.

Example 1 — Higher

What mass of calcium chloride ($CaCl_2$) is produced when 3.7 g of calcium hydroxide ($Ca(OH)_2$) reacts with an excess of hydrochloric acid (HCl)?

1. The balanced symbol equation for this reaction is: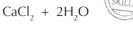

$$Ca(OH)_2 + 2HCl \rightarrow CaCl_2 + 2H_2O$$

2. The limiting reactant is $Ca(OH)_2$. The product you want is $CaCl_2$.

M_r of $Ca(OH)_2 = 40 + (2 \times (16 + 1)) = 74$
M_r of $CaCl_2 = 40 + (2 \times 35.5) = 111$

3. Calculate the number of moles of calcium hydroxide in 3.7 g.

Number of moles = mass $\div M_r = 3.7 \div 74 = 0.050$ mol

4. Look at the ratio of moles in the equation to work out how many moles of calcium chloride will be formed.

1 mole of $Ca(OH)_2$ reacts to produce 1 mole of $CaCl_2$ — the same number of moles are produced. So 0.05 moles of $Ca(OH)_2$ will react to produce 0.05 moles of $CaCl_2$.

5. Calculate the mass of $CaCl_2$ produced.

mass = moles $\times M_r = 0.050 \times 111 = 5.6$ g

> **Exam Tip**
> In the exam, you might be expected to know the equation for a reaction (if it's one you've studied), or you might be given the balanced symbol equation in the question.

> **Tip:** **H** This is just the moles = mass $\div M_r$ equation rearranged.

Example 2 — Higher

What mass of aluminium oxide is produced when 135 g of aluminium is burned in air?

1. The balanced symbol equation for this reaction is:

$$4Al + 3O_2 \rightarrow 2Al_2O_3$$

2. The limiting reactant is Al. The product you want is Al_2O_3.

A_r of Al = 27
M_r of $Al_2O_3 = (2 \times 27) + (3 \times 16) = 102$

3. Calculate the number of moles of aluminium in 135 g.

Number of moles = mass $\div M_r = 135 \div 27 = 5$ mol

4. Look at the ratio of moles in the equation to work out how many moles of aluminium oxide will be formed.

4 moles of Al react to produce 2 moles of Al_2O_3 — half the number of moles are produced. So 5 moles of Al will react to produce 2.5 moles of Al_2O_3.

5. Calculate the mass of Al_2O_3 produced.

mass = moles $\times M_r = 2.5 \times 102 = 255$ g

> **Tip:** **H** If a reaction is said to be carried out 'in air', then any gases in the reaction that are found in air (e.g. oxygen) will be in <u>excess</u> (unless you're told otherwise).

Figure 1: *Aluminium powder burning in air.*

Calculating the mass of a reactant

You can use the same basic method as on page 114 to find how much reactant you'd need to use to make a certain mass of product.

Example — Higher

How much zinc carbonate ($ZnCO_3$) would need to decompose to form 24.2 g of zinc oxide (ZnO)?

1. The balanced symbol equation for this reaction is:

$$ZnCO_3 \rightarrow ZnO + CO_2$$

2. The reactant is $ZnCO_3$. The product you know the mass of is ZnO.

$$M_r \text{ of } ZnCO_3 = 65 + 12 + (3 \times 16) = 125$$
$$M_r \text{ of } ZnO = 65 + 16 = 81$$

3. Calculate the number of moles of zinc oxide in 24.2 g.

number of moles = mass $\div M_r$ = 24.2 $\div$ 81 = 0.29... mol

4. Look at the ratio of moles in the equation to work out how many moles of zinc carbonate are needed to produce this.

1 mole of $ZnCO_3$ decomposes to produce 1 mole of ZnO — the same number of moles are produced. So 0.29... moles of ZnO will be produced by 0.29... moles of $ZnCO_3$.

5. Calculate the mass of $ZnCO_3$ that reacts.

mass = moles $\times M_r$ = 0.29... $\times$ 125 = 37 g

Practice Questions — Fact Recall

Q1 What is a limiting reactant?

Q2 State the term used to describe the reactants in a reaction that aren't limiting.

Practice Questions — Application

Q1 During an experiment, a small piece of sodium was added to a bowl of water. The sodium reacted with the water until the entire piece disappeared. Identify:

a) the limiting reactant.

b) the reactant(s) in excess.

Tip: It's useful to know how to calculate the amount of reactant needed to make a set amount of product when you're planning experiments. If you know how much product you want to end up with, you can then work out the minimum amount of reactant needed to make this quantity.

Tip: H This time it's the amount of product you know, so in step 3 you have to find the number of moles of product rather than reactant.

Q2 3.25 g of zinc reacts with an excess of hydrochloric acid to form 6.80 g of zinc chloride.

a) Describe what would happen to the amount of zinc chloride produced if the amount of zinc that reacted was doubled and the amount of hydrochloric acid remained in excess.

b) How much zinc chloride would be produced by 13.0 g of zinc in an excess of hydrochloric acid?

c) How much zinc would react in an excess of hydrochloric acid to produce 1.36 g of zinc chloride?

Tip: H You don't need to work out the symbol equation for the reaction in Q2 — you just have to work out how the relative amounts of products and reactants will change.

Q3 Calculate the mass of potassium chloride (KCl) that will be formed if 36.2 g of aqueous potassium bromide (KBr) reacts with an excess of chlorine. The balanced symbol equation for this reaction is:

$$2KBr + Cl_2 \rightarrow 2KCl + Br_2$$

Tip: H Use the periodic table on the back cover to answer questions 3-8.

Q4 Calculate the mass of aluminium chloride ($AlCl_3$) that will be made if 15.4 g of hydrochloric acid (HCl) reacts with an excess of aluminium. The balanced symbol equation for this reaction is:

$$6HCl + 2Al \rightarrow 2AlCl_3 + 3H_2$$

Q5 28.5 g of calcium carbonate ($CaCO_3$) reacts with an excess of sulfuric acid (H_2SO_4) to form calcium sulfate ($CaSO_4$), carbon dioxide (CO_2) and water (H_2O). Calculate the mass of calcium sulfate that will be formed in this reaction.

Tip: H For Q5 you need to write and balance the symbol equation yourself — but all the information you need is given in the question.

Q6 Calculate the mass of potassium hydroxide (KOH) that would be needed to form 25.0 g of potassium nitrate (KNO_3) in this reaction:

$$HNO_3 + KOH \rightarrow KNO_3 + H_2O$$

Q7 Ethanol (C_2H_6O) can be made from ethene (C_2H_4) using this reaction:

$$C_2H_4 + H_2O \rightarrow C_2H_6O$$

Calculate the mass of ethene that would be needed to make 60.0 g of ethanol using this reaction.

Tip: H These questions are quite tricky, so have another read of the method and examples on the last few pages if you need a hand.

Q8 Iron oxide (Fe_2O_3) can be reduced with carbon to form iron (Fe) and carbon dioxide, as shown by the equation below.

$$2Fe_2O_3 + 3C \rightarrow 4Fe + 3CO_2$$

Calculate the amount of iron oxide needed to form 32.0 g of iron.

- Know that lots of
reactions happen in
solution.
- Know that the
concentration of
a solution can be
measured by the mass
of solute in a given
volume of solution,
such as in g/dm³.
- **H** Be able to explain
the relationship
between the mass of
solute, the volume
of solution and the
concentration of
solution.
- Be able to use the
concentration of a
solution to calculate
the mass of solute in a
given volume.
- Know that
measurements always
have some uncertainty
to them.
- Be able to show how
distributed results
are and calculate
the uncertainty of a
measurement from a
range.

Specification Reference
5.3.1.4, 5.3.2.5

6. Concentrations

*Solutions are mixtures that contain one substance (the solute) dissolved in
another substance (the solvent). The easiest way to describe the amount of
solute in a solvent is by its concentration.*

What is concentration?

Lots of reactions in chemistry take place between substances that are
dissolved in a solvent to form a solution. The amount of a substance (e.g. the
mass or the number of moles) in a certain volume of a solution is called its
concentration. The more solute (the substance that's dissolved) there is in a
given volume, the more concentrated the solution.

Calculating concentration in terms of mass

One way to calculate the concentration of a solution is by working out the
mass of a substance in a given volume of solution. The units will be 'units of
mass'/'units of volume'. Here's how to calculate the concentration of a
solution in g/dm³:

$$\text{concentration (g/dm}^3) = \frac{\text{mass of solute (g)}}{\text{volume of solution (dm}^3)}$$

Example 1

**What's the concentration in g/dm³ of a solution of sodium chloride
where 30 g of sodium chloride is dissolved in 0.20 dm³ of water?**

$$\text{concentration} = \frac{30}{0.20} = 150 \text{ g/dm}^3$$

Example 2

**What's the concentration in g/dm³ of iron chloride solution
where 10 g of iron chloride is dissolved in 25 cm³ of water?**

First, change the units of volume from cm³ to dm³.

volume = 25 ÷ 1000 = 0.025 dm³

Then use the equation to find the concentration of the solution.

$$\text{concentration} = \frac{10}{0.025} = 400 \text{ g/dm}^3$$

Tip: The state symbol
for a substance in
solution is 'aq'.

Tip: There's more
information about how
to convert between units
on pages 18-19.

H The greater the mass of solute in a given volume, the higher the
concentration. So if you take a solution and dissolve more of the solute in it,
the concentration will increase. If you do anything to increase the volume
(e.g. adding more solvent) without also increasing the amount of solute then
the concentration will decrease.

Finding the mass of solute in a solution

You can rearrange the equation from the previous page to calculate the mass of solute in a given volume of solution if you know the concentration.

Tip: A <u>solute</u> is a substance that is dissolved in a liquid (the solvent). When a solute is dissolved in a <u>solvent</u> they form a <u>solution</u>.

> ### Example
>
> **What's the mass of copper chloride in 20 cm³ of an 80 g/dm³ solution of copper chloride?**
>
> First, change the units of volume from cm³ to dm³.
> volume = 20 ÷ 1000 = 0.020 dm³
>
> Rearrange the equation to make mass the subject by multiplying each side by volume:
> mass = concentration × volume = 80 × 0.020 = 1.6 g

Exam Tip
Always double check the units of any data you're given before you use it in a calculation, in case you need to convert them first.

Uncertainties in measurements

All measurements have some uncertainty to them. Experiments will often be repeated, and then an average (mean) of any repeated measurements will be calculated. The range of the results can also be found, and can be used to give you an idea of how uncertain the mean value is (see p.14). The greater the range (the more distributed the results), the higher the uncertainty will be.

Tip: This handy formula triangle might help when rearranging the equation for concentration:

```
    mass
 conc. × vol.
```

(See page 245 for how to use formula triangles.)

> ### Example
>
> A student carries out an investigation to find the volume of a solution needed to neutralise an acid. She repeats her experiment four times. Her results are shown below.
>
> | Repeat | 1 | 2 | 3 | 4 |
> |---|---|---|---|---|
> | Volume (cm³) | 15.2 | 15.0 | 14.9 | 15.3 |
>
> The mean volume is (15.2 + 15.0 + 14.9 + 15.3) ÷ 4 = 15.1 cm³
>
> The range of results is 15.3 − 14.9 = 0.4 cm³
>
> To calculate the uncertainty, you divide the range by 2.
>
> So the uncertainty is 0.4 ÷ 2 = ±0.2 cm³.
>
> This can be shown as 15.1 ± 0.2 cm³

Practice Questions — Fact Recall

Q1   What is concentration?

Q2   State the equation that links the concentration of a solution in g/dm³ with the mass of the solute and the volume of the solution.

Practice Questions — Application

Q1   Calculate the concentrations of the following solutions, in g/dm³.

   a) A solution containing 150 g of iron chloride in 3 dm³ of solvent.

   b) A solution containing 48 g of hydrochloric acid in 0.4 dm³ of solvent.

Figure 1: *Copper sulfate solution.*

Q2 Calculate the concentrations of the following solutions, in g/dm³.

a) A solution containing 60 g of sodium hydroxide in 120 cm³ of solvent.

b) A solution containing 2.4 g of sodium chloride in 8 cm³ of solvent.

Q3 Calculate the mass of solute in the following solutions.

a) The mass of sodium carbonate in 2.5 dm³ of a 32 g/dm³ solution of sodium carbonate.

b) The mass of copper sulfate in 0.35 dm³ of a 60 g/dm³ solution of copper sulfate.

Q4 Calculate the mass of solute in the following solutions.

a) The mass of sulfuric acid in 80 cm³ of a 200 g/dm³ solution of sulfuric acid.

b) The mass of magnesium chloride in 15 cm³ of a 120 g/dm³ solution of magnesium chloride.

Q5 A student has two solutions, A and B. He measures the volume of each solution three times and calculates a mean result. His measurements for the volume of solution A have a range of 0.5 cm³, and his measurements for the volume of solution B have a range of 0.2 cm³.

a) Which result has a greater uncertainty?

b) Calculate the uncertainty of the student's result for solution B.

Topic Checklist — Make sure you know...

Relative Formula Mass

☐ How to calculate the relative formula mass (M_r) of a substance by adding up the relative atomic masses (A_r) of all the atoms in the formula.

☐ How to calculate the percentage mass of an element in a compound.

The Mole

☐ **H** That the Avogadro constant has the value 6.02×10^{23}.

☐ **H** That amounts in chemistry can be measured in moles, and have the units 'mol'.

☐ **H** That the number of particles (atoms, ions or molecules) in one mole of any substance is equal to the Avogadro constant.

☐ **H** That the relative formula mass of a substance is the same as the mass, in grams, of one mole of that substance.

☐ **H** How to convert mass to moles and vice versa using the formula moles = mass ÷ M_r.

☐ **H** How to rearrange a mathematical equation.

cont...

Conservation of Mass

☐ What the law of conservation of mass is.

☐ That the law of conservation of mass can be used to write balanced symbol equations, where the number of atoms in the reactants and products is the same.

☐ That the mass of the products in a reaction is equal to the mass of the reactants.

☐ How to calculate the masses of substances in a reaction using balanced symbol equations.

☐ That if the mass of the substances in a reaction seems to increase, it's usually because at least one of the reactants is a gas, and all the products are solids, liquids or solutions.

☐ That if the mass of the substances in a reaction seems to decrease, it's usually because at least one of the products is a gas, and all the reactants are solids, liquids or solutions.

☐ How to explain observations of mass change in terms of the particle model.

The Mole and Equations

☐ ⒣ That symbol equations give you the ratio of the number of moles of each substance in a reaction.

☐ ⒣ How to balance a chemical equation using the masses of the reactants and products.

Limiting Reactants

☐ ⒣ That the reactant that gets used up first in a chemical reaction is known as the limiting reactant.

☐ ⒣ That the limiting reactant controls how much product is formed.

☐ ⒣ How the amount of product formed will change if the amount of limiting reactant is changed.

☐ ⒣ How to calculate the mass of product formed in a reaction from the balanced symbol equation and the mass of the limiting reactant.

☐ ⒣ How to calculate the mass of reactant needed to make a given amount of product from the balanced symbol equation.

Concentrations

☐ That there are many reactions that happen in solution.

☐ That the concentration of a solution is determined by the mass of solute and volume of solvent.

☐ That the units of concentration can be given in 'units of mass'/'units of volume', such as g/dm^3.

☐ How to calculate the concentration of a solution in g/dm^3.

☐ That the greater the mass of solute in a given volume of solution, the higher its concentration.

☐ How to calculate the mass of solute in a volume of solution from the concentration in g/dm^3.

☐ That all measurements have some uncertainty to them, and that you can estimate uncertainties from the range of results.

Exam-style Questions

1 A scientist carries out an experiment to react copper with oxygen to form copper oxide. The balanced equation for the reaction is: $2Cu_{(s)} + O_{2(g)} \rightarrow 2CuO_{(s)}$

The scientist heats 2.54 g of copper in an unsealed container. Once all the copper has reacted, she finds that the mass of the reaction container has increased by 0.64 g.

1.1 Calculate the relative formula mass of copper oxide.
Relative atomic masses (A_r): O = 16, Cu = 63.5

(1 mark)

1.2 Explain how the balanced symbol equation follows the law of conservation of mass.

(1 mark)

1.3 What mass of oxygen reacts with the copper in this experiment?

(1 mark)

1.4 Explain why the mass inside the reaction vessel increases during this experiment.

(2 marks)

2 A student prepares a 150 g/dm³ solution of magnesium chloride ($MgCl_2$).

2.1 What mass of magnesium chloride would there be in 30 cm³ of this solution?

(2 marks)

2.2 The student adds 60 cm³ of water to the 30 cm³ of 150 g/dm³ solution.
What is the concentration of the diluted solution in g/dm³?

(2 marks)

3 Calcium carbonate decomposes when it's heated to form calcium oxide and carbon dioxide. The balanced equation for the reaction is: $CaCO_{3(s)} \rightarrow CaO_{(s)} + CO_{2(g)}$

During an experiment, 7.0 g of calcium oxide and 5.5 g of carbon dioxide are formed.

3.1 What mass of calcium carbonate was there at the beginning of the reaction?

(1 mark)

3.2 Predict the mass of calcium oxide that would be produced if the same reaction was carried out using three times as much calcium carbonate.

(1 mark)

3.3 Calculate the relative formula masses of each of the substances in the reaction.
Relative atomic masses (A_r): C = 12, O = 16, Ca = 40

(3 marks)

3.4 Use your answer to 3.3 to show that mass is conserved in this reaction.

(2 marks)

4   In a reaction, 0.50 g of hydrogen and 4.0 g of oxygen react to form 4.5 g of water.

4.1   Use the data to write a balanced symbol equation for this reaction.

(4 marks)

The reaction is carried out again using 0.20 g of hydrogen
and the same mass of oxygen.

4.2   Explain why hydrogen will be a limiting reactant in this reaction.

(1 mark)

4.3   Using your knowledge of how changing the amount of limiting reactant changes the
amount of product formed, predict the mass of water made during this reaction.

(1 mark)

5   4.8 g of magnesium reacts in an excess of zinc chloride solution to form magnesium
chloride and zinc. The equation for this reaction is:

$$Mg + ZnCl_2 \rightarrow MgCl_2 + Zn$$

5.1   How many moles of magnesium react?

(1 mark)

5.2   What mass of magnesium chloride is produced by this reaction?

(3 marks)

5.3   At the start of the reaction, the solution contained 35 g of zinc chloride. What mass of
zinc chloride will be left in the solution after the reaction has taken place?

(4 marks)

5.4   The reaction is repeated using the same amount of magnesium, but this
time a volume of zinc chloride solution that contains 20 g of zinc chloride.
State, with reasoning, whether the zinc chloride is still in excess.

(2 marks)

6   A mixture is being made that will contain 8% bromine by mass.

6.1   What mass of calcium bromide, $CaBr_2$, is needed to provide enough bromine to make
30 g of this mixture?

(4 marks)

6.2   The calcium bromide is made by reacting calcium iodide with bromine.
The equation for this reaction is: $CaI_2 + Br_2 \rightarrow CaBr_2 + I_2$
Calculate the mass of calcium iodide that will react to form the mass of calcium
bromide needed in the mixture. If you didn't get an answer to 5.1, you can assume the
mass of calcium bromide needed is 1.5 g. This is not the correct value.

(4 marks)

Learning Objectives:

- Know that how acidic or alkaline a solution is can be measured on the pH scale, which runs from 0 to 14.

- Know that a neutral substance has a pH of 7, an acidic solution has a pH less than 7 and an alkaline solution has a pH more than 7.

- Be able to describe how you could measure the pH of a solution using a wide range indicator, such as Universal indicator, or by using a pH probe.

- Know that it is hydrogen ions (H^+) that make a solution acidic and hydroxide ions (OH^-) that make a solution alkaline.

- Know that in a neutralisation reaction between an acid and an alkali, hydrogen ions (H^+) react with hydroxide ions (OH^-) to produce water.

Specification References
5.4.2.4

1. Acids and Alkalis

Solutions can be classed as acidic, alkaline or neutral depending on their pH. How acidic or basic a solution is can tell you a lot about its chemistry.

The pH scale

pH is a measure of how acidic or alkaline a solution is. The **pH scale** goes from 0 to 14 (see Figure 1).

- Anything that forms a solution with a pH of less than 7 is an **acid**. The lower the pH, the more acidic the solution.

- Anything that forms a solution with a pH of greater than 7 is an **alkali**. The higher the pH, the more alkaline the substance is.

- **Neutral substances** are neither acidic nor alkaline and have a pH of exactly 7. Pure water is an example of a neutral substance.

Testing pH

One way to test the pH of a solution is to use an **indicator**. An indicator is a dye that changes colour depending on whether it's above or below a certain pH. Some indicators contain a mixture of dyes that means they gradually change colour over a broad range of pHs. These are called **wide range indicators** and they're useful for estimating the pH of a solution. For example, **Universal indicator** gives the colours shown in Figure 1.

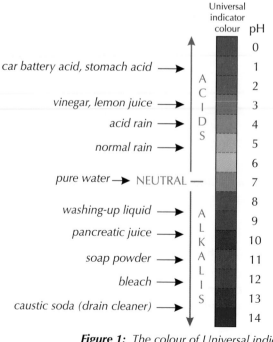

Figure 1: The colour of Universal indicator at different pHs.

Another method is to use a pH probe attached to a pH meter which can measure pH electronically. The probe is placed in the solution you are measuring and the pH is given on a digital display as a numerical value, meaning it's more accurate than an indicator.

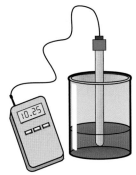

Figure 2: *A pH meter and probe.*

Figure 3: *A student using a pH meter and probe while conducting a titration experiment.*

Acids and alkalis

Whether a substance is an acid or an alkali depends on the type of ions that are released when the substance is dissolved in water. Acids form hydrogen ions (H^+) when dissolved in water and alkalis form hydroxide ions (OH^-).

Neutralisation reactions

An acid will react with an alkali to form a salt and water — this is called a **neutralisation** reaction. The general equation for a neutralisation reaction is shown below.

$$\text{acid} + \text{alkali} \rightarrow \text{salt} + \text{water}$$

Neutralisation reactions between acids and alkalis can also be shown in terms of H^+ and OH^- ions. During neutralisation reactions, hydrogen ions (H^+) from the acid react with hydroxide ions (OH^-) from the alkali to produce water. The equation for this reaction is:

$$H^+_{(aq)} + OH^-_{(aq)} \rightarrow H_2O_{(l)}$$

When an acid neutralises an alkali (or vice versa), the solution that's formed is neutral — it has a pH of 7. An indicator can be used to show that a neutralisation reaction is over.

Tip: Neutralisation reactions are a good chance to measure changes in pH using Universal indicator or a pH probe.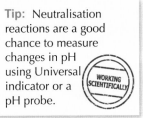

Tip: You'll often see equations involving ions with state symbols. There's more on state symbols on page 99.

> **Example**
>
> Universal indicator turns green at the end of a neutralisation reaction — see Figure 4. This shows that the solution has become neutral (and therefore that the reaction has finished).

Figure 4: *Universal indicator turning green at the end of a neutralisation reaction.*

Practice Questions — Fact Recall

Q1   What is pH a measure of?

Q2   If a solution is neutral, what pH will it have?

Q3   What range of pHs show that a substance is an alkali?

Q4   a) What type of ions are released when an acid dissolves in water?

b) What type of ions are released when an alkali dissolves in water?

Q5   What is the product of the reaction between hydrogen ions (H^+) and hydroxide ions (OH^-)?

Tip: An alkali is a soluble base.

Practice Questions — Application

Q1   State whether the following solutions are acidic or alkaline.

a) A solution of hydrogen sulfide with a pH of 4.2.

b) A solution of calcium hydroxide with a pH of 12.4.

Q2   a) After adding Universal indicator to a colourless solution, the colour changes to yellow. Suggest the pH of this solution.

b) Another solution has a pH of 9. Suggest what colour this solution will go if Universal indicator is added to it.

Q3   The alkali lithium hydroxide reacts with hydrochloric acid.

a) What type of reaction is this?

b) A salt is formed. What is the other product of this reaction?

Tip: Remember that acidic solutions have a pH less than 7 and alkaline solutions have a pH greater than 7.

2. Strong Acids and Weak Acids Higher

Not all acids are created equal, some like to give up more of their H+ ions in water than others — some are strong, some are weak.

Dissociation of acids

When acids are added to an aqueous solution they ionise to produce H+ ions.

| Example | Higher |

Hydrogen chloride dissolves in water to form hydrogen ions and chloride ions:

$$HCl_{(g)} \rightarrow H^+_{(aq)} + Cl^-_{(aq)}$$

Acid strength

The strength of an acid tells you about the proportion of acid particles that will dissociate to produce H+ ions in solution.

Strong acids

Strong acids, such as sulfuric (H_2SO_4), hydrochloric (HCl) and nitric acid (HNO_3), ionise completely in water — all the acid particles dissociate to release H+ ions.

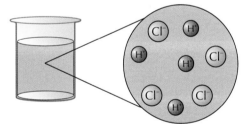

Figure 1: Hydrochloric acid dissociates completely in water.

| Examples | Higher |

Nitric acid ionises completely in water to form hydrogen ions and nitrate ions:

$$HNO_{3(l)} \rightarrow H^+_{(aq)} + NO_3^-{}_{(aq)}$$

Sulfuric acid also ionises completely but releases two hydrogen ions for every molecule of sulfuric acid:

$$H_2SO_{4(l)} \rightarrow 2H^+_{(aq)} + SO_4^{2-}{}_{(aq)}$$

Weak acids

Weak acids only partially ionise in water — if you put a sample of a weak acid in water, only some of the acid molecules will ionise and release H+ ions. Carboxylic acids are weak acids (they don't ionise completely when dissolved in water) as are citric and carbonic acids.

Learning Objectives:

- **H** Know that strong acids ionise completely in water.
- **H** Know that weak acids partially ionise in water.
- **H** Be able to give examples of strong and weak acids.
- **H** Know that a change of H+ ion concentration by a factor of 10 will result in a change of 1 on the pH scale.
- **H** Be able to compare the relative acidity or neutrality of solutions from their pH or hydrogen ion concentrations.
- **H** Understand that a solution of a strong acid will have a lower pH than a solution of a weaker acid with the same concentration.
- **H** Know the difference between a concentrated acid and a strong acid.

Specification Reference 5.4.2.5

Tip: **H** Acids don't produce hydrogen ions until they meet water. So, for example, hydrogen chloride gas isn't acidic.

Tip: **H** An H+ ion is just a proton.

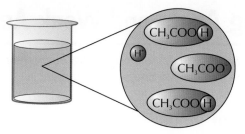

Figure 2: Ethanoic acid dissociates partially in water.

Tip: In a reversible reaction, the products are able to react together to form the reactants again. The symbol '$\rightleftharpoons$' is used in place of a normal reaction arrow for reversible reactions to show that the reaction can go both ways. For more on this, have a look at page 181.

Tip: If the equilibrium is to the left there are more reactants than products.

Tip: There's more about the factors that affect reaction rate on pages 165-166.

Ionisation of a weak acid is a reversible reaction, which sets up an equilibrium between the undissociated and dissociated acid. Since only a few of the acid particles release H^+ ions, the position of equilibrium lies well to the left.

Examples — **Higher**

Ethanoic acid does not fully ionise in water, creating an equilibrium:

$$CH_3COOH_{(aq)} \rightleftharpoons H^+_{(aq)} + CH_3COO^-_{(aq)}$$

Carbonic acid also only partially ionises in water:

$$H_2CO_{3(aq)} \rightleftharpoons 2H^+_{(aq)} + CO_3^{2-}_{(aq)}$$

Effect of acid strength on reactivity

Reactions of acids involve the H^+ ions reacting with other substances. If the concentration of H^+ ions is higher, the rate of reaction will be faster. Since strong acids dissociate more than weak acids, a strong acid will be more reactive than a weak acid of the same concentration.

Effect of acid strength on pH

The pH is a measure of the concentration of H^+ ions in a solution. The lower the pH, the higher the concentration of H^+ ions and so the more acidic the solution is. The pH of a strong acid will be lower than a weak acid if both acids are at the same concentration. This is because strong acids dissociate more than weak acids resulting in a larger concentration of H^+ ions.

For every decrease of 1 on the pH scale, the concentration of H^+ ions increases by a factor of 10.

Examples — **Higher**

- An acid that has a pH of 4 has 10 times the concentration of H^+ ions of an acid that has a pH of 5.

- For a decrease of 2 on the pH scale, the concentration of H^+ ions increases by a factor of $(10 \times 10) = 100$.

- For an increase of 3 on the pH scale, the concentration of H^+ ions decreases by a factor of $(10 \times 10 \times 10) = 1000$.

You can calculate the change in H^+ concentration with the equation:

Factor H^+ ion concentration changes by $= 10^{-X}$ *X = difference in pH*

Example — **Higher**

The pH of a neutral aqueous solution fell from 7 to 4 following the addition of hydrochloric acid. This means the difference in pH following the addition of hydrochloric acid is $(4 - 7) = -3$.

Factor H^+ ion concentration changes by $= 10^{-X}$
Factor H^+ ion concentration changes by $= 10^{-(-3)} = 10^3$.

This means the H^+ ion concentration in the solution is now $(10 \times 10 \times 10) = 1000$ times higher.

Exam Tip H
You can check your answer by making sure that, if the pH has decreased, then the concentration of H^+ ions has increased.

Concentration and strength of acids

Acid strength (i.e. strong or weak) tells you what proportion of the acid molecules ionise in water. However, the **concentration** of an acid is different. Concentration measures the total number of dissolved acid molecules there are in a certain volume of water, not the number of molecules that are ionised to produce hydrogen ions at any given moment — it's basically a measure of how watered down your acid is.

Tip: H There's more about concentration on pages 118-120.

The larger the amount of acid there is in a certain volume of liquid, the more concentrated the acid is. This means you can have a dilute (not very concentrated) but strong acid, or a concentrated but weak acid. The pH will decrease with increasing acid concentration, regardless of whether it's a strong or weak acid.

Practice Questions — Fact Recall

Q1 Give the definition of a strong acid and name an example.

Q2 Give the definition of a weak acid and name an example.

Q3 Give the equation for the dissociation of ethanoic acid (CH_3COOH).

Q4 Give the equation that describes how the concentration of H^+ ions changes for a given change in pH.

Q5 Describe the difference between the strength and the concentration of an acid.

Practice Questions — Application

Q1 Explain why a 1 mol/dm³ solution of hydrochloric acid will have a lower pH than a 1 mol/dm³ solution of ethanoic acid.

Q2 A student added acid to an alkaline solution. The pH of the solution changed from 9 to 7. By how many times did the concentration of H^+ ions change?

Q3 Following the addition of alkali to an acid solution the pH of the solution changed from 4 to 7. By how many times did the concentration of H^+ ions change?

Learning Objectives:

■ Know that acids can react with bases, such as metal oxides and metal hydroxides, to form salts and water.

■ Know that the salt formed depends on the positive ion in the base and the acid it reacts with.

■ Know that acids can react with metal carbonates to form salts, water and carbon dioxide.

■ Be able to predict the products of a neutralisation reaction from the reactants.

■ Know how to make a pure dry sample of a soluble salt from the reaction of an acid with an insoluble oxide or carbonate (Required Practical 8).

Specification References
5.4.2.2, 5.4.2.3

3. Reactions of Acids

Acids can react with all sorts of things, most of the time through neutralisation reactions. Here are some you need to know...

Reaction with metal oxides and metal hydroxides

Bases are substances that can react with acids in neutralisation reactions. All metal oxides and hydroxides are bases. Soluble metal hydroxides are alkalis because they dissolve in water to form OH^- ions. The products of these neutralisation reactions are a salt and water. So the general equation for the reaction of metal oxides or metal hydroxides with acids is:

$$\text{acid} + \frac{\text{metal oxide}}{\text{or metal hydroxide}} \rightarrow \text{salt} + \text{water}$$

Which salt is formed?

The name of the salt produced depends on the metal ion in the oxide or hydroxide and the acid that is used. The first part of the name of the salt is the metal ion in the oxide/hydroxide and the second part of the name comes from the acid that is used.

> **Example**
>
> Reacting hydrochloric acid with copper oxide will give you copper chloride:
>
> hydrochloric acid + copper oxide → copper chloride + water

Reaction with hydrochloric acid gives chlorides, with sulfuric acid gives sulfates and with nitric acid gives nitrates.

> **Examples**
>
> hydrochloric acid + sodium hydroxide → sodium chloride + water
> $HCl_{(aq)}$ + $NaOH_{(aq)}$ → $NaCl_{(aq)}$ + $H_2O_{(l)}$
>
> sulfuric acid + zinc oxide → zinc sulfate + water
> $H_2SO_{4(aq)}$ + $ZnO_{(s)}$ → $ZnSO_{4(aq)}$ + $H_2O_{(l)}$
>
> sulfuric acid + calcium hydroxide → calcium sulfate + water
> $H_2SO_{4(aq)}$ + $Ca(OH)_{2(s)}$ → $CaSO_{4(aq)}$ + $2H_2O_{(l)}$
>
> nitric acid + magnesium oxide → magnesium nitrate + water
> $2HNO_{3(aq)}$ + $MgO_{(s)}$ → $Mg(NO_3)_{2(aq)}$ + $H_2O_{(l)}$
>
> nitric acid + potassium hydroxide → potassium nitrate + water
> $HNO_{3(aq)}$ + $KOH_{(aq)}$ → $KNO_{3(aq)}$ + $H_2O_{(l)}$

Tip: To work out the formula of an ionic compound, you need to balance the charges of the positive and negative ions so the overall charge of a compound is neutral. For more on ionic formulas, see p.76.

Tip: Whether you use an oxide or a hydroxide isn't important — it's the metal in the compound that determines which salt you'll get.

Metal carbonates and acid

Metal carbonates are also bases. Metal carbonates react with acids to make a salt, carbon dioxide and water. The general equation for the reaction of metal carbonates and acids is:

> metal carbonate + acid → metal salt + carbon dioxide + water

The type of salt produced depends on the type of acid used and the metal in the carbonate.

Figure 1: *Reaction of calcium carbonate and hydrochloric acid forming calcium chloride, carbon dioxide and water.*

Examples

If calcium carbonate reacts with sulfuric acid, a sulfate is produced.

calcium carbonate + sulfuric acid → calcium sulfate + carbon dioxide + water

$$CaCO_3 + H_2SO_4 \rightarrow CaSO_4 + CO_2 + H_2O$$

If calcium carbonate reacts with hydrochloric acid, a chloride is produced.

calcium carbonate + hydrochloric acid → calcium chloride + carbon dioxide + water

$$CaCO_3 + 2HCl \rightarrow CaCl_2 + CO_2 + H_2O$$

When zinc carbonate reacts with nitric acid, zinc nitrate is formed.

zinc carbonate + nitric acid → zinc nitrate + carbon dioxide + water

$$ZnCO_3 + 2HNO_3 \rightarrow Zn(NO_3)_2 + CO_2 + H_2O$$

Exam Tip
You might be asked to write equations for the reactions of different carbonates with different acids, so make sure you can work them out. Remember, with sulfuric acid you always get a sulfate, with hydrochloric acid you always get a chloride and with nitric acid you always get a nitrate.

Making soluble salts   REQUIRED PRACTICAL **8**

Soluble salts can be made by reacting an acid with a metal or an insoluble base (such as a metal oxide, metal hydroxide or metal carbonate). When making a soluble salt, the first thing you need to do is choose appropriate reagents to produce that particular salt. You should be able to work out which are the right reagents to choose from the name of the salt you want to produce.

Tip: You could also react hydrochloric acid with copper carbonate to make copper chloride.

Example

If you want to make copper chloride, you could mix hydrochloric acid and copper oxide:

$$2HCl_{(aq)} + CuO_{(s)} \rightarrow CuCl_{2(aq)} + H_2O_{(l)}$$

Making soluble salts from acids and insoluble bases

If you are making a soluble salt by adding an insoluble reagent to an acid, you can add it in excess and separate it out at the end of the reaction using filter paper. Many metal oxides and some metal carbonates are insoluble, so this is the method you'd use if you're using any of those. Here's what you do:

Tip: Make sure you carry out a risk assessment before doing any practical and that you use the correct safety equipment.

1. Put the acid in a beaker. Gently warm the dilute acid using a Bunsen burner, then turn off the Bunsen burner.

2. Add the insoluble reactant (the metal oxide or metal carbonate) and stir — it will form a soluble product in the acid as it reacts.

3. Keep adding the insoluble reactant until it is in excess. You'll know when this is because there will be some left over that won't react — this shows that all the acid has been neutralised and the reaction has finished.

4. Then you need to filter out the excess insoluble reactant to get the salt solution. This is done using filter paper and a filter funnel (see Figure 2).

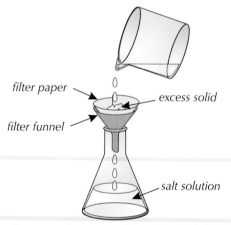

filter paper

excess solid

filter funnel

salt solution

Figure 2: *Filtering out the excess insoluble reactant using filter paper and a filter funnel.*

Tip: If you want to know more about crystallisation have a look at page 38.

5. You'll be left with a salt solution at the end of the filtration. You can convert this into pure, solid crystals of salt using crystallisation. To do this you first need to heat the salt solution using a water bath or an electric heater, in order to evaporate some of the water and make the solution more concentrated. Then, stop heating it and leave the solution to cool. Crystals of the salt should form, which can be filtered out of the solution and then dried.

Practice Questions — Application

Q1 a) Name the salt that is produced when magnesium carbonate reacts with hydrochloric acid.

b) Balance the following equation:
$MgCO_3 + HCl \rightarrow MgCl_2 + CO_2 + H_2O$

Q2 A scientist is making the soluble salt zinc chloride ($ZnCl_2$) by reacting the insoluble base, zinc oxide (ZnO), with hydrochloric acid (HCl).

a) Write the word equation for this reaction.

b) Describe the experimental method used to make this salt.

4. Reactivity of Metals

The reactivity series tells you how reactive a metal is relative to another. This is very useful when predicting how metals are likely to react.

The reactivity series

The **reactivity series** is a list of metals that are arranged in order of how reactive they are. The most reactive metals are at the top and the least reactive are at the bottom.

The reactivity of a metal is derived from how easily it forms positive ions. A metal which easily forms positive ions (i.e. loses electrons) will be more reactive and therefore further to the top of the reactivity series than a metal that doesn't form positive ions so easily.

Learning Objectives:

- Know that metals can be placed in order of reactivity, and that this is known as the reactivity series.
- Understand that the reactivity of a metal is due to how easily it forms positive ions.
- Know that potassium, sodium, lithium, calcium, magnesium, zinc, iron and copper can be put in order of reactivity based on their reactions with acid and water.
- Know that carbon and hydrogen are often included in the reactivity series, even though they are non-metals.
- Be able to use experimental results to work out an order of reactivity.
- Be able to describe the reactions, if any, of these metals with dilute acids to form a salt and hydrogen.
- Be able to describe the reactions, if any, of these metals with water to form a metal hydroxide and hydrogen gas.
- Know that more reactive metals are able to displace less reactive ones from compounds.

Specification References 5.4.1.2, 5.4.2.1

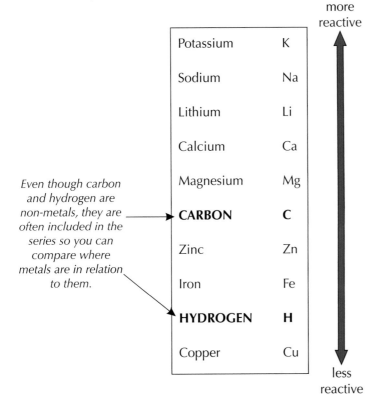

Even though carbon and hydrogen are non-metals, they are often included in the series so you can compare where metals are in relation to them.

Figure 1: *The reactivity series.*

Finding an order of reactivity from experiments

If you compare the relative reactivity of different metals with either an acid or water and put them in order from most reactive to the least reactive, the order you get is a reactivity series. The higher a metal is in the reactivity series, the more easily it reacted with the water or acid.

You can also investigate the reactivity of metals by measuring the temperature change of the reaction with an acid or water over a set time period. If you use the same mass and surface area of metal each time, then the more reactive the metal, the greater the temperature change should be.

Reactions of metals with acids

Tip: This reaction can be used to make soluble salts using the technique shown on page 132.

The reaction of a metal and acid produces a salt and hydrogen, as shown in the equation below.

$$acid \ + \ metal \ \rightarrow \ salt \ + \ hydrogen$$

Reactivity of metals with acids

You can see how reactive different metals are by monitoring the rate of hydrogen production when they react with an acid. The more reactive the metal, the faster the reaction will go. The speed of the reaction is indicated by the rate at which bubbles of hydrogen are given off — a speedy reaction is shown by bubbles being produced rapidly.

Tip: The reactions of some Group 1 metals and acids are very dangerous and should not be attempted in a classroom.

Very reactive metals like potassium, sodium, lithium and calcium react explosively, but less reactive metals such as magnesium, zinc and iron react less violently. Copper won't react with cold, dilute acids.

Tip: There's more about tests for gases on page 203.

The production of hydrogen can be detected using the burning splint test. This involves putting a lit splint at the mouth of the tube containing the metal and the acid. If hydrogen is there, you'll hear a 'squeaky pop'. The more reactive the metal, the more hydrogen is produced in a certain amount of time and the louder the 'squeaky pop'.

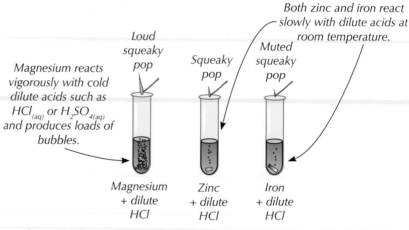

Both zinc and iron react slowly with dilute acids at room temperature.

Magnesium reacts vigorously with cold dilute acids such as $HCl_{(aq)}$ or $H_2SO_{4(aq)}$ and produces loads of bubbles.

Loud squeaky pop — Magnesium + dilute HCl

Squeaky pop — Zinc + dilute HCl

Muted squeaky pop — Iron + dilute HCl

Figure 2: *The reactivity of different metals in the presence of hydrochloric acid.*

Figure 3: *Magnesium reacting with hydrochloric acid.*

Which salt is formed?

The name of the salt produced depends on which metal and acid are used. The first part of the name of the salt comes from the metal and the second part of the name comes from the acid that is used.

Tip: The way to remember which acid produces which salt is in the name. Hydro<u>chlor</u>ic acid produces <u>chloride</u> salts and <u>sulfur</u>ic acid produces <u>sulfate</u> salts.

Example

When you react magnesium with hydrochloric acid you get magnesium chloride:

hydrochloric acid + magnesium → magnesium chloride + hydrogen

---

Hydrochloric acid always produces chloride salts.

Exam Tip
In the exam you might be asked to work out the salt formed from two reactants or the reactants need to make a particular salt.
So it's important that you understand these examples.

Examples

hydrochloric acid	+	iron	$\rightarrow$	iron chloride	+ hydrogen
$2HCl_{(aq)}$	+	$Fe_{(s)}$	$\rightarrow$	$FeCl_{2(aq)}$	+ $H_{2(g)}$
hydrochloric acid	+	zinc	$\rightarrow$	zinc chloride	+ hydrogen
$2HCl_{(aq)}$	+	$Zn_{(s)}$	$\rightarrow$	$ZnCl_{2(aq)}$	+ $H_{2(g)}$

Sulfuric acid always produces sulfate salts.

Examples

sulfuric acid	+	magnesium	$\rightarrow$	magnesium sulfate	+ hydrogen
$H_2SO_{4(aq)}$	+	$Mg_{(s)}$	$\rightarrow$	$MgSO_{4(aq)}$	+ $H_{2(g)}$
sulfuric acid	+	zinc	$\rightarrow$	zinc sulfate	+ hydrogen
$H_2SO_{4(aq)}$	+	$Zn_{(s)}$	$\rightarrow$	$ZnSO_{4(aq)}$	+ $H_{2(g)}$

Figure 4: *Reaction of zinc and sulfuric acid with bubbles of hydrogen gas forming.*

Reactions of metals with water

Some metals form positive ions when they react with water, so the reaction can be used to compare their reactivity. The reaction at room temperature produces a metal hydroxide and hydrogen gas as shown in the general equation below.

| metal | + | water | $\rightarrow$ | metal hydroxide | + | hydrogen |

Examples

calcium	+	water	$\rightarrow$	calcium hydroxide	+ hydrogen
$Ca_{(s)}$	+	$2H_2O_{(l)}$	$\rightarrow$	$Ca(OH)_{2(aq)}$	+ $H_{2(g)}$
potassium	+	water	$\rightarrow$	potassium hydroxide	+ hydrogen
$K_{(s)}$	+	$H_2O_{(l)}$	$\rightarrow$	$K(OH)_{(aq)}$	+ $H_{2(g)}$

Exam Tip
You can see more on the reactions of Group 1 metals with water on pages 57-58.

Metals that aren't very reactive, such as zinc, iron and copper won't react with water. However, more reactive metals such as the Group 1 metals potassium, sodium and lithium as well as the Group 2 metal calcium, will all react.

Displacement reactions

Displacement reactions involve one metal replacing another one out of a compound. A more reactive metal will displace a less reactive metal from its compound.

If you put a more reactive metal in the solution of a dissolved metal compound containing a less reactive metal ion, the reactive metal will replace the less reactive metal in the compound.

Exam Tip
In the exam, you may need to write word or symbol equations to show displacement reactions.

Figure 5: *Displacement reaction of zinc and copper sulfate. The blue colour of the copper sulfate solution fades as copper metal is precipitated out of solution.*

Tip: The more reactive the metal is compared to the metal ion, the more vigorous the reaction will be.

Examples

If you place iron in a solution of copper(II) sulfate ($CuSO_4$), the more reactive iron will 'kick out' the less reactive copper from the solution. You end up with iron(II) sulfate in solution and copper metal as a precipitate.

iron	+ copper(II) sulfate	→	iron(II) sulfate	+	copper
$Fe_{(s)}$	+ $CuSO_{4(aq)}$	→	$FeSO_{4(aq)}$	+	$Cu_{(s)}$

As zinc is a more reactive metal than iron, if you add zinc to a solution of iron(II) sulfate, the zinc will displace the iron from the solution. You end up with zinc sulfate in solution and iron metal as a precipitate.

zinc	+ iron(II) sulfate	→	zinc sulfate	+	iron
$Zn_{(s)}$	+ $FeSO_{4(aq)}$	→	$ZnSO_{4(aq)}$	+	$Fe_{(s)}$

Practice Questions — Fact Recall

Q1 Is an element at the top of the reactivity series more or less reactive than the elements below it?

Q2 Which is more reactive: calcium or zinc?

Q3 Write a word equation for the general reaction of a metal with acid.

Practice Questions — Application

Q1 Give the balanced equation for the reaction of iron and hydrochloric acid. The salt produced is iron chloride ($FeCl_2$).

Q2 Name the salt produced in the following reactions.

   a) Sulfuric acid reacting with iron.

   b) Water reacting with calcium.

Q3 Three metals, A, B and C were placed into a test tube containing dilute hydrochloric acid. Metal A reacted vigorously and produced a gas which gave a loud squeaky popping noise on testing with a lit splint. Metal B did not react on addition of dilute hydrochloric acid but produced some bubbles of gas upon heating. Metal C produced a lower rate of bubbles than A and gave a quiet squeaky pop when tested with a lit splint.

   a) Give the order of reactivity of the metals A, B and C, going from least to most reactive.

   b) Give the identity of the gas produced.

Q4 A student added zinc to a solution of iron(II) sulfate. A reaction occurred forming a precipitate.

   a) Give the word equation for this reaction.

   b) In a second experiment, copper was used instead of zinc. Explain why no reaction occurred.

Tip: By using the reactivity series you can work out whether a metal will displace another one in a compound.

5. Metal Oxides and Redox

Most metals are not found in the ground in pure form, they have to be extracted from their ores somehow. Here are some of the ways it's done...

Extracting metals from ores

A few unreactive metals, like gold, are found in the Earth as the metal itself, rather than as a compound. The rest of the metals we get by extracting them from **metal ores**, which are mined from the ground. A metal ore is a rock which contains enough metal to make it profitable to extract the metal from it. In many cases the ore is an oxide of the metal. For example, the main aluminium ore is called bauxite — it's aluminium oxide (Al_2O_3).

A reaction that forms a metal oxide from its metal is known as **oxidation**.

> Oxidation can be defined as the gain of oxygen by an element or compound.

Examples

Magnesium is oxidised to make magnesium oxide.

2Mg	+	O_2	→	2MgO
magnesium	+	oxygen	→	magnesium oxide

Copper is oxidised to make copper oxide.

2Cu	+	O_2	→	2CuO
copper	+	oxygen	→	copper oxide

A reaction that separates a metal from its oxide is called **reduction**.

> Reduction can be defined as the loss of oxygen from a compound.

Examples

Copper oxide is reduced to make copper.

2CuO	+	C	→	2Cu	+	CO_2
copper oxide	+	carbon	→	copper	+	carbon dioxide

Zinc oxide is reduced to make zinc.

2ZnO	+	C	→	2Zn	+	CO_2
zinc oxide	+	carbon	→	zinc	+	carbon dioxide

Extraction of metals by reduction with carbon

A metal below carbon in the reactivity series can be extracted from its ore by reducing it in a reaction with carbon. In this reaction, the ore is reduced as oxygen is removed from it and carbon gains oxygen so is oxidised.

Learning Objectives:

- Know that a few metals are found as themselves in the earth but most are compounds that need extraction.
- Know that metals can react with oxygen to form metal oxides.
- Know that oxidation can be defined as the gain of oxygen.
- Know that reduction can be defined as the loss of oxygen.
- Be able to identify species that have been oxidised or reduced.
- Metals lower than carbon in the reactivity series can be extracted by carbon by a reduction reaction.
- Metals above carbon in the metal reactivity series need to be extracted by electrolysis.
- Be able to explain why metals are extracted in certain ways from given information.

Specification References 5.4.1.1, 5.4.1.3, 5.4.3.3

Tip: H Oxidation and reduction can also be defined in terms of the loss and gain of electrons (see page 139).

Tip: During a reduction reaction, oxygen is removed from the ore and the ore is said to be <u>reduced</u>.

Figure 1: A blast furnace.

Exam Tip
Make sure you can explain why different metals are extracted from their ores in different ways, as well as how they are extracted.

Example

Iron(III) oxide (the ore of iron) is reduced in a blast furnace to make iron. Iron is less reactive than carbon so when iron oxide and carbon react the oxygen is removed from the iron ore, leaving iron metal.

$$2Fe_2O_3 \quad + \quad 3C \quad \rightarrow \quad 4Fe \quad + \quad 3CO_2$$

iron(III) oxide + carbon → iron + carbon dioxide

Metals below carbon in the reactivity series can be extracted by reduction using carbon. This is because carbon can only take the oxygen away from metals which are less reactive than carbon itself.

Metals higher than carbon in the reactivity series, or that react in different ways with carbon, have to be extracted using electrolysis, which is expensive.

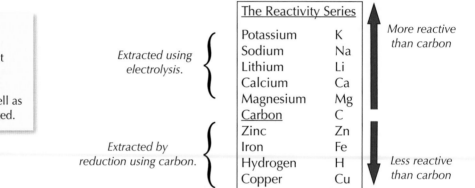

Figure 2: The reactivity series of metals showing which are extracted using reduction with carbon and which are extracted via electrolysis.

Practice Questions — Fact Recall

Q1 Name a metal which is found in the earth as the metal itself.

Q2 Define oxidation in terms of the loss or gain of oxygen.

Q3 What is formed when a metal reacts with oxygen?

Q4 Define reduction in terms of the loss or gain of oxygen.

Practice Questions — Application

Tip: Have a look at the reactivity series above to help you with these questions.

Q1 Name a process that could be used to extract each of these metals from their metal oxides.

a) Iron   b) Calcium

c) Zinc   d) Potassium

Q2 Lithium is commonly extracted from lithium chloride using electrolysis. Explain why reducing lithium chloride with carbon doesn't work.

6. Redox Reactions   Higher

Oxidation and reduction aren't just the gain or loss of oxygen. Confusingly, they can also mean the loss or gain of electrons by a chemical species.

What is a redox reaction?

Redox reactions occur when electrons are transferred between substances.

> - Oxidation is a loss of electrons.
> - Reduction is a gain of electrons.

Both oxidation and reduction happen at the same time, hence the term redox. Oxidation and reduction can also be defined in terms of loss or gain of oxygen (p.137) but on this page they're referring to the transfer of electrons.

Displacement reactions and redox

Displacement reactions are a type of redox reaction. In displacement reactions, it's always the metal ion that gains electrons and is reduced. The metal atom always loses electrons and is oxidised.

Example — **Higher**

If you place zinc in a solution of copper sulfate ($CuSO_4$), the more reactive zinc will displace the less reactive copper from the solution.

$$\text{zinc} \quad + \quad \text{copper sulfate} \quad \rightarrow \quad \text{zinc sulfate} \quad + \quad \text{copper}$$
$$Zn_{(s)} \quad + \quad CuSO_{4(aq)} \quad \rightarrow \quad ZnSO_{4(aq)} \quad + \quad Cu_{(s)}$$

Zinc loses 2 electrons to become a 2+ ion — it's oxidised.

$$Zn \rightarrow Zn^{2+} + 2e^-$$

The copper ion gains 2 electrons to become a copper atom — it's reduced.

$$Cu^{2+} + 2e^- \rightarrow Cu$$

Ionic equations of displacement reactions

Ionic equations show only the particles that react and the products they form. Ionic equations for redox reactions only concentrate on the substances which are oxidised or reduced.

Example — **Higher**

The equation for the displacement reaction between copper sulfate and zinc (shown above) can be written out so that you can see all the ions:

$$Zn_{(s)} + Cu^{2+}{}_{(aq)} + SO_4{}^{2-}{}_{(aq)} \rightarrow Zn^{2+}{}_{(aq)} + SO_4{}^{2-}{}_{(aq)} + Cu_{(s)}$$

The sulfate ions don't change in the reaction so can be ignored:

$$Zn_{(s)} + Cu^{2+}{}_{(aq)} + \cancel{SO_4{}^{2-}{}_{(aq)}} \rightarrow Zn^{2+}{}_{(aq)} + \cancel{SO_4{}^{2-}{}_{(aq)}} + Cu_{(s)}$$

So the ionic equation is:

$$Zn_{(s)} + Cu^{2+}{}_{(aq)} \rightarrow Zn^{2+}{}_{(aq)} + Cu_{(s)}$$

Learning Objectives:

- **H** Know that oxidation is when a species loses electrons and reduction is when a species gains electrons.
- **H** Know that displacement reactions are redox reactions.
- **H** Be able to identify for displacement reactions which species is being oxidised and which is being reduced from a symbol equation or half equation.
- **H** Be able to write ionic equations for displacement reactions.
- **H** Know that the reactions of acids with metal are redox reactions.
- **H** Be able to identify which species are being oxidised and reduced in the reactions of acids and metals.

Specification References
5.4.1.4, 5.4.2.1

Tip: H A useful mnemonic to use to remember what oxidation and reduction are is OIL RIG: Oxidation Is Loss, Reduction Is Gain.

Tip: H Equations that show electrons being lost or gained are called half equations. There's more about them on pages 142-143.

Redox reactions of acids and metals

Tip: **H** All the reactions of metals and acids on pages 134-135 are redox reactions.

When acids react with metals they form salts and release hydrogen (p.134). These reactions are redox reactions as the metal atoms lose electrons (they are oxidised) and the hydrogen ions gain them (they are reduced).

Example — **Higher**

Iron and hydrochloric acid react to form iron chloride and hydrogen:

$$Fe_{(s)} + 2HCl_{(aq)} \rightarrow FeCl_{2(aq)} + H_{2(g)}$$

Iron atoms are oxidised to Fe^{2+} ions and H^+ ions are reduced to hydrogen:

$$Fe_{(s)} + 2H^+_{(aq)} \rightarrow Fe^{2+}_{(aq)} + H_{2(g)}$$

The iron atoms lose electrons. They are oxidised by the hydrogen ions:

$$Fe_{(s)} \rightarrow Fe^{2+}_{(aq)} + 2e^-$$

Hydrogen ions gain electrons. They are reduced by the iron atoms:

$$2H^+_{(aq)} + 2e^- \rightarrow H_{2(g)}$$

Figure 1: *The reaction of iron and hydrochloric acid.*

Sulfuric acid also contains hydrogen ions, so the half equations for the reaction of a metal with sulfuric acid are the same as for the reaction of that metal with hydrochloric acid.

Exam Tip **H**
You need to be able to identify which species are oxidised and which are reduced by looking at the chemical equations of reactions between either iron, zinc or magnesium and hydrochloric acid or sulfuric acid.

Practice Questions — Fact Recall

Q1 Define oxidation in terms of the transfer of electrons.

Q2 Define reduction in terms of the transfer of electrons.

Q3 During a displacement reaction are metal atoms oxidised or reduced?

Q4 Is the metal oxidised or reduced during a reaction with acid?

Practice Questions — Application

Tip: **H** You should use the reactivity series on page 133 to help you answer Q1.

Q1 A student carried out a reaction of zinc with an aqueous solution of copper sulfate: $Zn_{(s)} + CuSO_{4(aq)} \rightarrow$ Products

a) Give the formulas, including state symbols, of the products of this reaction.

b) State whether zinc is being oxidised or reduced.

c) Give the ionic equation for this reaction.

Q2 Magnesium reacts with sulfuric acid to form magnesium sulfate and hydrogen: $Mg + H_2SO_4 \rightarrow MgSO_4 + H_2$

a) Explain why the above reaction is considered a redox reaction.

b) Write the ionic equation for the reaction above.

7. Electrolysis

You've met electrolysis briefly before — it's used to extract metals from their ores. You need to know a bit more about it now though. Here we go...

What is electrolysis?

If you pass an electric current through an ionic substance that's molten or in solution, the ions in the liquid or solution will move towards the electrodes, where they can react, causing the ionic substance to decompose. This is called **electrolysis**. For example, the electrolysis of molten aluminium oxide breaks aluminium oxide down into aluminium and oxygen.

Electrolytes

Electrolysis requires a liquid to conduct the electricity, called the **electrolyte**. Electrolytes contain free ions — they're usually a molten or dissolved ionic substance (see Figure 1). In either case, it's the free ions which conduct the electricity and allow the whole thing to work.

Sodium chloride solution (sodium chloride dissolved in water).

The ions are free to move throughout the substance, so can carry an electric charge.

Molten sodium chloride.

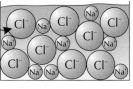

Figure 1: *Free ions in molten and dissolved sodium chloride.*

How electrolysis works

Electrolysis is based on an electrical circuit that includes an electrolyte and two **electrodes** — an electrode is a solid that conducts electricity and is submerged in the electrolyte. In electrolysis, the electrodes are placed into the electrolyte and ions move from one electrode to the other — this allows the conduction of electricity through the circuit. The positive ions in the electrolyte will move towards the negative electrode (the cathode) and gain electrons. The negative ions in the electrolyte will move towards the positive electrode (the anode) and lose electrons. As ions gain or lose electrons they become atoms or molecules and are released. These atoms or molecules are the products of electrolysis.

Electrolysis and redox `Higher`

Electrolysis always involves an oxidation reaction and a reduction reaction. Reduction is occurring at the negative electrode as the positive ions are gaining electrons. Oxidation occurs at the positive electrode as the negative ions are losing electrons.

Learning Objectives:

- Know that when an electric current is passed through a molten or dissolved ionic compound it decomposes and that this is called electrolysis.
- Know what an electrolyte is.
- Know that dissolved or molten ionic substances contain free ions.
- Be able to describe electrolysis in terms of the movement of positive and negative ions towards electrodes.
- **H** Know that, during electrolysis, positive ions are reduced at the cathode and negative ions are oxidised at the anode.
- Know that the electrolysis of a molten, simple ionic compound results in the formation of the metal element at the cathode and the non-metal element at the anode.
- Be able to predict the products that will form from the electrolysis of a molten, binary ionic compound.
- **H** Be able to write half equations for the reactions at the electrodes during electrolysis.

Specification References
5.4.3.1, 5.4.3.2, 5.4.3.5

Practice Questions — Fact Recall

Q1   Why are dissolved ionic substances able to conduct electricity?

Q2   What type of ions are attracted towards the negative electrode?

Electrolysis of molten ionic substances

Tip: Electrodes should be made out of an inert material, such as graphite or platinum, so they don't react.

Binary compounds are ionic compounds containing two elements which are ions — a positive metal ion and a negative non-metal ion. Electrolysis of the molten binary compounds gives the neutral metal and non-metal elements. During the electrolysis of these substances, the metal ions move to the cathode and gain electrons to become neutral, while the non-metal ions move to the anode and lose electrons to become neutral.

Tip: Lead bromide only contains two elements so can be described as a binary compound.

Example

Lead bromide ($PbBr_2$) is an ionic compound, so when it is molten, it will conduct electricity. Electrolysis of lead bromide breaks it down into lead (Pb) and bromine (Br_2). So, the electrolyte is lead bromide and the products of electrolysis are lead and bromine. Here's how it works...

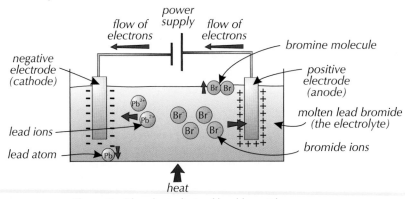

Figure 2: The electrolysis of lead bromide.

Molten lead bromide contains positively charged lead ions and negatively charged bromide ions.

- The positive ions are attracted towards the negative electrode. Here, each lead ion gains two electrons and becomes a lead atom.

- The negative ions are attracted towards the positive electrode. Here, bromide ions lose one electron each and form bromine molecules (Br_2).

Tip: How many electrons each ion needs to gain or lose to become an atom or molecule depends on the charge on the ion. Have a look back at pages 70-71 for more on this.

Tip: [H] During the electrolysis of lead bromide, lead ions gain electrons. This is a reduction reaction, and the lead ions are said to be reduced. Bromide ions lose electrons. This is an oxidation reaction, and the bromide ions are said to be oxidised.

Half equations Higher

Half equations show the reactions at the electrodes. Here's how to write a half equation for the reaction that takes place at the negative electrode:

Step 1: Write the symbol for the positive ion in the electrolyte on the left-hand side of the equation.

Step 2: Write the symbol for the neutral atoms or molecules produced on the right-hand side of the equation.

Step 3: Balance the number of atoms in the equation.

Step 4: Balance the charges by adding or subtracting electrons (shown as e⁻).

You can do the same to get the half equation for the reaction at the positive electrode, starting with the negative ion on the left-hand side of the equation.

These are the half equations for the electrolysis of lead bromide:

Negative electrode:

Step 1: Pb^{2+}

Step 2: $Pb^{2+} \rightarrow Pb$

Step 3: There's one lead ion on the left and one lead atom on the right, so the number of atoms is balanced.

Step 4: A charge of 2+ on the left hand side needs to be balanced out by two electrons, so that the overall charge of both sides is the same (0). So the half equation for the reaction at the negative electrode is:

$$Pb^{2+} + 2e^- \rightarrow Pb$$

Positive electrode:

Step 1: Br^-

Step 2: $Br^- \rightarrow Br_2$

Step 3: There are two bromine atoms on the right so there need to be two bromide ions on the left to balance the equation.

$$2Br^- \rightarrow Br_2$$

Step 4: A charge of 2– on the left hand side needs to be balanced out by two electrons on the right hand side, so that the overall charge on both sides is equal (2–). So the half equation for the reaction at the negative electrode is:

$$2Br^- \rightarrow Br_2 + 2e^-$$

Or, you could subtract two electrons from the left-hand side to give both sides a charge of zero. This would give you this half equation:

$$2Br^- - 2e^- \rightarrow Br_2$$

The charges in this half equation are still balanced because $(-2) - (-2) = 0$

Tip: [H] For the half equation to show the reaction at the positive electrode, you can balance the charges by adding or subtracting electrons. For the half equation for the negative electrode you can only add electrons.

Tip: [H] These equations are called half equations because each one only shows half of the overall reaction that takes place.

Exam Tip [H]
You can check your half equations are correct by making sure that the charges balance and the atoms balance. If they don't, you've gone wrong somewhere.

Practice Questions — Application

Q1 Molten zinc chloride can undergo electrolysis. The ions in the electrolyte are Zn^{2+} and Cl^-. The electrodes are made of graphite.

a) Give the name of the electrolyte.

b) Which electrode do the Cl^- ions move towards?

c) Describe what happens to the Cl^- ions at this electrode.

d) Are the zinc ions oxidised or reduced during electrolysis?

Q2 Complete the half equations below to show the reactions that happen during the electrolysis of two different solutions:

a) $Br^- \rightarrow Br_2$ and $H^+ \rightarrow H_2$

b) $Cu^{2+} \rightarrow Cu$ and $O^{2-} \rightarrow O_2$

- Know that if metals are too reactive to be extracted from their ores using carbon, they can be extracted using electrolysis.
- Be able to explain why extracting metals using electrolysis is a very high energy process.
- Know that aluminium is extracted from aluminium oxide by electrolysis.
- Know why the electrolyte is a mixture of aluminium oxide and molten cryolite.
- Be able to explain why the positive electrode, made of carbon, needs replacing regularly.
- **H** Be able to write half equations for the reactions at the electrodes during electrolysis of aluminium oxide.

Specification References
5.4.3.1, 5.4.3.3

8. Electrolysis of Metal Ores

Next up, the electrolysis of aluminium oxide to get pure aluminium. The basics of electrolysis are all the same here, but there are a few twists to learn...

Extracting metals using electrolysis

If a metal is too reactive to be reduced with carbon (see page 138), then electrolysis can be used to extract it. Extracting metals via this method is very expensive as lots of energy is needed to melt the ore and produce the current.

Extracting aluminium by electrolysis

The main ore of aluminium is bauxite, which can be mined and purified to give aluminium oxide, Al_2O_3. Aluminium is then extracted by electrolysis.

Aluminium oxide (Al_2O_3) has a very high melting point of over 2000 °C — so melting it would be very expensive. Instead, the aluminium oxide is dissolved in molten cryolite (a less common ore of aluminium). This brings the melting point down to about 900 °C, which saves energy, making the process cheaper and easier. The electrolysis of aluminium oxide is shown in Figure 1.

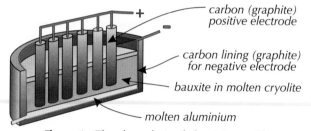

carbon (graphite) positive electrode
carbon lining (graphite) for negative electrode
bauxite in molten cryolite
molten aluminium

Figure 1: *The electrolysis of aluminium oxide.*

The electrodes are made of carbon (graphite), a good conductor of electricity. The positive Al^{3+} ions are attracted to the negative electrode where they each pick up three electrons and turn into neutral aluminium atoms. These sink to the bottom of the electrolysis tank. The negative O^{2-} ions are attracted to the positive electrode where they each lose two electrons. The neutral oxygen atoms combine to form O_2 molecules. Some of the oxygen produced reacts with the carbon in the electrode to produce carbon dioxide. This means that the positive electrodes gradually get 'eaten away' and have to be replaced every now and again.

The overall equation for the reaction is: $2Al_2O_3 \rightarrow 4Al + 3O_2$

Half equations   Higher

The half equations for the reactions taking place at the electrodes when aluminium oxide is electrolysed are:

Negative electrode: $Al^{3+} + 3e^- \rightarrow Al$

Positive electrode: $2O^{2-} \rightarrow O_2 + 4e^-$

Exam Tip **H**
Make sure you're happy with how to work out these half equations (Have a look at page 142 for the steps).

> ### Practice Questions — Fact Recall
>
> Q1   Why is aluminium oxide dissolved in molten cryolite before it undergoes electrolysis?
>
> Q2   Why do the positive electrodes have to be replaced over time?

9. Electrolysis of Aqueous Solutions

When you electrolyse substances dissolved in water, you need to think about the ions in the water when working out what the products will be.

Predicting the products of electrolysis

Sometimes there are more than two types of free ions in the electrolyte. For example, if a salt is dissolved in water there will be some H^+ and OH^- ions as well as the ions from the salt in the solution. In this situation, the products of electrolysis depend on how reactive the elements involved are.

At the negative electrode, if metal ions and H^+ ions are present, the metal ions will stay in solution if the metal is more reactive than hydrogen.
This is because the more reactive an element, the more likely it is to stay as ions. So, hydrogen will be produced unless the metal is less reactive than it.

At the positive electrode, if OH^- and halide ions (Cl^-, Br^-, I^-) are present then molecules of chlorine, bromine or iodine will be formed. If no halide is present, then the OH^- ions are discharged and oxygen and water will be formed.

Example 1

A solution of copper(II) sulfate ($CuSO_4$) contains four different ions: Cu^{2+}, SO_4^{2-}, H^+ and OH^-.

Copper metal is less reactive than hydrogen. So at the cathode, copper metal is produced and coats the electrode.

$$Cu^{2+} + 2e^- \rightarrow Cu$$

There aren't any halide ions present so at the anode oxygen and water are produced. The oxygen can be seen as bubbles.

$$4OH^- \rightarrow O_2 + 2H_2O + 4e^-$$

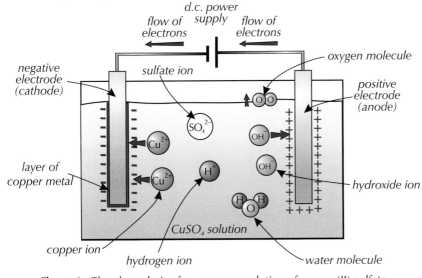

Figure 1: The electrolysis of an aqueous solution of copper(II) sulfate.

Learning Objectives:

- Know that the products of the electrolysis of an aqueous solution using inert electrodes are determined by how reactive the elements involved are.
- Understand that hydrogen will be produced at the cathode, when electrolysing aqueous solutions, if the metal is more reactive than hydrogen.
- Understand that oxygen and water will be produced at the anode, when electrolysing aqueous solutions, unless the solution contains halide ions in which case the halogen will be produced.
- Be able to predict the products that will form from the electrolysis of an aqueous solution containing one ionic compound.
- **H** Be able to write half equations for the reactions at the electrodes during electrolysis of aqueous solutions.
- Be able to set up an electrolysis experiment using inert electrodes and identify the products (Required Practical 9).

Specification References
5.4.3.1, 5.4.3.4, 5.4.3.5

Figure 2: Electrolysis of an aqueous solution of NaCl.

> **Exam Tip** **H**
> If you are taking the higher tier paper, you need to know how to write half equations for the electrolysis of aqueous solutions.

> **Tip:** If you're drawing the apparatus for an electrolysis experiment, remember to include a d.c. power supply, wires and labels for the anode and the cathode. The anode is the electrode on the same side as the longer line of the d.c. power supply symbol.

> **Tip:** Make sure you do a risk assessment before doing any electrolysis in class.

Example 2

A solution of sodium chloride (NaCl) contains four different ions: Na^+, Cl^-, OH^- and H^+.

Sodium metal is more reactive than hydrogen. So, at the cathode, hydrogen gas is produced: $2H^+ + 2e^- \rightarrow H_2$.

Chloride ions are present in the solution. So, at the anode, chlorine gas is produced: $2Cl^- \rightarrow Cl_2 + 2e^-$.

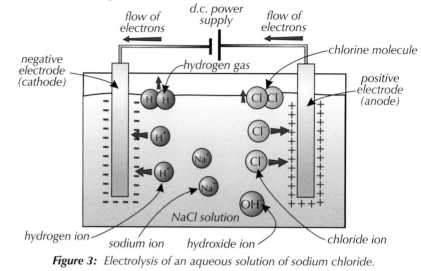

Figure 3: *Electrolysis of an aqueous solution of sodium chloride.*

Investigating electrolysis of an aqueous solution

You need to be able to identify what's been made in an electrolysis experiment. Here's how you set up the electrolysis of an aqueous solution:

> REQUIRED PRACTICAL **9**

- Get two inert electrodes (e.g. platinum or carbon). Clean the surfaces of the electrodes using a piece of emery paper (or sandpaper).

- From this point on, be careful not to touch the surfaces of the metals with your hands — you could transfer grease back onto the electrodes.

- Place both electrodes into a beaker filled with your electrolyte and position them so they are inside inverted test tubes containing the aqueous solution.

- Connect the electrodes to a power supply using crocodile clips and wires.

As the reaction progresses, gases may form and collect inside the test tubes.

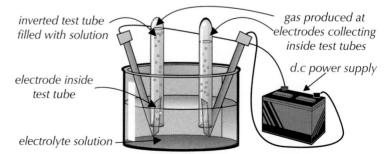

Figure 4: *Diagram of the experimental set-up for an electrolysis experiment.*

Once the experiment is finished, you can test any gaseous products to work out what was produced:

- Chlorine bleaches damp litmus paper turning it white.

- Hydrogen makes a 'squeaky pop' with a lighted splint.

- Oxygen will relight a glowing splint.

Tip: It's really important to make sure any gas being formed at each electrode is being collected in the test tubes.

Tip: For more on the tests for gases turn to page 203.

Practice Questions — Fact Recall

Q1 What determines the products of electrolysis of an aqueous solution using inert electrodes?

Q2 If a metal is more reactive than hydrogen will it be produced at the cathode when carrying out electrolysis on an aqueous solution?

Q3 When carrying out electrolysis of an aqueous solution containing bromide ions, what will be produced at the anode?

Practice Questions — Application

Q1 When aqueous calcium bromide solution is electrolysed, hydrogen is produced at the cathode. Explain why calcium is not produced.

Q2 Electrolysis is carried out on an aqueous solution of zinc sulfate. Suggest the products of the reaction. Give reasons for your answer.

Q3 A student suggests that the electrolysis of an aqueous solution of magnesium chloride will produce hydrogen and chlorine gas.

  a) Describe how the student could carry out an experiment to investigate her prediction.

  b) Is the student correct? Explain your answer.

Q4 The electrolysis of an aqueous solution of sodium carbonate produces oxygen and hydrogen gas. Give half equations for the reactions at the anode and cathode.

Tip: You can find out if a metal is more or less reactive than hydrogen by using the reactivity series — there's one on page 133.

Topic Checklist — Make sure you know...

Acids and Alkalis

☐ That the pH scale measures how acidic or alkaline a solution is.

☐ That solutions with a pH of less than 7 are acidic, solutions with a pH of more than 7 are alkaline and solutions with a pH of exactly 7 are neutral.

☐ That an alkali is a base that is soluble in water.

☐ That acids release H^+ ions in solution and alkalis release OH^- ions in solution.

☐ That in a neutralisation reaction, water is produced when hydrogen ions react with hydroxide ions.

cont...

Strong Acids and Weak Acids

- [ ] [H] That acids that ionise completely are strong acids and acids that partially ionise are weak acids.
- [ ] [H] That the pH of a solution changes by 1 if the H^+ ion concentration changes by a factor of 10.
- [ ] [H] How the relative acidity of a substance depends on its pH and its H^+ ion concentration.
- [ ] [H] That a strong acid will have a lower pH than a weak acid with the same concentration.
- [ ] [H] The difference between the concentration of an acid and the strength of an acid.

Reactions of Acids

- [ ] That the reaction of an acid with a metal hydroxide or a metal oxide forms a salt and water.
- [ ] That the salt formed when an acid and base react depends on the acid and the metal ion in the base.
- [ ] That carbon dioxide, a salt and water are formed from the reaction of a metal carbonate and an acid.
- [ ] How soluble salts can be made from acids and insoluble bases or metals.

Reactivity of Metals

- [ ] That the reactivity series places metals and some non-metals in order of their ability to form positive ions, and so their reactivity.
- [ ] That the more reactive a metal is, the more easily it forms positive ions.
- [ ] That the order of reactivity of metals can be found based on their reactions with acids and water.
- [ ] That the reaction of metals with dilute acids produces salts and hydrogen.
- [ ] That the reaction of certain metals and water forms metal hydroxides and hydrogen.
- [ ] That a more reactive metal will displace a less reactive one in a compound.

Metal Oxides and Redox

- [ ] That most metals are found as compounds in the earth.
- [ ] That oxidation can be defined as the gain of oxygen and reduction as the loss of oxygen.
- [ ] That a metal less reactive than carbon can be extracted from its oxide by reduction with carbon.
- [ ] That a metal more reactive than carbon has to be extracted by electrolysis.

Redox Reactions

- [ ] [H] That oxidation is the loss of electrons and reduction is the gain of electrons.
- [ ] [H] How to identify which species are being oxidised and reduced in displacement reactions.
- [ ] [H] How to write ionic equations for displacement reactions.
- [ ] [H] That the reactions of acids with metals are redox reactions.
- [ ] [H] How to identify what is being oxidised and reduced in reactions between metals and acids.

cont...

Electrolysis

☐ That a dissolved or molten ionic compound will break down if a current is passed through it.

☐ That electrolytes are substances containing free ions, such as molten or dissolved ionic compounds.

☐ That during electrolysis, the positive ions in the electrolyte move towards the negative electrode and the negative ions move towards the positive electrode.

☐ **H** That, in electrolysis, positive ions are reduced and negative ions are oxidised at the electrodes.

☐ That when an ionic compound containing two elements is melted and electrolysed, the metal forms at the negative electrode and the non-metal forms at the positive electrode.

☐ **H** How to write half equations for the reactions that occur at the electrodes.

Electrolysis of Metal Ores

☐ That electrolysis is used to extract metals, such as aluminium, from their ores if they're too reactive to be extracted by reduction with carbon.

☐ That aluminium oxide is dissolved in molten cryolite before electrolysis takes place, as this reduces the temperature at which it can be melted, and so reduces the cost.

☐ That during the electrolysis of aluminium oxide, aluminium is formed at the negative electrode and oxygen is formed at the positive electrode.

☐ That the oxygen produced reacts with the carbon in the electrode to form carbon dioxide.

☐ **H** How to write half equations for the electrolysis of aluminium oxide.

Electrolysis of Aqueous Solutions

☐ That the products of the electrolysis of an aqueous solution using inert electrodes are determined by the reactivity of the elements.

☐ That water can break down into H^+ and OH^- ions and these ions can be discharged in electrolysis.

☐ That if the metal ion dissolved in the aqueous solution forms an elemental metal that is more reactive than hydrogen, then hydrogen will be formed at the cathode.

☐ That if the solution contains halide ions, then the halogen will be formed at the anode, but, if no halides are present, then oxygen will be produced.

☐ **H** How to write half equations for reactions taking place in the electrolysis of an aqueous solution.

☐ How to investigate the electrolysis of an aqueous solution with experiments.

Exam-style Questions

1   A solution can either be acidic, basic or neutral. For each of the questions below, choose which phrase **A**, **B**, or **C**, best describes the substance.

1.1   Toothpaste has a pH of 8.2.

      A It is an acid.

      B It is an alkali.

      C It is neutral.

(1 mark)

1.2   Sodium hydroxide is an alkali.

      A It is insoluble in water.

      B It dissolves in water to release OH^- ions.

      C It dissolves in water to release H^+ ions.

(1 mark)

1.3   A student has two solutions. Solution A contains a strong acid and solution B contains a weak acid. Both solutions are the same concentration.

      A Solution A will have a lower pH than solution B.

      B Solution A will have a higher pH than solution B.

      C Both solutions will have the same pH.

(1 mark)

2   Niall has a substance with a pH of 4.

2.1   Which of the following, **A**, **B**, or **C** could Niall add to his solution to neutralise it?

      A Potassium hydroxide (pH 13)   **B** Pure water (pH 7)   **C** Sulfuric acid (pH 1)

(1 mark)

2.2   Describe how Niall could determine when the neutralisation reaction has finished.

(2 marks)

2.3   Write an ionic equation, including state symbols, for a neutralisation reaction.

(2 marks)

3   There are a number of different ways to make soluble salts.
One way of making soluble salts involves reacting acids with metal oxides.

3.1   Copy and complete the general equation for this reaction shown below:

      acid + metal oxide → _____ + _____

(2 marks)

3.2   What type of reaction is the reaction between a metal oxide and an acid?

(1 mark)

4 Acids can have different strengths.

4.1 Ethanoic acid is a weak acid. Describe how ethanoic acid ionises in solution.

(1 mark)

4.2 A 1 mol/dm^3 solution of hydrochloric acid has a pH of 0 and a 1 mol/dm^3 solution of citric acid has a pH of 3. State which acid is stronger.

(1 mark)

4.3 Sulfuric acid is a stronger acid than ethanoic acid. State which of the acids you would expect to react more vigorously with magnesium.

(1 mark)

5 Magnesium (Mg) is placed in an aqueous solution of copper sulfate ($CuSO_4$) and a displacement reaction occurs.

5.1 Give the word equation for the reaction.

(1 mark)

5.2 State which species has been oxidised and which species has been reduced.

(1 mark)

5.3 Give the ionic equation for this reaction, including state symbols.

(3 marks)

5.4 The reaction was attempted again with iron instead of magnesium.
Would you expect a reaction to occur? Explain your answer.

(2 marks)

5.5 Magnesium also reacts with dilute hydrochloric acid. Describe in terms of oxidation and reduction what happens in the reaction. Write an ionic equation for the reaction.

(4 marks)

6 Copper chloride is an ionic compound. When dissolved in water it forms copper chloride solution. Copper chloride solution can undergo electrolysis.

6.1 Give the name of the electrolyte used in this electrolysis.

(1 mark)

6.2 The ions present in the electrolyte are Cu^{2+}, Cl^-, H^+ and OH^-.
What compound do the H^+ and OH^- ions come from?

(1 mark)

6.3 Copper ions move towards the negative electrode.
Describe what happens to the copper ions at the negative electrode.

(2 marks)

6.4 Complete the half equation for the reaction that occurs at the positive electrode.

$$........Cl^- \rightarrow Cl_2 + ...e^-$$

(1 mark)

6.5 Give the half equation for the reaction that occurs at the negative electrode.

(2 marks)

Learning Objectives:

- Know that during a chemical reaction the total amount of energy in the universe stays the same.
- Know that energy is transferred to or from the surroundings during a chemical reaction.
- Know that if a reaction transfers energy to the surroundings it is exothermic and the temperature of the surroundings will increase.
- Know some examples of exothermic reactions and their uses.
- Know that if a reaction absorbs energy from the surroundings it is endothermic and the temperature of the surroundings will decrease.
- Know some examples of endothermic reactions and their uses.
- Be able to investigate how different variables affect the temperature change of a reaction in solution (Required Practical 10).

Specification Reference 5.5.1.1

Figure 1: A chemical hand warmer. It uses an exothermic reaction.

1. Energy Transfer in Reactions

During reactions, energy is transferred between the reaction mixture and the surroundings. Some reactions give out heat, while others take heat in.

Energy transfer

Chemicals store a certain amount of energy — and different chemicals store different amounts. If the products of a reaction store more energy than the original reactants, then they must have taken in the difference in energy between the products and reactants from the surroundings during the reaction. But if they store less, then the excess energy was transferred to the surroundings during the reaction.

The energy that is transferred between the reactants and the surroundings during a chemical reaction is usually transferred by heating. If energy is transferred to the surroundings, the temperature of the surroundings will increase. If energy is transferred from the surroundings, the temperature of the surroundings will decrease.

The overall amount of energy in the reactants and the surroundings doesn't change. This is because energy is conserved in reactions — it can't be created or destroyed, only moved around. This means the amount of energy in the universe always stays the same.

Exothermic reactions

An **exothermic reaction** is one which transfers energy to the surroundings. This is shown by a rise in temperature in the surroundings. The best example of an exothermic reaction is burning fuels (**combustion**). This gives out a lot of energy — it's very exothermic. **Neutralisation reactions** (between an acid and an alkali) are also exothermic as are many **oxidation** reactions.

Examples

- The reaction of potassium hydroxide with hydrochloric acid is a neutralisation reaction. This reaction releases energy — it's exothermic.

- When sodium is added to water, it's oxidised, releases energy and moves about on the surface of the water. The fact that energy is released shows that this is an exothermic reaction.

Uses of exothermic reactions

Exothermic reactions have lots of everyday uses.

Examples

- Some hand warmers use the exothermic oxidation of iron in air (with a salt solution catalyst) to release energy.

- Self-heating cans of hot chocolate and coffee also rely on exothermic reactions between chemicals in their bases.

Endothermic reactions

An **endothermic reaction** is one which takes in energy from the surroundings. This is shown by a fall in the temperature of the surroundings. Endothermic reactions are much less common than exothermic reactions, but the reaction between citric acid and sodium hydrogencarbonate is a good example, as are thermal decomposition reactions.

Tip: Physical processes can also take in or release energy. E.g. freezing is an exothermic process, melting is endothermic.

> **Example**
>
> The thermal decomposition of calcium carbonate is endothermic. Heat must be supplied to make calcium carbonate decompose into calcium oxide and carbon dioxide. The equation for this reaction is:
>
> $$CaCO_3 \rightarrow CaO + CO_2$$

Uses of endothermic reactions

Endothermic reactions also have everyday uses.

> **Example**
>
> A sports injury pack is a cold pack that can be placed on an injury like a sprain or strain to reduce swelling. Some sports injury packs use endothermic reactions — they take in heat and the pack becomes very cold. This is much more convenient than carrying ice around. Also, this type of cold pack is much more flexible than a block of ice, so it can be wrapped around an injury more easily.

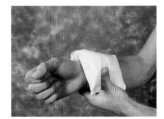

Figure 2: A cold pack which uses an endothermic reaction being used to treat a sprained wrist.

Energy transfer of reactions REQUIRED PRACTICAL 10

The amount of energy transferred during a reaction is proportional to the temperature change of that reaction. So, if you measure the temperature change of a reaction under different conditions (such as with different amounts of reactants), you can compare how the energy transfer changes.

Tip: Always carry out a risk assessment before you do any experiments in class.

You can find the temperature change of a reaction where at least one reactant is a liquid or solution by taking the temperature of the reactants, mixing everything together in a polystyrene cup and measuring the temperature of the solution at the start and at the end of the reaction (see Figures 3 and 4).

The biggest problem with taking measurements like this is the amount of energy that's lost to the surroundings. Using a polystyrene cup helps to insulate the reaction mixture more than a glass beaker would, but some energy is still transferred by heating. You can reduce it a bit more by putting the polystyrene cup into a beaker of cotton wool to give more insulation, and putting a lid on the cup to reduce energy lost by evaporation.

Figure 3: A reaction taking place in a polystyrene cup with no insulation and no lid — it will lose lots of energy to the surroundings.

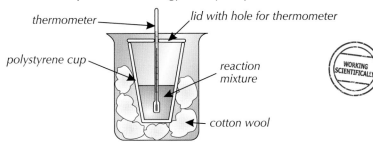

thermometer — lid with hole for thermometer
polystyrene cup — reaction mixture
cotton wool

WORKING SCIENTIFICALLY

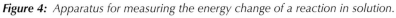

Figure 4: Apparatus for measuring the energy change of a reaction in solution.

Tip: When investigating how one variable affects the temperature change, you need to make sure that all the other variables (e.g. the amounts of the other reactants) stay the same each time you carry out the experiment — otherwise the test won't be valid (see p.10).

Tip: The acid and the alkali have to start at the same temperature, otherwise your results won't be valid. See page 9 for more on validity.

Tip: If you were investigating the temperature change of an endothermic reaction then, during step 4, you'd record the lowest temperature that the reaction reaches.

Exam Tip
In the exams, you might be asked to spot problems with a method, or suggest improvements. So make sure you understand what all the pieces of apparatus are for, and why each step in the method is needed.

This method works for reactions of solids with liquids (e.g. reactions between metals and acid, or metal carbonates and acid) as well as for reactions where you mix two solutions, like neutralisation reactions (reactions between alkalis and acids).

You can use this method to investigate what effect different **variables** have on the temperature change, and so the amount of energy transferred. For example, you could investigate the effect that changing the amount of reactant has on the energy transferred. This could be done by repeating the experiment with a different mass or concentration of one of the reactants each time.

Example

Here's how you could test the effect of acid concentration on the temperature change in a neutralisation reaction between hydrochloric acid (HCl) and sodium hydroxide (NaOH):

1. Using a measuring cylinder, measure out 25 cm³ of 1.00 mol/dm³ hydrochloric acid and transfer it into a beaker. Measure out 25 cm³ of 1.00 mol/dm³ sodium hydroxide and put it in a separate beaker.

2. Measure the temperature of both solutions. They need to be at the same temperature. (If they aren't, just put them both in a water bath at 30 °C for a while.) Record the initial temperature of both solutions.

3. Pour the hydrochloric acid from the beaker into a polystyrene cup. Add the sodium hydroxide to the hydrochloric acid and quickly put the lid on the cup (as in Figure 4). Carefully stir the mixture through the lid.

4. Observe the temperature of the solution shown on the thermometer, and record the highest temperature that it reaches.

5. Repeat steps 1-4 using 1.50 mol/dm³ and then 2.00 mol/dm³ of hydrochloric acid.

If the reaction is exothermic, energy will be released and the temperature of the solution will increase. The more energy is released, the bigger the increase in temperature will be. If the reaction is endothermic, energy will be absorbed and the temperature of the solution will decrease. The more energy that is absorbed, the bigger the decrease in temperature will be.

Practice Questions — Fact Recall

Q1 What happens to the total energy in the universe during a chemical reaction?

Q2 a) What is an exothermic reaction?

b) Name one type of reaction that is exothermic.

Q3 a) When an endothermic reaction takes place, the temperature around the reaction decreases. Explain why.

b) Give one example of an everyday use of an endothermic reaction.

Q4 a) Describe how you could measure the energy released by a chemical reaction between two solutions.

b) State a possible source of errors in this type of experiment.

2. Reaction Profiles

You can illustrate the energy changes that happen during a reaction using reaction profiles. You need to be able to interpret reaction profiles... so these pages are well worth a bit of concentration.

What are reaction profiles?

A **reaction profile** (or **energy level diagram**) is a graph that shows how the energy in a reaction changes as the reaction progresses. The graph starts at the energy level of the reactants and finishes at the energy level of the products. These two points are usually joined by a smooth curve — see Figure 1.

There are three useful pieces of information you can find from a reaction profile:

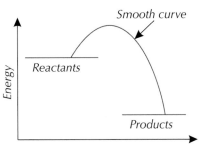

Figure 1: *A reaction profile showing how the energy in a reaction changes over time.*

1. The overall energy change

The overall energy change of a reaction is the difference between the energy of the reactants and the energy of the products. You can find the overall energy change of a reaction from a reaction profile by looking at the difference in height between the reactants and the products — see Figure 2.

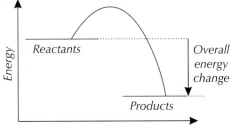

Figure 2: *Finding the overall energy change from a reaction profile.*

2. Whether the reaction is exothermic or endothermic

Reaction profiles show the relative energies of the reactants and the products, so you can use them to work out whether a reaction is exothermic or endothermic.

In an exothermic reaction, the reactants have more energy than the products, because energy is released during the reaction. This means the reaction profile will start high and finish lower than where it started.

In an endothermic reaction, the products have more energy than the reactants, because energy is taken in during the reaction. This means the reaction profile will start low and finish higher than where it started — see Figure 3.

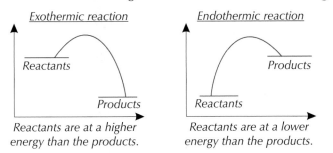

Figure 3: *The reaction profiles of an exothermic reaction and an endothermic reaction.*

Learning Objectives:
- Know that reaction profiles are used to show the relative energies of the reactants and products in reactions.
- Know how to find the overall energy change for a reaction from a reaction profile.
- Know how to determine if a reaction is exothermic or endothermic using a reaction profile.
- Be able to draw reaction profiles for exothermic and endothermic reactions.
- Know that the activation energy of a reaction is the minimum amount of energy that particles must have when they collide in order to react.
- Know how to find the activation energy of a reaction from a reaction profile.

Specification Reference 5.5.1.2

Tip: [H] You can also find the overall energy change of a reaction using bond energies — see pages 158-159 for more.

Tip: Don't forget — an <u>exothermic</u> reaction transfers energy <u>to</u> the surroundings and an <u>endothermic</u> reaction takes in energy <u>from</u> the surroundings (see pages 152-153 for more).

3. The activation energy

Tip: See pages 166-167 for more on activation energy.

Reaction profiles don't normally go straight from the reactants to the products — the graph will curve upwards before it starts to go down again. This is because some energy usually has to be put in to break the bonds in the reactants and get the reaction started.

The **activation energy** (E_a) is the minimum amount of energy the reactant particles need when they collide with each other in order to react. The greater the activation energy, the more energy that is needed to start the reaction — this has to be supplied, e.g. by heating the reaction mixture.

You can find the activation energy of a reaction from its reaction profile by looking at the difference between where the curve starts and the highest point on the curve — see Figure 4.

Tip: Adding a catalyst to the reaction mixture changes the shape of the reaction profile by decreasing the activation energy — see page 167 for more.

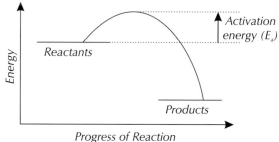

Figure 4: Finding the activation energy from a reaction profile.

Practice Questions — Fact Recall

Exam Tip
You need to be able to <u>draw</u> reaction profiles, as well as interpret them, so make sure you know how they're set up and how the axes are labelled.

Q1 Sketch a reaction profile for an exothermic reaction and add the following labels to it.

a) The energy of the reactants.   b) The energy of the products.

c) The activation energy.   d) The overall energy change.

Q2 Define the term 'activation energy'.

Practice Questions — Application

Q1 Are the following reactions exothermic or endothermic?

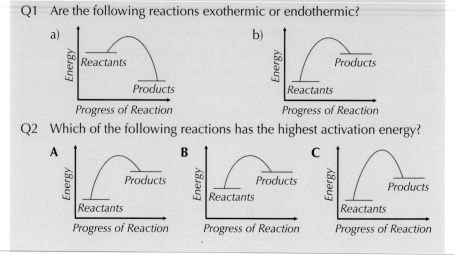

Q2 Which of the following reactions has the highest activation energy?

3. Energy in Reactions Higher

Chemical reactions are all about breaking old bonds and making new ones. You need to put in energy to break bonds, but making bonds releases energy. That's why there's a change in energy when a chemical reaction happens.

Units of energy

Energy is usually measured in **joules** (J). Large energy values are often given in kilojoules (kJ) — there are 1000 joules in a kilojoule.

When measuring energy transfer in reactions, the amount of energy released or absorbed will depend on how much reactant is used. As a result, energy transfer is usually measured in kilojoules per mole of reactant (kJ/mol), so that comparisons can be made between different reactions.

Energy and bonding

Energy is transferred in chemical reactions because old bonds are broken and new bonds are formed.

- Energy must be supplied to break existing bonds — so bond breaking is an **endothermic** process (see Figure 1).

- Energy is released when new bonds are formed — so bond formation is an **exothermic** process (see Figure 1).

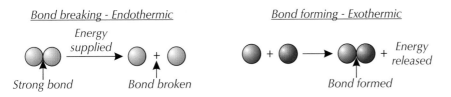

Bond breaking - Endothermic   *Bond forming - Exothermic*

Figure 1: *Energy changes during bond breaking and bond forming.*

Bond energy and overall energy change

Whether a reaction is exothermic or endothermic depends on what bond breaking and bond making is going on. It all comes down to whether the amount of energy absorbed when the bonds in the reactants are broken is more or less than the amount of energy released when the bonds in the products are made.

In an exothermic reaction, the energy released in bond formation is greater than the energy used in breaking old bonds. The leftover energy is released into the surroundings and the temperature rises.

In an endothermic reaction, the energy required to break old bonds is greater than the energy released when new bonds are formed. The extra energy needed is absorbed from the surroundings and the temperature falls.

Learning Objectives:

- **H** Know that bond breaking requires energy while bond making releases energy.
- **H** Be able to explain why reactions are exothermic or endothermic in terms of the amount of energy transferred when bond breaking compared to the amount of energy transferred when bond making.
- **H** Know that the amount of energy absorbed when bonds are broken, or released when bonds are made, can be calculated using bond energies.
- **H** Know that the overall energy change of a reaction is equal to the difference between the total energy needed to break the bonds in the reactants and the total energy released when the new bonds in the products are formed.
- **H** Be able to calculate energy transfer in reactions using bond energies.

Specification Reference 5.5.1.3

Figure 2: *Sodium reacting with water. This is a very exothermic reaction — it gives off lots of energy.*

Bond energy calculations

Not all bonds are the same strength — it requires more energy to break some bonds than others. Every chemical bond has a particular **bond energy** associated with it.

Tip: H There are 1000 J in a kJ, so 348 kJ is the same as 348 000 J.

Examples — **Higher**

- A carbon-carbon (C–C) bond has a bond energy of 348 kJ/mol. This means that it takes 348 kJ of energy to break one mole of C–C bonds. It also means that 348 kJ of energy is released when one mole of C–C bonds is formed.

- A carbon-hydrogen (C–H) bond has a bond energy of 413 kJ/mol. It takes 413 kJ of energy to break one mole of C–H bonds and 413 kJ of energy is released when one mole of C–H bonds are made.

You can use these bond energies to calculate the overall energy change for a reaction. Here's what you have to do:

Exam Tip H
Bond energies vary slightly depending on what compound the bond is in. But don't worry about this — you'll be given any bond energies that you need in the exam.

- Draw out the displayed formulas of the molecules in the reaction so you can see all the bonds that are being broken and made.

- Work out the amount of energy used in bond breaking by adding up the bond energies of all the bonds in all the reactants.

- Work out the amount of energy given out from bond making by adding up the bond energies of all the bonds in all the products.

- Then, use this formula to work out the overall energy change:

> Energy change = Energy of bond breaking − Energy of bond making

---

Example — **Higher**

Calculate the overall energy change for this reaction: $H_2 + Cl_2 \rightarrow 2HCl$

The bond energies you need are:
H–H: 436 kJ/mol; Cl–Cl: 242 kJ/mol; H–Cl: 431 kJ/mol.

If you draw out the displayed formulas of the molecules in this reaction, it looks like this:

$$H-H \ + \ Cl-Cl \rightarrow \begin{matrix} H-Cl \\ H-Cl \end{matrix}$$

As you can see, one mole of H–H bonds and one mole of Cl–Cl bonds are being broken and two moles of H–Cl bonds are being formed.

The amount of energy used in bond breaking is 436 + 242 = 678 kJ/mol

The amount of energy released in bond making is 2 × 431 = 862 kJ/mol

So the overall energy change of the reaction is 678 − 862 = −184 kJ/mol

---

The overall energy change for a reaction can be positive or negative. If the energy change is negative, it shows that more energy was released in bond making than was used in bond breaking — so the reaction is exothermic. If the energy change is positive, it shows that more energy was used in bond breaking than was released in bond making — so the reaction is endothermic.

You can't compare the overall energy changes of reactions unless you know the numerical differences in the bond energies.

Exam Tip H
You can use the sign of the energy change to check your answer. If you know a reaction is exothermic and you end up with a positive energy change, you must have gone wrong somewhere.

Example — **Higher**

Chlorine and bromine react with hydrogen in similar ways:

$$Cl_2 + H_2 \rightarrow 2HCl \qquad\qquad Br_2 + H_2 \rightarrow 2HBr$$

Br–Br bonds are weaker than Cl–Cl bonds and H–Br bonds are weaker than H–Cl bonds. So less energy is needed to break the bonds in the reaction with bromine, but less energy is released when the new bonds form. So unless you know the exact difference, you can't say which reaction releases more energy.

Bond energies from overall energy changes

You can also find one of the bond energies in the reaction if you have the energy change of the reaction and the bond energies of all the other bonds that are made or broken in the reaction.

Tip: H You don't have to draw out the displayed formulas if you don't want to, but it makes it much easier to see all the bonds if you do.

Example — **Higher**

The overall energy change for: $CH_4 + 2O_2 \rightarrow CO_2 + 2H_2O$ is –818 kJ/mol.

Calculate the bond energy of one C–H bond. The other bond energies are: O=O: 498 kJ/mol, C=O: 805 kJ/mol, O–H: 464 kJ/mol.

Drawing out the displayed formulas of the molecules in this reaction gives you this:

$$
\begin{array}{c}
H \\
| \\
H-C-H \\
| \\
H
\end{array}
+
\begin{array}{c}
O=O \\
O=O
\end{array}
\rightarrow
O=C=O
+
\begin{array}{c}
H-O-H \\
H-O-H
\end{array}
$$

Four moles of C–H bonds and two moles of O=O bonds are being broken. Two moles of C=O bonds and four moles of O–H bonds are being formed.

The amount of energy used in bond breaking is
(4 × C–H) + (2 × 498) = (4 × C–H) + 996 kJ/mol

The amount of energy released in bond making is
(2 × 805) + (4 × 464) = 3466 kJ/mol

So the overall energy change of the reaction is
(4 × C–H) + 996 – 3466 = –818 kJ/mol

You can rearrange this equation to make (4 × C–H) the subject:
(4 × C–H) = –818 – 996 + 3466 = 1652 kJ/mol

So C–H = 1652 ÷ 4 = 413 kJ/mol

Exam Tip H
Bond energies should always be positive, so if your answer is negative you should go back and check your working.

Q1 Are the following processes exothermic or endothermic?

   a) Breaking chemical bonds.

   b) Making chemical bonds.

Q2 Explain why energy is released to the surroundings during an exothermic reaction.

Q3 Give the formula that you could use to calculate the energy change of a reaction from the relevant bond energies.

Practice Questions — Application

Q1 Use the information in the table to calculate the overall energy change for the reaction, $2H_2 + O_2 \rightarrow 2H_2O$.

Bond	Bond energy (kJ/mol)
H–H	436
O=O	498
O–H	464

Q2 Methanol burns in air to form carbon dioxide and water, as shown by this equation:

$$2\,H-\underset{\underset{H}{|}}{\overset{\overset{H}{|}}{C}}-O-H \; + \; 3\,O{=}O \; \rightarrow \; 2\,O{=}C{=}O \; + \; 4\,H-O-H$$

Calculate the overall energy change for this reaction.
Bond energies: C–H = 413 kJ/mol, C–O = 358 kJ/mol, O–H = 464 kJ/mol, O=O = 498 kJ/mol, C=O = 805 kJ/mol.

Q3 Ethene reacts with bromine, as shown by this equation:

$$\underset{H}{\overset{H}{}}{\scriptstyle\diagdown}C{=}C{\scriptstyle\diagup}\underset{H}{\overset{H}{}} \; + \; Br-Br \; \rightarrow \; H-\underset{\underset{H}{|}}{\overset{\overset{Br}{|}}{C}}-\underset{\underset{H}{|}}{\overset{\overset{Br}{|}}{C}}-H$$

The overall energy change for this reaction is –122 kJ/mol.
Calculate the bond energy of the C–Br bond.
Bond energies: C–H = 413 kJ/mol, C=C = 612 kJ/mol, Br–Br = 193 kJ/mol, C–C = 348 kJ/mol

Q4 The following reaction occurs between methane and chlorine:

$$CH_4 + 4Cl_2 \rightarrow CCl_4 + 4HCl$$

   a) Use these bond energies to calculate the overall energy change for this reaction.

   Bond energies: C–H = 413 kJ/mol, Cl–Cl = 242 kJ/mol, C–Cl = 327 kJ/mol, H–Cl = 431 kJ/mol

   b) Is this reaction exothermic or endothermic? Explain your answer.

Figure 3: *Methanol burning in air.*

Topic Checklist — Make sure you know...

Energy Transfer in Reactions

☐ That during a chemical reaction, energy is either transferred from the reaction to the surroundings, or from the surroundings to the reaction.

☐ That the total energy of the universe stays the same before, during and after a chemical reaction.

☐ That exothermic reactions are reactions which transfer energy to the surroundings, resulting in an increase in temperature.

☐ That combustion, neutralisation reactions and some oxidation reactions are exothermic.

☐ That exothermic reactions are used in hand warmers and self-heating cans.

☐ That an endothermic reaction is a reaction which takes energy in from the surroundings, resulting in a decrease in temperature.

☐ That thermal decomposition reactions and the reaction between citric acid and sodium hydrogencarbonate are examples of endothermic reactions.

☐ That endothermic reactions are used in some sports injury packs.

☐ How you can find the energy change of a reaction in solution by mixing the reactants in a well-insulated polystyrene cup and measuring the change in temperature of the reaction.

Reaction Profiles

☐ That a reaction profile starts at the energy level of the reactants, ends at the energy level of the products and shows how the energy in a reaction changes as the reaction progresses

☐ That on a reaction profile, the overall energy change of the reaction is the difference in height from where the graph starts to where it finishes.

☐ How to use a reaction profile to determine if a reaction is exothermic or endothermic.

☐ That the activation energy is the minimum amount of energy the reactant particles need when they collide with each other in order to react.

☐ That on a reaction profile, the activation energy is the difference in height from where the graph starts to the highest point on the curve.

Energy in Reactions

☐ H That energy is released when bonds are made (bond making is exothermic) and energy must be absorbed to break bonds (bond breaking is endothermic).

☐ H That in an exothermic reaction, more energy is released forming the bonds in the products than is absorbed breaking the bonds in the reactants — so energy is given out to the surroundings.

☐ H That in an endothermic reaction, more energy is absorbed breaking the bonds in the reactants than is released forming the bonds in the products — so energy is absorbed from the surroundings.

☐ H How to calculate the overall energy change for a reaction from given bond energies.

Exam-style Questions

1   The diagram below shows the reaction profile for an endothermic reaction:

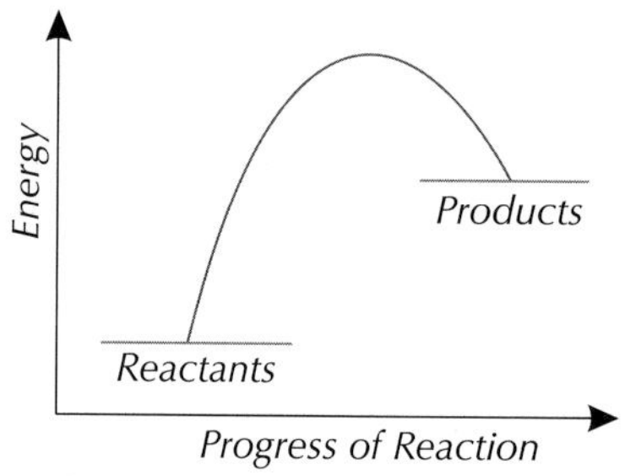

1.1   Predict what will happen to the temperature of the surroundings when this reaction takes place.

(1 mark)

1.2   During the reaction, the energy initially rises before falling again.
What does this initial rise represent?

(1 mark)

1.3   Suggest what type of reaction this could be.

(1 mark)

1.4   The total bond energy of the products is 1590 kJ/mol, and the total bond energy of the reactants is 1845 kJ/mol. Calculate the overall energy change of this reaction.

(1 mark)

2   When magnesium reacts with sulfuric acid to form magnesium sulfate and hydrogen gas, energy is released.

2.1   Draw a reaction profile to show how energy changes during the reaction.

(3 marks)

A student investigates how the concentration of the acid affects the amount of heat given out by the reaction. She carries out the reaction in a polystyrene cup and measures the initial and maximum temperatures of the reaction mixture.
She repeats the experiment with different concentrations of acid, but keeping everything else the same.

2.2   Suggest why the student uses a polystyrene cup, rather than a glass beaker.

(1 mark)

2.3   Why does she keep all the factors other than the concentration of the acid the same in each experiment?

(1 mark)

3 The Haber process is used to manufacture ammonia from nitrogen and hydrogen in the following reaction:

$$N_{2(g)} + 3H_{2(g)} \rightleftharpoons 2NH_{3(g)}$$

Here is the reaction profile for this reaction:

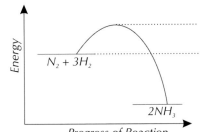

3.1 Use the reaction profile to explain whether the formation of ammonia is endothermic or exothermic.

(2 marks)

The bond energies of the bonds that are broken and made during this reaction are:
H–H = 436 kJ/mol, N≡N = 945 kJ/mol, N–H = 391 kJ/mol.

3.2 Calculate the overall energy change for this reaction.

(3 marks)

3.3 Draw and label an arrow on a sketch of the reaction profile to show the overall energy change for this reaction.

(1 mark)

4 Hydrogen reacts with oxygen as shown in this equation: $2H_2 + O_2 \rightarrow 2H_2O$
This reaction is exothermic and has an energy change of –486 kJ/mol.

4.1 Sketch an energy level diagram to represent the energy changes that occur during this reaction.

(3 marks)

4.2 State, with reference to the overall energy change, whether the energy needed to break the bonds in this reaction will be more or less than the energy released as bonds are formed.

(2 marks)

4.3 The H–H bond energy is 436 kJ/mol, and the O=O bond energy is 498 kJ/mol. Calculate the bond energy of an H–O bond in H_2O.

(3 marks)

4.4 The reaction of hydrogen and oxygen is an example of a combustion reaction. Name one other type of reaction that tends to be exothermic.

(1 mark)

Learning Objectives:

- Know that, according to collision theory, particles must collide with enough energy in order to react.

- Be able to explain how temperature, concentration, pressure (for reactions with gases) and surface area to volume ratio (for reactions with solids) affect the rate of a reaction in terms of collision theory.

- Be able to predict how changing these conditions may affect the rate of a reaction.

- Be able to define the term activation energy.

- Be able to use ideas about proportionality and collision theory to explain the effect of changing conditions on the rate of reaction.

- Know that catalysts speed up a reaction without being changed or used up and how they work.

- Be able to identify catalysts from the fact that they increase the rate of a reaction but don't appear in the chemical equation.

- Be able to interpret reaction profiles to show reactions with and without catalysts.

- Know that enzymes are biological catalysts.

Specification References
5.6.1.2-5.6.1.4

1. Rate of Reaction

Chemical reactions don't all happen at the same rate. There are a number of factors that affect how quickly a reaction goes. Read on to find out more...

What is rate of reaction?

The **rate** of a chemical reaction is how fast the reactants are changed into products. Reactions can go at all sorts of different rates. Some reactions happen very quickly, while others happen really slowly.

> **Examples**
>
> - The rusting of iron is a pretty slow reaction.
>
> - A moderate speed reaction is a metal (like magnesium) reacting with acid to produce a gentle stream of bubbles.
>
> - A really fast reaction is an explosion.

Factors that affect the rate of a reaction

There are four main factors that affect how quickly a reaction goes:

1. Temperature — the higher the temperature, the faster the reaction.

2. Concentration (or pressure for gases) — the more concentrated the reactants (or the higher the pressure), the faster the reaction goes.

3. Surface area (which depends on the size of solid pieces) — the larger the surface area (the smaller the pieces), the faster the reaction goes.

4. Catalysts — reactions with a catalyst can go faster than reactions without.

Collision theory

Reaction rates are explained by **collision theory**. Collision theory just says that the rate of a reaction depends on two things:

> 1. The collision frequency of reacting particles (how often they collide). The more there are in a certain amount of time, the faster the reaction is.
>
> 2. The energy transferred during a collision. Particles have to collide with enough energy to be successful.

Changing either of these factors will change the rate of reaction, meaning there are two ways to increase the rate of a reaction. One way is to increase the frequency of collisions, so that the probability of a **successful collision** (a collision that results in a reaction) increases. The other way is to increase the energy of the collisions, so that more of the collisions are successful.

1. Increasing the frequency of collisions

The effects of temperature, concentration (or pressure) and surface area on the rate of reaction can be explained in terms of how often the reacting particles collide.

Temperature

When the temperature is increased the particles all move quicker. If they're moving quicker, they're going to collide more often and more collisions means a faster rate of reaction — see Figure 1.

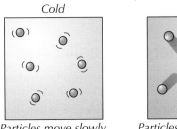

Cold	Hot
Particles move slowly. Not many collisions.	Particles move quickly. Lots of collisions.

Figure 1: A diagram showing why increasing the temperature increases the rate of a reaction.

Concentration (or pressure)

If a solution is made more concentrated it means there are more particles of reactant knocking about between the water molecules, which makes collisions between the important particles more likely.

Similarly, in a gas, increasing the pressure means the particles are more squashed up together, so there will be more frequent collisions (see Figure 2). More frequent collisions means a faster rate of reaction.

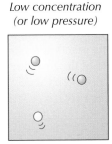

Low concentration (or low pressure)

High concentration (or high pressure)

The particles are far apart — they don't collide often.

The particles are close together — they collide often.

Figure 2: A diagram showing why increasing the concentration (or pressure) increases the rate of a reaction.

Surface area

If one of the reactants is a solid then breaking it up into smaller pieces will increase its surface area to volume ratio. This means that, for the same volume of solid, the particles around it in the solution will have more area to work on, so there'll be more frequent collisions and the rate of reaction will be faster — see Figure 4.

Tip: Being able to use a theoretical model, such as collision theory, to explain an experimental observation is an important part of Working Scientifically.

WORKING SCIENTIFICALLY

Tip: Increasing the temperature also increases the energy of the collisions — more on this on the next page.

Tip: This makes sense if you think about it — you're much more likely to bump into someone when you're in a crowd of people than when there aren't many people around.

Tip: You get the fastest rates of reactions with powders because powders have a very large surface area.

Figure 3: *Powdered calcium carbonate (top) has a larger surface area than a piece of calcium carbonate (above).*

Small surface area

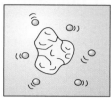

Less area for collisions. Collisions are less frequent.

Large surface area

More area for collisions. Collisions are more frequent.

Figure 4: *A diagram showing why increasing the surface area increases the rate of a reaction.*

2. Increasing the energy of collisions

The effect of temperature on reaction rate can also be explained in terms of how much energy the particles have when they collide. A higher temperature doesn't only increase the frequency of collisions — it also increases the energy of the collisions, because it makes all the particles move faster.

Reactions only happen if the particles collide with enough energy. The minimum amount of energy that particles must have in order to react is called the **activation energy**. At a higher temperature there will be more particles colliding with enough energy to make the reaction happen.

Tip: For a collision to be successful, the energy of the particles must be greater than or equal to the activation energy. If the particles don't have enough energy, they will just bounce off each other without reacting.

Rate and proportionality

The rate of a reaction is directly proportional to the frequency of successful collisions. This means that, if the frequency of successful collisions doubles, the rate will also double. If the frequency of successful collisions triples, the rate triples, and so on.

Tip: See page 168 for more on how to calculate the mean rate of a reaction.

| Example |

Magnesium and hydrochloric acid react to form magnesium chloride and hydrogen gas. When the temperature at which the reaction is carried out at is increased from 15 °C to 25 °C, the mean rate of the reaction is found to have doubled. So the frequency of successful collisions at 25 °C must be double the frequency of successful collisions at 15 °C.

Catalysts

Many reactions can be speeded up by adding a **catalyst**.

Tip: You'll come across a few catalysts later on. For example, aluminium oxide is a catalyst used in cracking (p.194).

A catalyst is a substance which can speed up a reaction, without being changed or used up in the reaction.

As they're not used up or changed in reactions, catalysts don't appear in the chemical equation for the reaction. Sometimes they're written in over the arrow, but they'll never be shown in the reactants or products.

Different catalysts are needed for different reactions, but they all work by decreasing the activation energy needed for the reaction to occur. They do this by providing an alternative reaction pathway with a lower activation energy (see Figure 5).

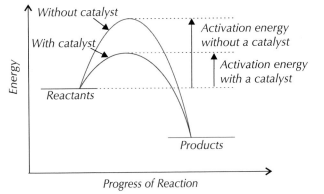

Figure 5: The reaction profiles of the same reaction with and without a catalyst.

Biological catalysts are known as **enzymes**. Like other catalysts, they work by lowering the activation energy of a reaction. An enzyme will generally only catalyse a certain reaction for a specific molecule. For example, some enzymes help to break down specific molecules in food, whilst there are others which catalyse processes in the formation of proteins.

Tip: Figure 5 shows an exothermic reaction — the products are at a lower energy than the reactants. If the reaction were endothermic, the products would be at a higher energy than the reactants. The activation energy of the catalysed reaction would still be lower than the activation energy of the uncatalysed reaction.

Tip: There's more about reaction profiles on pages 155-156.

Figure 6: A molecular model showing an enzyme found in saliva that catalyses the breakdown of starch.

Practice Questions — Fact Recall

Q1 What must happen for a reaction to occur between two particles?

Q2 Give two reasons why increasing the temperature increases the rate of a reaction.

Q3 Explain why increasing the concentration of the reactants increases the rate of a reaction.

Q4 What is the definition of a catalyst?

Q5 How do catalysts increase the rate of a chemical reaction?

Q6 What is an enzyme?

Practice Question — Application

Q1 The table below shows some rate of reaction data for the reactions of hydrochloric acid with different forms of calcium carbonate:

Form of calcium carbonate	Marble chips	Crushed marble chips	Powdered chalk
Initial rate of reaction (cm³/min)	0.6	1.2	5.6

a) Describe and explain the trend in these results.

b) The rate of reaction for the crushed marble chips is double the rate for the marble chips. State how the frequency of the collisions between particles has changed between these two reactions.

Tip: Don't worry too much about what the units mean in Q1 for now — how to calculate rates of reaction is coming up later on in the topic.

- Know that the rate of a reaction can be calculated by dividing either the amount of reactant used or the amount of product formed by time.
- Know that the amount of a reactant or product may be measured in terms of mass in g or volume in cm³, and that the units of rate may be given in g/s or cm³/s.
- **H** Know that the amount of a reactant or product may be given in moles and that the units of rate may be given in mol/s.
- Be able to investigate the rate of a reaction by measuring the time it takes for a solution to become cloudy, the loss in mass of reactants or the volume of a gas produced.

Specification References
5.6.1.1, 5.6.1.2

2. Measuring Rates of Reaction

If you want to measure the rate of a reaction, you're going to need a way to follow what's happening. Here's a guide to measuring rates of reaction...

Calculating rates of reaction

You can find the rate of a reaction either by measuring how quickly the reactants are used up or how quickly the products are formed (although it's usually a lot easier to measure the products forming). Once you've taken these measurements, you can work out the mean reaction rate using this formula:

$$\text{Mean rate of reaction} = \frac{\text{Quantity of reactant used or product formed}}{\text{Time}}$$

Example

In a reaction, 14.4 cm³ of oxygen gas was produced in the first 8 seconds. Calculate the mean rate of this reaction.

$$\text{Mean rate} = \frac{\text{Quantity of product formed}}{\text{Time}} = \frac{14.4}{8} = \textbf{1.8 cm}^3\textbf{/s}$$

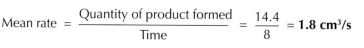

Units of rate

The units of rate will depend on the units you used to measure the amount of product or reactant. The general form of the units will be 'units of amount of substance'/'units of time'. For example, when the product or reactant is a gas you usually measure the amount in cm³. If it's a solid, then you use grams (g). Time is often measured in seconds (s). This means that the units for rate may be in cm³/s or in g/s.

H The amount of a product or reactant can be given in moles, so the units of rate could also be mol/s.

Measuring the formation of product

There are a few different ways that you can measure the formation of products during a reaction, and so calculate the rate.

Precipitation

You can record the visual change in a reaction if the initial solution is transparent and the product is a **precipitate** which clouds the solution (so it becomes opaque). You can observe a mark through the solution and measure how long it takes for the mark to disappear (see Figure 1). The quicker the mark disappears, the quicker the reaction.

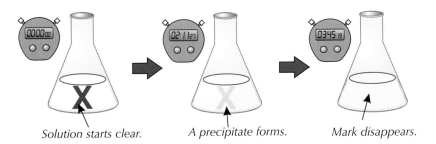

Solution starts clear. *A precipitate forms.* *Mark disappears.*

Figure 1: *Measuring the rate of a precipitation reaction.*

Figure 2: *A reaction that produces a precipitate. When enough precipitate has formed, the cross disappears.*

If the reactants are coloured and the products are colourless (or vice versa), you can time how long it takes for the solution to lose (or gain) colour.

This method is simple and easy to do but it only works for reactions where there's a visual change in the solution as the reaction occurs. The results are very subjective — different people might not agree over the exact point when the mark 'disappears' or the solution changes colour. Also, if you use this method, you can't plot a rate of reaction graph from the results.

Tip: Choosing the right method and equipment to make sure an investigation is accurate and reliable is an important part of Working Scientifically.

WORKING SCIENTIFICALLY

Change in mass

You can measure the speed of a reaction that produces a gas using a mass balance. You just place the reaction vessel on the balance. Then add your reactants to a conical flask and put a piece of cotton wool in the neck. As the gas is released the mass disappearing is easily measured — see Figure 3. The quicker the reading on the balance drops, the faster the reaction.

If you take measurements at regular intervals, you can plot a graph of the mass against time which can be used to find the rate at a particular point (see page 173 for more).

Tip: Some gases don't weigh very much so the change in mass can be quite small. The trick is to use a mass balance with a high <u>resolution</u>, so that very small changes in mass can be detected. See page 12 of the Working Scientifically section for more on resolution.

Gas released into the room.

The cotton wool lets the gas escape but stops the acid spitting out.

Mass decreases over time.

Figure 3: *Measuring the rate of a reaction using a change in mass.*

This is the most accurate of the three methods described here because the mass balance is very accurate. But it has the disadvantage of releasing the gas straight into the room, which isn't very good if the gas is dangerous.

Volume of gas given off

You can also measure the rate of a reaction that produces a gas by using a gas syringe to measure the volume of gas given off — see Figures 4 and 5. The more gas given off during a given time interval, the faster the reaction. You can take measurements at regular intervals and plot a graph of the volume of gas given off against time in order to find the rate of the reaction at a particular point.

Tip: ⬛ The mean rate of a reaction tells you what the average rate was as a certain amount of product was formed. But rate isn't constant during a reaction, it slows down. So drawing a graph can let you calculate the rate of reaction at a particular point in time during the reaction.

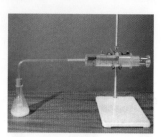

Figure 4: *The volume of gas produced in a reaction being measured.*

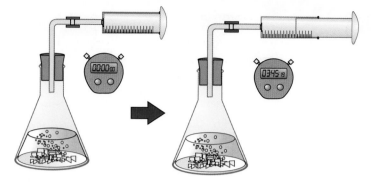

Figure 5: *Measuring the rate of a reaction using the volume of gas produced.*

Gas syringes usually give volumes to the nearest cm³, so they're quite sensitive. Also, the gas isn't released into the room, which is useful if the gas produced is poisonous. You have to be quite careful though — if the reaction is too vigorous, you can easily blow the plunger out of the end of the syringe.

Practice Questions — Fact Recall

Q1   What is the formula for calculating the mean rate of a reaction?

Q2   Describe how you could measure the rate of a reaction between two solutions where one of the products was a precipitate.

Q3   A student is measuring the rate of a reaction using a gas syringe.

   a) Discuss the advantages and disadvantages of this technique.

   b) Suggest another method that the student could use to measure the rate of this reaction.

Tip: Remember — the tiny letters in brackets that you find in some equations are called state symbols. They tell you what state each chemical is in:
- (s) means solid,
- (l) means liquid,
- (g) means gas,
- (aq) means dissolved in water.

For more about state symbols, see page 99.

Practice Questions — Application

Q1   The equation below shows the reaction between sulfuric acid and sodium hydrogen carbonate:

$$H_2SO_{4(aq)} + 2NaHCO_{3(s)} \rightarrow Na_2SO_{4(aq)} + 2H_2O_{(l)} + 2CO_{2(g)}$$

Suggest a method for measuring the rate of this reaction.

Q2   The equation below shows the reaction of sodium hydroxide with magnesium chloride:

$$2NaOH_{(aq)} + MgCl_{2(aq)} \rightarrow 2NaCl_{(aq)} + Mg(OH)_{2(s)}$$

Suggest a method for measuring the rate of this reaction. (If you need a clue, have a look at Figure 6.)

Q3   A reaction produced 4.3 cm³ of carbon dioxide gas in the first 5.0 seconds. Calculate the rate of this reaction in cm³/s.

Q4   Some lithium metal was added to water and the change in mass was measured on a mass balance. In the first 8.0 seconds, the mass of the reaction decreased from 34.31 g to 32.63 g. Calculate the rate of this reaction in g/s.

Figure 6: *The reaction of sodium hydroxide with magnesium chloride.*

3. Rate of Reaction Graphs

Once you've measured the amount of product made or reactant used over time, you can plot your data on a graph.

Graphs showing the rate of a reaction

If you plot the amount of product formed or the amount of reactant left in a reaction against time you'll get a graph similar to one of the ones in Figure 1.

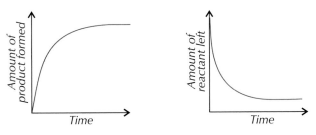

Figure 1: *Typical graphs of the amount of product formed against time and the amount of reactants left against time.*

On a graph showing the amount of product or reactant against time, the rate of the reaction is shown by the gradient (steepness) of the line. The steeper the line, the faster the rate (because it shows that products are being formed, or reactants used up, more quickly).

Graphs of product formed or reactant left against time aren't straight lines — they're curves that start steep, get shallower and then level off. This is because reactions start quickly, then slow down and eventually stop. The point at which the reaction has finished is the point at which the line on the graph goes flat.

Reactions start quickly because at the beginning of the reaction there are lots of reactant particles around, so collisions between them are very frequent. As the reaction progresses, the reactants get used up so the number of reactant particles decreases. This means collisions between reactant particles get less frequent and the reaction slows down. The reaction stops when all of the particles from at least one of the reactants are used up.

Comparing rates of reaction

You can compare the rate of a reaction performed under different conditions (e.g. at different temperatures) by plotting a series of lines on one graph. All of the lines will be curves, but the exact shape of each curve will depend on the rate of reaction and the amount of reactants that you started with.

- The fastest reaction will be the line with the steepest slope at the beginning. Also, the faster a reaction goes, the sooner it finishes, which means that the line will become flat earlier.

- Reactions that start off with the same amount of reactants will give lines that finish at the same level on the graph.

Learning Objectives:
- Be able to draw and interpret graphs showing the amount of product formed or reactant used against time.
- Be able to draw tangents to the curves of these graphs, and use the slopes of tangents to describe the rate of reaction.
- **H** Be able to calculate the gradient of a tangent to one of these curves in order to find the rate of a reaction at a given time.

Specification Reference 5.6.1.1

Tip: Have a look at page 16 for tips on how to draw graphs from a table of data.

Exam Tip
Always look really carefully at any graphs you're asked to interpret — don't assume you know what they show. Make sure you read the labels for each axis and the units that the data is in.

Tip: There are more examples of rate of reaction graphs coming up on the next few pages.

Exam Tip
You need to be able to interpret graphs like this in your exam so make sure you understand why the shapes of these curves are different.

> ### Example
>
> A student added some magnesium metal to an excess of hydrochloric acid that had been heated to 30 °C. He recorded the amount of gas formed at regular intervals.
>
> The student repeated the experiment with the acid heated to 40 °C and then to 50 °C. Finally he tried heating the acid to 50 °C and adding double the mass of magnesium. This graph shows all of his results:
>
>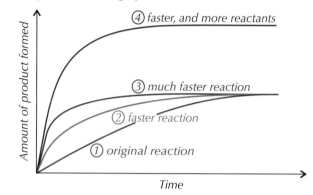
>
> - Line 1 shows the original (fairly slow) reaction at 30 °C. The graph isn't very steep at the start and it takes a long time to level off.
>
> - Lines 2 and 3 show the same reaction taking place at 40 °C and 50 °C. The initial rate of the reaction gets faster as the temperature increases, so the slope of the graphs gets steeper too.
>
> - Lines 1, 2 and 3 all end up at the same level because they produce the same amount of product (though they take different times to get there).
>
> - Line 4 shows the reaction taking place at 50 °C with double the mass of magnesium. It goes faster than the original reaction. It also finishes at a higher level because more reactants were added to begin with.

Mean rates from graphs

To find the mean rate for the whole reaction from a graph of the amount of a substance against time, you just work out the overall change in the y-value (the amount of substance) and then divide this by the total time taken for the reaction. You can also use the graph to find the mean rate of reaction between any two points in time:

Exam Tip
If you're asked to find the mean rate of reaction for the whole reaction, remember that the reaction finishes as soon as the line on the graph goes flat.

> ### Example
>
> **The graph shows the volume of gas released by a reaction, measured at regular intervals. Find the mean rate of reaction between 20 s and 40 s.**
>
>
>
> Mean rate = change in y ÷ change in x
> = (19 cm³ – 15 cm³) ÷ 20 s
> = **0.2 cm³/s**
>
>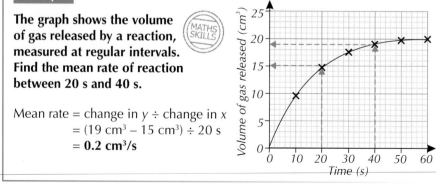

Rates and tangents

To get an idea of how fast the rate is at a particular point in the reaction you need to find out how steep the curve is at that point. And to do that you need to be able to draw a **tangent** to the curve. A tangent is a straight line that touches the curve at a particular point without crossing it.

Example

Here's how to draw a tangent at 90 s on the graph below. (MATHS SKILLS)

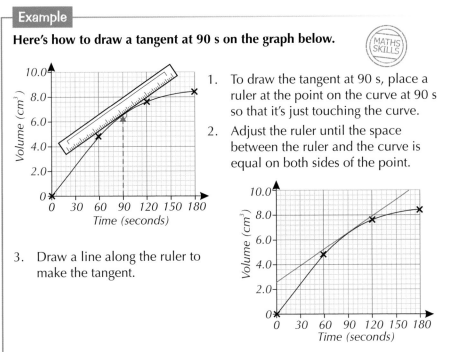

1. To draw the tangent at 90 s, place a ruler at the point on the curve at 90 s so that it's just touching the curve.

2. Adjust the ruler until the space between the ruler and the curve is equal on both sides of the point.

3. Draw a line along the ruler to make the tangent.

> **Exam Tip**
> Always use a ruler and a sharp pencil to draw tangents.

By drawing tangents at various points along the curve of a reaction, you can see how the rate changes over time.

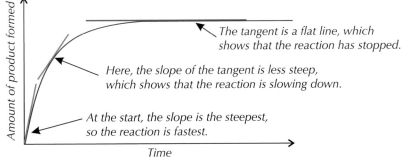

The tangent is a flat line, which shows that the reaction has stopped.

Here, the slope of the tangent is less steep, which shows that the reaction is slowing down.

At the start, the slope is the steepest, so the reaction is fastest.

Figure 2: *A graph of amount of product formed against time for a reaction.*

> **Tip:** For graphs showing amount of reactant left against time, the tangents will point from the top of the graph to the bottom, rather than from bottom to top. But it's still the case that, the steeper the line, the faster the rate.

Calculating rates from tangents `Higher`

As well as drawing the tangent of a curve, you can also calculate the gradient of the tangent. The value you calculate will be equal to the rate of the reaction at that particular point in time.

> **Tip:** **H** See pages 246-247 for more on calculating gradients.

$$\text{gradient} = \frac{\text{change in } y}{\text{change in } x}$$

Find the rate at 40 seconds for the reaction shown in the following graph:

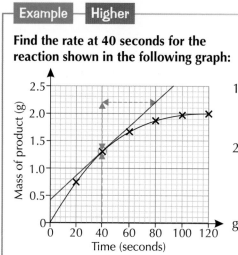

MATHS SKILLS

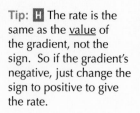

Tip: H The rate is the same as the <u>value</u> of the gradient, not the sign. So if the gradient's negative, just change the sign to positive to give the rate.

1. Draw a tangent to the curve at the point where you want to know the rate — here it's 40 s.

2. Pick two points on the line that are easy to read. Use them to calculate the gradient of the tangent in order to find the rate:

gradient = change in y ÷ change in x
= $(2.2 - 1.3) \div (80 - 40)$
= $0.90 \div 40 = 0.023$

So, the rate of reaction at 40 s was **0.023 g/s**.

Practice Questions — Application

Q1 Some tangents to a curve of a graph showing the amount of reactant left against time are shown below:

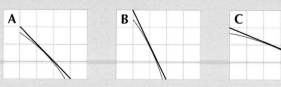

Put these tangents in order from the one showing that the rate is fastest, to the one showing that the rate is slowest.

Q2 A reaction took 200 s to finish and produced 24 cm³ of gas.

a) Which of the graphs below shows the volume of gas produced against time over the course of this reaction?

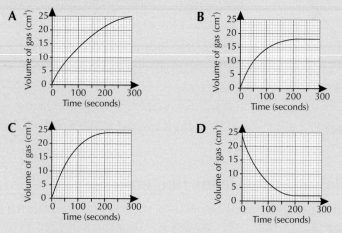

b) Under different conditions the reaction took 150 s to finish and produced 24 cm³ of gas. At the beginning of this reaction, would you predict the gradient of a graph of the amount of gas produced against time to be steeper or shallower than the original reaction?

Q3 The graph below shows the same reaction performed at three different temperatures. All other conditions were kept the same.

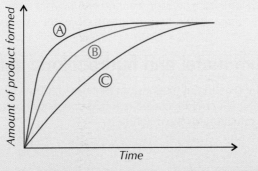

Tip: See page 165 for more on how and why temperature affects the rate of reaction.

Which of these reactions (A, B or C) was performed at the highest temperature? Explain your answer.

Q4 The graph below shows the amount of product formed over time in a reaction.

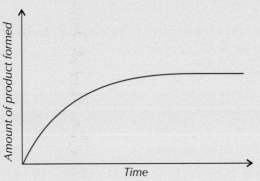

Copy this graph and sketch on the curves that would be produced if the reaction was performed:

a) with double the amount of reactant.

b) with the same amount of reactant but in the presence of a catalyst.

Tip: Don't forget — a catalyst is a substance that can speed up the rate of a reaction without being changed or used up in the reaction.

Q5 The graph below shows the change in concentration of a reactant against time during a reaction. After 60 seconds, the reaction is complete.

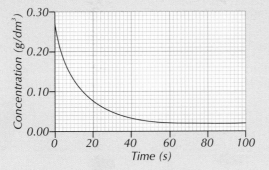

a) Find the mean rate of the entire reaction.

b) Find the rate of the reaction at 20 seconds.

Exam Tip
If you need to draw on a graph make sure you use a pencil rather than a pen. If you use pen you won't be able to rub it out if you make a mistake. Also, if you obscure something on the graph that you later need to read you'll be in trouble.

Learning Objectives:

- Know how to investigate the affect of concentration on the rate of reaction by measuring the volume of gas produced, or observing a precipitate forming or a colour change occurring (Required Practical 11).

Specification Reference 5.6.1.2

To really understand how rates of reaction can be measured you need to know some examples of reaction rate experiments. Like the examples coming up...

Magnesium metal and hydrochloric acid

You can use the reaction of magnesium metal with dilute hydrochloric acid to investigate the effect of increased reactant concentration on the rate of a reaction. The equation for the reaction is:

$$2HCl_{(aq)} + Mg_{(s)} \rightarrow MgCl_{2(aq)} + H_{2(g)}$$

This reaction gives off hydrogen gas, so you can follow the rate of the reaction by measuring the volume of gas produced using a gas syringe. Here's what you do:

Tip: Always carry out a risk assessment before you do an experiment in class.

- Measure out 50 cm^3 of dilute hydrochloric acid using a measuring cylinder, and add this to a conical flask.

- Add some magnesium ribbon to the acid and quickly attach an empty gas syringe to the flask.

- Start the stopwatch.

Tip: You could also measure the amount of hydrogen produced using a mass balance. The apparatus you'd use for this experiment is shown on page 169. Rather than measuring the volume at various intervals, you'd be measuring the mass of the reaction vessel, and using these values to work out the mass of gas lost during the reaction.

- Take readings of the volume at regular intervals (e.g. every 30 seconds) until the volume hasn't changed for three readings in a row.

- Put the results in a table. Plot a graph with time on the x-axis and volume of gas produced on the y-axis.

- Repeat with more concentrated acid solutions. Variables such as the mass and surface area of magnesium ribbon, the temperature of the reaction and the volume of acid used should be kept the same each time — only change the acid's concentration. This is to make your experiment a fair test — see page 10.

Sodium thiosulfate and hydrochloric acid

Sodium thiosulfate and hydrochloric acid are both clear solutions. They react together to form a yellow precipitate of sulfur, so the reaction mixture will become more turbid (cloudy) as the reaction continues:

$$2HCl_{(aq)} + Na_2S_2O_{3(aq)} \rightarrow 2NaCl_{(aq)} + SO_{2(g)} + S_{(s)} + H_2O_{(l)}$$

This experiment involves looking through the reaction solution at a black cross and timing how long it takes to disappear (see Figure 2).

Figure 1: *Magnesium ribbon reacting with hydrochloric acid — you can see the bubbles of hydrogen gas being produced.*

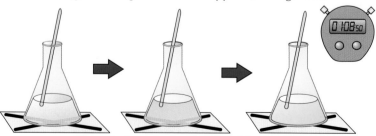

Figure 2: *Investigating the rate of the reaction between sodium thiosulfate and hydrochloric acid.*

- Start by adding 50 cm³ of dilute sodium thiosulfate solution to a flask.

- Place the flask on a piece of paper with a black cross drawn on it. Add 10 cm³ of dilute hydrochloric acid to the flask, give the flask a brief swirl to mix the reactants and start the stopwatch.

- Now watch the black cross through the cloudy sulfur and time how long it takes to disappear. Record your results in a table.

- Repeat the reaction in exactly the same way, using the same concentrations of reactants, and use your results to calculate a mean time for the cross to disappear. This will make your results more precise.

- The reaction can be repeated with solutions of either reactant at different concentrations. (Only change the concentration of one reactant at a time though.) The depth of the liquid must be kept the same each time, so make sure you use the same reaction flask each time. Also, different people might think the cross has disappeared at slightly different times, so the same person should observe the cross each time, to make it a fair test.

Tip: You could use a similar method to investigate the rate of a reaction that involves a colour change. Place the reaction vessel on a white tile (to make the colour change easier to spot) and time how long it takes for the colour change to happen.

Tip: Unlike the other experiments in this topic, this one doesn't give you a set of graphs. You just get one lot of readings telling you how long it took for the mark to disappear at each concentration. You could still plot these on a graph though.

Practice Questions — Fact Recall

Q1 Describe an experiment that could be used to demonstrate the effect of concentration on the rate of a reaction that produces a gas.

Q2 Describe one way that you could measure the rate of the reaction between sodium thiosulfate and hydrochloric acid.

Practice Question — Application

Q1 Two scientists investigate how long it takes for a colour change to happen in a reaction that takes place in solution at different temperatures. They repeat their experiment at each temperature a number of times.

a) State what the independent and dependent variables are in this experiment.

b) Name two other variables that should be controlled in this experiment.

c) What is the purpose of repeating the experiment at each temperature?

d) Why is it important that only one of the scientists decides when the colour change is complete for every repeat?

Topic Checklist — Make sure you know...

Rate of Reaction

☐ That in order for a reaction to take place, the reacting particles must collide with sufficient energy.

☐ That increasing the temperature, the concentration (or pressure), or the surface area of reactants will increase the rate of reaction, because they increase the frequency of collisions between particles.

☐ That increasing the temperature also increases the rate because it increases the energy of collisions.

☐ That the minimum amount of energy required for a reaction to occur is called the activation energy.

☐ That the rate of a reaction is proportional to the frequency of successful collisions between particles.

☐ That a catalyst increases the rate of a reaction without being changed or used up.

☐ That you can spot catalysts as they increase the rate of a reaction but aren't in the chemical equation.

☐ That catalysts work by providing a different reaction pathway that has a lower activation energy.

☐ How to draw reaction profiles to show the difference between a reaction with and without a catalyst.

☐ That catalysts in biological systems are known as enzymes.

Measuring Rates of Reaction

☐ That the mean rate of a reaction can be calculated by dividing either the amount of reactant used or the amount of product formed by time.

☐ That units of g/s and cm^3/s may be used to describe the rate of reactions.

☐ **H** That units of mol/s may be used to describe the rate of reactions.

☐ That the rate of a reaction that produces a precipitate can be measured by observing a mark through the solution and timing how long it takes for the mark to disappear.

☐ That the rate of a reaction that involves a colour change can be measured by timing how long it takes for the colour change to occur.

☐ That the rate of a reaction that produces a gas can be measured by monitoring the mass of the reaction over time (using a balance) or by measuring the volume of gas formed (using a gas syringe).

Rate of Reaction Graphs

☐ That if you plot a graph showing the amount of product formed (or reactant used) against time, the steepness of the curve shows the rate of the reaction — the steeper the curve, the faster the rate.

☐ That these types of graphs are usually curves because the reaction starts quickly, then slows down and eventually stops as the reactants get used up.

☐ How to use these graphs to find the mean rate of reaction between two points in time.

☐ **H** How to calculate the steepness of the curve at a particular point in time using a tangent.

Reaction Rate Experiments

☐ How to investigate how changing the concentration of a reactant affects the rate, for reactions where either a gas is produced, a precipitate is formed or there is a colour change.

Exam-style Questions

1   A student is investigating the rate of the reaction between nitric acid and zinc carbonate. The equation for this reaction is shown below:

$$2HNO_{3(aq)} + ZnCO_{3(s)} \rightarrow Zn(NO_3)_{2(aq)} + CO_{2(g)} + H_2O_{(l)}$$

The student measured the volume of carbon dioxide produced by this reaction and recorded the volume every 2 minutes for 20 minutes.

1.1   Suggest another technique that the student could have used to measure the rate of this reaction.

(1 mark)

The student's results are shown on this graph.

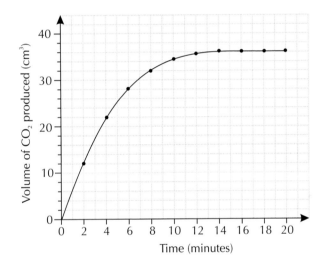

1.2   Use the graph to estimate how long it took for all of the reactants to be used up in this reaction.

(1 mark)

1.3   Calculate the rate of reaction during the first 2 minutes of this reaction. Give your answer in cm³/min.

(2 marks)

1.4   Explain why the rate of this reaction decreased as the reaction progressed.

(2 marks)

1.5   The student repeated his experiment at a higher temperature. All other conditions were kept the same.

Sketch out a copy of the graph above and sketch a second curve on the same axes to show the results he might expect.

(2 marks)

2   A student mixes ethanol, ethanoic acid and hydrochloric acid together in a beaker. The following reaction takes place:

ethanol + ethanoic acid → ethyl ethanoate + water

The student carries out the experiment again, but this time leaves out the hydrochloric acid. The same reaction takes place, but it happens at a much slower rate.

2.1   State two pieces of evidence that suggest that hydrochloric acid is a catalyst for the reaction.

(2 marks)

2.2   Explain how catalysts work.

(2 marks)

2.3   Draw a reaction profile diagram to show the reaction between ethanol and ethanoic acid with and without hydrochloric acid. The reaction is exothermic.

(3 marks)

2.4   Other than adding hydrochloric acid, suggest one thing the student could do to increase the rate of the reaction.

(1 mark)

3   A student is investigating how the rate changes over the course of the following reaction:

$$2HCl_{(aq)} + Mg_{(s)} \rightarrow MgCl_{2(aq)} + H_{2(g)}$$

She does this by measuring the volume of hydrogen gas produced at regular intervals. Her results are shown in the table below.

Time (s)	0	20	40	60	80	100	120	140	160	180
Volume of gas produced (cm^3)	0.0	13.0	18.0	20.5	22.0	23.0	23.5	24.0	24.0	24.0

3.1   State a piece of equipment the student could have used to accurately measure the volume of gas produced.

(1 mark)

3.2   Plot a graph of the student's results. Draw a line of best fit.

(4 marks)

3.3   State the units of the rate that would be given using these results.

(1 mark)

3.4   Calculate the rate of reaction at 20 seconds.

(3 marks)

3.5   After 40 s, the rate of reaction was half the rate it had been at 20 s. State how the frequency of successful collisions changed between 20 s and 40 s.

(1 mark)

1. Reversible Reactions

If a reaction is reversible this means it can run in both directions. Sounds a bit complicated, but don't worry — all will be revealed in the next few pages.

What is a reversible reaction?

A **reversible reaction** is one where the products of the reaction can themselves react to produce the original reactants. Reversible reactions can be represented like this:

$$A + B \rightleftharpoons C + D$$

The double arrow means that the reaction can go in either direction. By changing the conditions of a reaction, the overall direction can be changed and the relative amounts of products and reactants can be altered.

> **Example**
>
> Ammonium chloride can thermally decompose to form ammonia and hydrogen chloride. This reaction can also run in reverse — ammonia and hydrogen chloride can react with each other to form ammonium chloride.
>
> ammonium chloride $\rightleftharpoons$ ammonia + hydrogen chloride
>
> Heating the reaction means that more of the products are produced (more ammonia and hydrogen chloride) and cooling it means that more of the reactants are produced (more ammonium chloride).

Equilibrium

If a reversible reaction takes place in a closed system then a state of **equilibrium** will always be reached. Equilibrium is when the amounts of reactants and products reach a balance — their concentrations stop changing. A 'closed system' just means that none of the reactants or products can escape and nothing else can get in.

As the reactants react in a reversible reaction, their concentrations fall — so the forward reaction will slow down. But as more and more products are made and their concentrations rise, the backward reaction will speed up. After a while the forward reaction will be going at exactly the same rate as the backward one — the system has reached equilibrium. Both reactions are still happening, but the overall effect is nil because the forward and reverse reactions cancel each other out.

Learning Objectives:

- Know that in reversible reactions the products can react together to form the original reactants.
- Know how reversible reactions are represented.
- Know that the reaction conditions affect the direction of the reaction and the relative amounts of reactants and products.
- Know that a reversible reaction reaches equilibrium when the forward and reverse reactions occur at exactly the same rate.
- Know that if a reversible reaction is endothermic in one direction it will be exothermic in the other.
- Know that in a reversible reaction the energy absorbed by the endothermic reaction is equal to the energy released by the exothermic reaction.

Specification References 5.6.2.1-5.6.2.3

Exam Tip
Remember, if you come across a reaction you're not familiar with in an exam you can tell whether it's reversible by the arrow symbol. Double arrows ($\rightleftharpoons$) mean it's reversible.

Tip: You might come across double arrow symbols with words above and below them. For example:

$$\xrightleftharpoons[\text{cool}]{\text{heat}} \quad \xrightleftharpoons[\text{exothermic}]{\text{endothermic}}$$

The words 'heat' and 'cool' indicate how the conditions need to change for the reaction to run in the direction indicated — e.g. heat causes the reaction to run to the right.

The words 'endothermic' and 'exothermic' indicate what type of reaction is taking place in each direction (endo or exothermic).

Tip: Remember, an endothermic reaction takes in energy <u>from</u> the surroundings. An exothermic reaction transfers energy <u>to</u> the surroundings. See pages 152-153 for more.

Tip: "<u>Anhydrous</u>" just means "without water", and "<u>hydrated</u>" means "with water".

When a reaction's at equilibrium it doesn't mean the amounts of reactants and products are equal:

- If the equilibrium lies to the right, the concentration of products is greater than that of the reactants.

- If the equilibrium lies to the left, the concentration of reactants is greater than that of the products.

Energy transfer in reversible reactions

In reversible reactions, if the reaction is **endothermic** in one direction, it will be **exothermic** in the other direction. The energy absorbed by the endothermic reaction is equal to the energy released by the exothermic reaction.

Example 1

A good example of a reversible reaction is the thermal decomposition of hydrated copper sulfate. The equation for this reaction is:

hydrated copper sulfate $\rightleftharpoons$ anhydrous copper sulfate + water

- If you heat blue hydrated copper sulfate crystals it drives the water off and leaves white anhydrous copper sulfate powder. This is endothermic.

- If you then add a couple of drops of water to the white powder you get the blue crystals back again and energy is given out. This is exothermic.

The amount of energy that you have to put in to drive all the water out of the hydrated copper sulfate is the same as the amount of energy that is given out when you re-form hydrated copper sulfate.

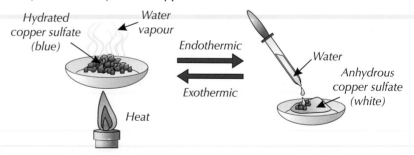

Figure 1: The reversible reaction that forms hydrated copper sulfate or anhydrous copper sulfate.

Figure 2: Hydrated copper sulfate (blue) being heated to form anhydrous copper sulfate (white).

Example 2

The thermal decomposition of $CaCO_3$ is another example of a reversible reaction. The equation is shown below.

$$CaCO_3 \rightleftharpoons CaO + CO_2$$

The decomposition of calcium carbonate to form calcium oxide and carbon dioxide gas is an endothermic reaction requiring constant heating.

If the temperature is reduced energy will be released, as the formation of calcium carbonate is an exothermic process.

Practice Questions — Fact Recall

Q1 What is a reversible reaction?

Q2 A reversible reaction involves the reactants A and B and the products C and D. Write an equation to represent this reaction.

Q3 If you run a reversible reaction in a closed system what will happen to the reaction?

Q4 Compare the rates of the forward and reverse reactions when equilibrium is reached.

Q5 If a reaction is exothermic in one direction will it give out energy or absorb energy in the opposite direction?

Practice Questions — Application

Q1 Hydrogen gas ($H_{2(g)}$) reacts with iodine vapour ($I_{2(g)}$) to form hydrogen iodide gas ($HI_{(g)}$). Write a chemical equation for this reversible reaction.

Q2 A student carries out the endothermic thermal decomposition of calcium carbonate to form calcium oxide and carbon dioxide in a closed system. The equation for the reaction is shown below.

$$CaCO_{3(s)} \rightleftharpoons CaO_{(s)} + CO_{2(g)}$$

a) After a period of heating, the reaction reached equilibrium. Describe what 'equilibrium' means.

b) Explain whether the reverse reaction is exothermic or endothermic.

Figure 3: When it's heated, calcium carbonate thermally decomposes to form calcium oxide and carbon dioxide.

Learning Objectives:

- **H** Know that Le Chatelier's principle states that if the conditions are changed for a reversible reaction at equilibrium the position of equilibrium will alter to counteract those changes.

- **H** Be able to predict how changing the temperature alters the yield of a reversible reaction.

- **H** Be able to predict how changing the pressure alters the yield of a reversible reaction involving gases.

- **H** Be able to predict how changing the concentration of reactants and products alters the yield of a reversible reaction.

Specification References
5.6.2.4-5.6.2.7

2. Le Chatelier's Principle Higher

Henri Le Chatelier (1850-1936) developed a principle to explain how yield is affected when you change conditions for a reversible reactions. Clever chap.

What is Le Chatelier's principle?

Le Chatelier's principle is the idea that if you change the conditions of a reversible reaction at equilibrium, the system will try to counteract the change. This means the effect of any changes to a system can be predicted. So by altering the temperature, pressure or concentration of the reactants, you can alter the **yield** of the reaction — making sure that you end up with more of the product you want (and less of the reactants).

Temperature

All reversible reactions are exothermic in one direction and endothermic in the other.

- If you raise the temperature, the yield of the endothermic reaction will increase and the yield of the exothermic reaction will decrease.

- If you reduce the temperature, the yield of the exothermic reaction will increase and the yield of the endothermic reaction will decrease.

Tip: The yield is the amount of product you get from a reaction.

Example Higher

The reaction below is used to make sulfur trioxide. It's exothermic in the forward direction and endothermic in the reverse direction.

$$Exothermic \rightarrow$$
$$2SO_{2(g)} + O_{2(g)} \rightleftharpoons 2SO_{3(g)}$$
$$\leftarrow Endothermic$$

- If you increase the temperature, the endothermic reverse reaction will be favoured and absorb the extra energy. This would result in a higher yield of SO_2 and O_2.

- If you decrease the temperature, the exothermic forward reaction will be favoured and release more energy. This would result in a higher yield of SO_3 — the product that you want.

Tip: **H** In descriptions of Le Chatelier's principle you might see different phrases like 'equilibrium shifts to the right', 'forward reaction is favoured' and 'yield of the forward reaction is increased' — they all mean the same thing.

Pressure

Changing the pressure affects reactions where the reactants and products are gases. Many of these reactions have a greater volume on one side (either of products or reactants). Greater volume means there are more gas molecules on that side of the equation and less volume means there are fewer gas molecules.

- Raising the pressure favours the reaction which produces less volume (the fewest number of gas molecules).

- Lowering the pressure favours the reaction which produces more volume (the greatest number of gas molecules).

Tip: **H** Changing the pressure <u>only</u> affects the equilibrium position of reactions where some of the reactants or products are gases.

Example — Higher

The reaction below is used to make hydrogen gas. It has two gas molecules on the left and four on the right.

$$CH_{4(g)} + H_2O_{(g)} \rightleftharpoons CO_{(g)} + 3H_{2(g)}$$

- If you increase the pressure, the reverse reaction will be favoured because the left side has fewer gas molecules than the right. This would result in a higher yield of CH_4 and H_2O.

- If you decrease the pressure, the forward reaction will be favoured because the right side has more gas molecules than the left. This would result in a higher yield of CO and H_2 — the products that you want.

Concentration

If you change the concentration of either the reactants or the products, the system will no longer be at equilibrium. So the system will respond to bring itself back to equilibrium again.

- If you increase the concentration of a reactant the system tries to decrease it by making more products.

- If you decrease the concentration of a product the system tries to increase it again by reducing the amount of reactants.

Tip: **H** The general idea here is that when you make any change to the conditions, the reaction will try to counteract it. In other words, it will do whatever it can to get the temperature or pressure or concentration back to what it was before you started meddling with it.

Example — Higher

Nitrogen and hydrogen can react together in a reversible reaction to form ammonia through the Haber process.

$$N_{2(g)} + 3H_{2(g)} \rightleftharpoons 2NH_{3(g)}$$

- If the concentration of N_2 or H_2 is increased, the forward reaction will be favoured so more NH_3 is produced.

- If NH_3 is removed, lowering the concentration, again, the forward reaction will be favoured so more NH_3 is produced.

Practice Questions — Fact Recall

Q1 What is the name of the principle which states that if you change the conditions of a reversible reaction at equilibrium, the system will try to counteract the change?

Q2 If you decrease the temperature of a reversible reaction, is the endothermic or exothermic reaction favoured?

Q3 In a reversible reaction involving gases, what effect does increasing the pressure have on the position of equilibrium?

Q4 What happens to the position of equilibrium if you decrease the concentration of the products in a reversible reaction?

Q1 Ammonium chloride decomposes when heated to 338 °C to form ammonia and hydrogen chloride. On cooling the reaction can be reversed. The equation for the reaction is shown below.

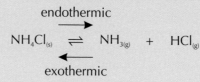

$$NH_4Cl_{(s)} \rightleftharpoons NH_{3(g)} + HCl_{(g)}$$

Figure 1: *Ammonium chloride thermally decomposing to form ammonia and hydrogen chloride.*

a) i) If you lower the temperature to 250 °C, which reaction will be favoured?

  ii) Which compound(s) will have a higher yield as a result?

b) i) If you raise the temperature to 400 °C, which reaction will be favoured?

  ii) Which compound(s) will have a higher yield as a result?

Q2 Sulfur dioxide reacts with oxygen to produce sulfur trioxide:

$$2SO_{2(g)} + O_{2(g)} \rightleftharpoons 2SO_{3(g)}$$

a) Which side of the equation has more volume?

b) State the effect of increasing the pressure on the yield of SO_3.

c) State the effect of decreasing the pressure on the yield of SO_3.

Topic Checklist — Make sure you know...

Reversible Reactions

☐ That the products of reversible reactions can react to re-form the original reactants.

☐ That the conditions the reaction takes place in affect the overall direction of the reaction and the relative amounts of reactants and products.

☐ That at equilibrium the forward and reverse reactions are occurring at exactly the same rate.

☐ That if a reversible reaction is endothermic in one direction it will be exothermic in the other direction.

☐ That in a reversible reaction the same amount of energy is absorbed by the endothermic reaction as is released by the exothermic reaction.

Le Chatelier's Principle

☐ **H** That Le Chatelier's principle states that if you change the conditions of a reversible reaction the system will react to counteract that change by shifting the position of equilibrium.

☐ **H** How changing temperature, pressure and concentration affects the yield of a reversible reaction.

Exam-style Questions

1   A reusable hand warmer contains a solution of sodium acetate trihydrate. When the hand warmer is activated, the sodium acetate trihydrate crystallises and energy is released. The word equation for this reaction is shown below:

$$\text{sodium acetate trihydrate solution} \rightleftharpoons \text{solid sodium acetate trihydrate}$$

1.1   What type of reaction is this? Choose the correct answer.

A neutralisation   **B** exothermic   **C** combustion   **D** endothermic

(1 mark)

1.2   Using the information above, explain why hand warmers that contain sodium acetate trihydrate are reusable.

(1 mark)

1.3   The hand warmer can be reset after use by heating it.
Suggest why heating the hand warmer makes it ready to be used again.

(2 marks)

2   Ethanol is produced using a reversible reaction between ethene and steam, as shown in the equation below.

$$\underset{\text{endothermic}}{\overset{\text{exothermic}}{C_2H_{4(g)} \quad + \quad H_2O_{(g)} \quad \rightleftharpoons \quad C_2H_5OH_{(g)}}}$$

This reaction is carried out at 300 °C and 60-70 atmospheres.

2.1   The reaction takes place in a closed system. Explain what this means.

(1 mark)

2.2   The temperature that the reaction is carried out at is increased.
What effect would this have on the yield of ethanol? Explain your answer.

(2 marks)

2.3   The pressure that the reaction is carried out at is increased.
What effect would this have on the yield of ethanol? Explain your answer.

(2 marks)

2.4   Explain why the amount of energy released when ethanol is produced is the same as the amount of energy used to break down ethanol into ethene and steam.

(1 mark)

Learning Objectives:
- Know that hydrocarbons only contain hydrogen and carbon.
- Be able to recognise hydrocarbons called alkanes from their molecular and displayed formulas.
- Know that methane, ethane, propane and butane are the first four alkanes.
- Know that alkanes have the general formula C_nH_{2n+2}.
- Know that alkenes are hydrocarbons and that they are more reactive than alkanes.
- Know how to test for alkenes using bromine water.
- Know that alkenes can be used as the starting materials for many chemicals, including polymers.
- Know how the boiling points, viscosity and flammability of alkanes change depending on the size of the molecules.
- Know that, when hydrocarbons combust completely, carbon and hydrogen are oxidised, that carbon dioxide and water are produced and that energy is released.
- Be able to write balanced equations for the complete combustion of hydrocarbons.

Specification References
5.7.1.1, 5.7.1.3, 5.7.1.4

1. Hydrocarbons

Organic chemistry is the study of substances that contain carbon atoms. Hydrocarbons are a really important part of organic chemistry as their properties make them very useful in modern life.

What is a hydrocarbon?

A **hydrocarbon** is any molecule that is formed from carbon and hydrogen atoms only. So $C_{10}H_{22}$ (decane, an alkane) is a hydrocarbon, but $CH_3COOC_3H_7$ (an ester) is not — it contains oxygen.

Alkanes

The simplest type of hydrocarbons are called **alkanes**. Alkanes are made up of chains of carbon atoms surrounded by hydrogen atoms. Carbon atoms form four bonds and hydrogen atoms only form one bond. In alkanes, there are no carbon-carbon double bonds so all the atoms have formed bonds with as many other atoms as they can — this means they're **saturated**. Different alkanes have chains of different lengths.

Examples

The first four alkanes are methane (natural gas), ethane, propane and butane.

Methane has just one carbon atom and four hydrogen atoms, so its chemical formula is CH_4. The displayed structure of methane is shown in Figure 1. The green lines in this structure represent covalent bonds.

Figure 1: *Methane.*

Ethane (C_2H_6) has a chain of two carbon atoms, propane (C_3H_8) has three carbon atoms and butane (C_4H_{10}) has four carbon atoms. Their displayed structures are shown in Figure 2.

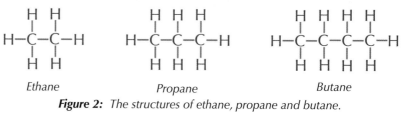

Ethane   *Propane*   *Butane*

Figure 2: *The structures of ethane, propane and butane.*

General formula of alkanes

Alkanes all have the general formula C_nH_{2n+2}. In this formula, n is the number of carbon atoms. So if an alkane has n carbon atoms, it will always have 2n + 2 hydrogen atoms.

Tip: You can work out the molecular formula of any alkane using the general formula, as long as you know how many carbon atoms it has.

Example

If an alkane has 5 carbons, it's got to have $(2 \times 5) + 2 = 12$ hydrogens.
So the chemical formula of an alkane with 5 carbon atoms is C_5H_{12}.

Alkenes

Alkenes are another family of hydrocarbons. They're more reactive than alkanes. This means they are useful starting materials for making other organic compounds and polymers.

As alkenes are more reactive than alkanes, you can distinguish between them using bromine water. When orange bromine water is added to an alkane, no reaction will happen and it'll stay bright orange. If it's added to an alkene, a reaction occurs and the bromine water is decolourised.

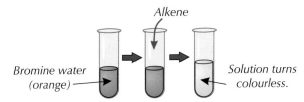

Alkene

Bromine water (orange)

Solution turns colourless.

Figure 3: *Using bromine water to test for alkenes.*

Figure 4: *The orange to colourless colour change when an alkene is added to bromine water.*

Properties of hydrocarbons

The properties of hydrocarbons change depending on how long the carbon chain is. There are three trends in the properties of hydrocarbons that you need to know.

- The shorter the molecules, the more runny the hydrocarbon is — that is, the less **viscous** it is.

- The shorter the molecules, the lower their boiling point is. So, the shorter the molecules, the lower the temperature at which they vaporise or condense.

- The shorter the molecules, the more **flammable** the hydrocarbon is.

So, hydrocarbons with very long carbon chains are viscous, have very high boiling points and are not very flammable.

Tip: How easy it is to ignite something shows how <u>flammable</u> it is.

Complete combustion of hydrocarbons

If you burn hydrocarbons, the carbon and hydrogen react with oxygen from the air to form carbon dioxide and water vapour. The carbon and hydrogen are said to be oxidised. Energy is also released.

When there's plenty of oxygen, all the carbon atoms are completely oxidised — this is called complete combustion. This is the equation for the complete combustion of a hydrocarbon:

hydrocarbon + oxygen → carbon dioxide + water vapour

Figure 5: *Bottled butane gas burning.*

Writing equations for combustion

In the exam, you could be asked to write a balanced symbol equation for the complete combustion of a particular hydrocarbon. All you have to do is put the molecular formula of your fuel and O_2 for oxygen on the left-hand side, CO_2 for carbon dioxide and H_2O for water on the right-hand side and then make sure the equation balances.

Tip: See pages 32-33 for more on balancing chemical equations.

Examples

Write an equation for the complete combustion of propane.

Propane has the formula C_3H_8.

If you put C_3H_8 and O_2 on the left-hand side of the equation and CO_2 and H_2O on the right-hand side of the equation you get:

$$C_3H_8 + O_2 \rightarrow CO_2 + H_2O$$

Balancing the equation gives you: $C_3H_8 + 5O_2 \rightarrow 3CO_2 + 4H_2O$

This is the equation for the complete combustion of propane.

Tip: Start by balancing the number of Cs on each side of the equation, then Hs and finally Os.

Write an equation for the complete combustion of butane.

Butane has the formula C_4H_{10}.

If you put C_4H_{10} and O_2 on the left-hand side of the equation and CO_2 and H_2O on the right-hand side of the equation you get:

$$C_4H_{10} + O_2 \rightarrow CO_2 + H_2O$$

Balancing the equation gives you: $C_4H_{10} + 6\frac{1}{2}O_2 \rightarrow 4CO_2 + 5H_2O$

This is the equation for the complete combustion of butane.

Tip: It's fine to use 13 instead of 6½ before O_2 but don't forget to double the other numbers on both sides to keep it balanced.

Practice Questions — Fact Recall

Q1 What is a hydrocarbon?

Q2 Name the alkane that has the chemical formula C_3H_8.

Q3 What happens to bromine water in the presence of an alkene?

Q4 Describe the trend in flammability of the alkanes.

Practice Questions — Application

Exam Tip
You need to know the names of the first four alkanes for your exam.

Q1 Octane has eight carbon atoms in it. What is its molecular formula?

Q2 Write a balanced symbol equation for the complete combustion of pentane (C_5H_{12}).

Q3 Write a balanced symbol equation for the complete combustion of methane.

Q4 The formulas of four compounds are:
A: $C_{12}H_{24}$ B: CH_2O C: C_5H_{12} D: C_3H_7OH

a) Which of the compounds are hydrocarbons?

b) Which of the compounds are alkanes?

2. Fractional Distillation of Crude Oil

Crude oil is a fossil fuel that is formed deep underground from the remains of plants and animals. Loads of useful products can be made from crude oil using a technique called fractional distillation.

What is crude oil?

Crude oil is a **mixture** of many different compounds. It's formed from the remains of plants and animals, mainly plankton, that died millions of years ago and were buried in mud. Over millions of years, with high temperature and pressure, the remains turn to crude oil, which can be drilled up from the rocks where it's found. Because it takes so long for crude oil to form it's said to be a finite resource — once it's used up we can't replace it.

Most of the compounds in crude oil are **hydrocarbon** molecules, and the majority of them are **alkanes**.

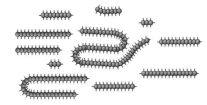

Figure 1: *Crude oil is a mixture of hydrocarbons.*

Fractional distillation

Crude oil can be split into separate groups of hydrocarbons using a technique called **fractional distillation**. The crude oil is pumped into a piece of equipment known as a fractionating column, which works continuously (it doesn't get switched off). This fractionating column has a temperature gradient running through it — it's hottest at the bottom and coldest at the top.

The crude oil is first heated so that it evaporates (turns into a gas) and is then piped in at the bottom of the column. The gas rises up the column and gradually cools. Different compounds in the mixture have different boiling points, so they condense (turn back into a liquid) at different temperatures. This means they condense at different levels in the fractionating column.

Hydrocarbons that have a similar number of carbon atoms have similar boiling points, so they condense at similar levels in the column.

> **Examples**
> - Hydrocarbons with lots of carbon atoms have high boiling points, so they condense near the bottom of the column.
> - Hydrocarbons with a small number of carbon atoms have low boiling points, so they condense near the top of the column.

The groups of hydrocarbons that condense together are called **fractions**. The various fractions are constantly tapped off from the column at the different levels where they condense.

The process of fractional distillation is illustrated in Figure 3.

Learning Objectives:
- Know that crude oil is a mixture of lots of different compounds.
- Know that crude oil is mainly formed from the remains of plankton and other plants and animals.
- Know that most of the compounds in crude oil are hydrocarbons.
- Know that the majority of hydrocarbons in crude oil are alkanes.
- Be able to explain how fractional distillation is used to separate crude oil into fractions.

Specification References
5.7.1.1, 5.7.1.2

Figure 2: *A fractionating column.*

Tip: The temperature at which a compound condenses is the same as its boiling point. E.g. if a compound had a boiling point of 120 °C, it would condense at 120 °C.

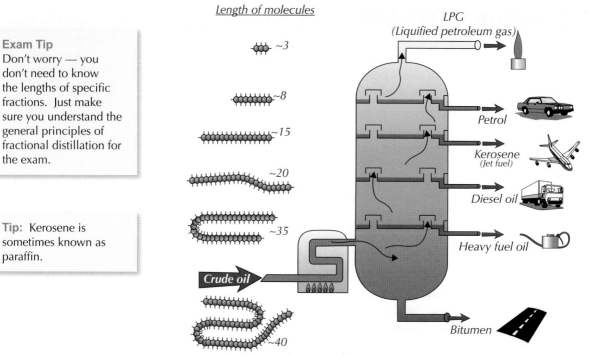

Figure 3: The process of fractional distillation.

Exam Tip
Don't worry — you don't need to know the lengths of specific fractions. Just make sure you understand the general principles of fractional distillation for the exam.

Tip: Kerosene is sometimes known as paraffin.

Practice Questions — Fact Recall

Q1   What is crude oil formed from?

Q2   What is the most common type of hydrocarbon in crude oil?

Practice Questions — Application

Q1   This table contains data on some of the fractions of crude oil that are separated out during fractional distillation.

Fraction	Petrol	Naphtha	Kerosene	Diesel
Approx. boiling temp. range (°C)	30 – 80	80 – 190	190 – 250	250 – 350

Tip: Don't forget — the fractionating column is hottest at the bottom and coolest at the top.

a) Which of the fractions in the table will be removed closest to the bottom of the fractionating column?

b) Hexane has a boiling point of 68 °C. At what temperature will hexane condense? In which fraction will it be found?

Q2   This table shows the number of carbon atoms in some of the hydrocarbons found in crude oil.

Hydrocarbon	Butane	Decane	Icosane	Tetracontane
Number of carbon atoms	4	10	20	40

Which of the hydrocarbons in the table will condense at the highest temperature?

3. Uses of Crude Oil

The fractions that you get when you separate crude oil have very different properties. This means they can be used for different things.

What can crude oil be used for?

Fractions from crude oil can be processed to provide the fuel for most modern transport. Diesel oil, petrol, kerosene, heavy fuel oil and LPG (liquefied petroleum gases) are used to fuel cars, trains, planes and other forms of transport. The uses of hydrocarbons depend on their properties.

Examples

The volatility helps decide what the fraction is used for.

- The LPG fraction has the lowest boiling point — in fact it's a gas at room temperature. This makes it ideal for using as bottled gas. It's stored under pressure as liquid in 'bottles'. When the tap on the bottle is opened, the fuel vaporises and flows to the burner where it's ignited.

- The petrol fraction has a higher boiling point. Petrol is a liquid at room temperature, which is ideal for storing in the fuel tank of a car. It can flow to the engine where it's easily vaporised to mix with the air before it is ignited.

The viscosity also helps decide how the hydrocarbons are used.

- The really gloopy, viscous hydrocarbons are used for lubricating engine parts or for covering roads.

The petrochemical industry uses some of the hydrocarbons from crude oil as a **feedstock** to make new compounds for use in things like polymers, solvents, lubricants, and detergents.

All the products you get from crude oil are examples of **organic compounds** (compounds containing carbon atoms). The reason you get such a large variety of products is because carbon atoms can bond together to form different groups called **homologous series**. These groups contain similar compounds that all have the same general formula and many properties in common. Alkanes, alkenes, as well as other families such as alcohols and carboxylic acids, are all examples of different homologous series.

Practice Question — Fact Recall

Q1 Crude oil can undergo fractional distillation to produce a variety of useful fuels.

   a) Give the name of a fuel obtained from crude oil.

   b) Give the name of one other product which can be derived from crude oil.

Learning Objectives:

- Know that fractions of crude oil can be used to make fuels or as starting materials for new compounds in the petrochemical industry.

- Know that fuels from crude oil fractions such as diesel oil, petrol, kerosene, heavy fuel oil and LPG are important for modern life.

- Understand that the properties of hydrocarbons affect how they are used.

- Know that many of today's useful compounds are produced by the petrochemical industry, including lubricants, solvents, polymers and detergents.

- Know that carbon compounds can form a wide variety of homologous series.

Specification References 5.7.1.2, 5.7.1.3

Figure 1: *Oil refineries process crude oil to form useful substances.*

Exam Tip
You need to learn the names of diesel oil, petrol, kerosene, heavy fuel oil and LPG for the exam and know that they come from crude oil.

Learning Objectives:

- Know that cracking is a process used to convert large hydrocarbon molecules into smaller, more useful hydrocarbons.
- Know that cracking produces some products that can be used as fuels.
- Be able to describe the processes of catalytic cracking and steam cracking.
- Know that cracking produces alkanes and alkenes.
- Know how to balance cracking equations.

Specification Reference
5.7.1.4

4. Cracking Crude Oil

Some fractions of crude oil are more useful than others — for example, short-chain hydrocarbons are often more useful than long-chain hydrocarbons. Cracking is used to break down long-chain hydrocarbons into shorter ones.

What is cracking?

Short-chain hydrocarbons are flammable so make good fuels and are in high demand. Long-chain hydrocarbons form thick gloopy liquids like tar which aren't all that useful, so a lot of the longer molecules produced from fractional distillation are turned into smaller, more useful ones by a process called **cracking**.

Some of the products of cracking are useful as fuels, like petrol for cars and paraffin for jet fuel. Cracking also produces substances like ethene, which are needed for making plastics. The process of cracking is illustrated in Figure 1.

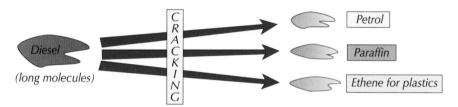

Figure 1: Cracking. In this example, diesel (a fraction containing long-chain hydrocarbons) is being broken down into shorter-chain hydrocarbons found in petrol, paraffin and ethene.

How cracking works

Figure 2: A catalytic cracker at an oil refinery.

Cracking is a **thermal decomposition** reaction — breaking molecules down by heating them. There are two methods that can be used to crack alkanes — catalytic cracking or steam cracking. In both methods, the first step is to heat the long-chain hydrocarbons to vaporise them (turn them into a gas). In catalytic cracking, the vapour is then passed over a hot, powdered **catalyst**. Aluminium oxide is one of the catalysts used. The long-chain molecules split apart or 'crack' on the surface of the specks of catalyst — see Figure 3.

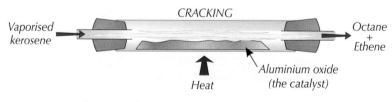

Figure 3: The cracking of kerosene into octane and ethene using an aluminium oxide catalyst.

Alternatively, in steam cracking, the vapour can be mixed with steam and heated to a very high temperature. This will also lead to thermal decomposition of long-chain hydrocarbon molecules to form smaller ones.

Products of cracking

Most of the products of cracking are alkanes and unsaturated hydrocarbons called **alkenes**.

Example

Decane is a long-chain hydrocarbon molecule (it has 10 carbon atoms). There's lots of decane in crude oil, but decane itself isn't that useful. Cracking is used to break decane down into octane and ethene (see Figure 5). Octane is a shorter-chain alkane which is useful for making petrol. Ethene is an alkene which is useful for making plastics.

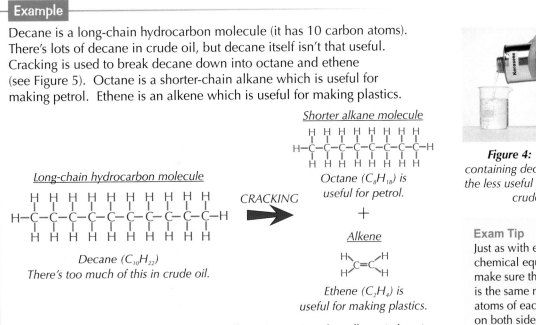

Figure 5: The cracking of decane into an alkane (octane) and an alkene (ethene).

Figure 4: Kerosene containing decane — one of the less useful products from crude oil.

Exam Tip
Just as with every chemical equation, make sure that there is the same number of atoms of each element on both sides so that it's balanced.

Practice Questions — Fact Recall

Q1 a) What is cracking and why is it useful?

b) Give two things that the products of cracking can be used for.

Q2 What type of reaction is cracking?

Q3 Name two types of hydrocarbon that are produced in cracking.

Practice Questions — Application

Q1 A long chain alkane, $C_{12}H_{26}$, undergoes a cracking reaction to form C_9H_{20} and an alkene.

a) Give the formula of the alkene product of the reaction.

b) Give the equation for the reaction.

Q2 A molecule of $C_{20}H_{42}$ is cracked into three products — two alkenes, C_5H_{10} and C_7H_{14}, and an alkane.

a) Give the formula of the alkane made.

b) Suggest one use for the two alkanes produced from the reaction.

Topic Checklist — Make sure you know...

Hydrocarbons

- [ ] That hydrocarbons are molecules that contain hydrogen and carbon atoms only.
- [ ] How to recognise alkanes from their molecular formulas and their displayed formulas.
- [ ] That methane, ethane, propane and butane are the first four alkanes.
- [ ] That the general formula for alkanes is C_nH_{2n+2}.
- [ ] That alkenes are a type of hydrocarbon that are more reactive than alkanes.
- [ ] How bromine water can be used to test for the presence of alkenes in solution.
- [ ] That many materials such as polymers use alkenes as starting materials.
- [ ] How the viscosity, boiling point and flammability of hydrocarbons change with molecular length.
- [ ] That when hydrocarbons undergo complete combustion they release energy and produce carbon dioxide and water. In the process, hydrogen and carbon are oxidised.
- [ ] How to write and balance equations for the complete combustion of alkanes.

Fractional Distillation of Crude Oil

- [ ] That crude oil is a mixture of many different compounds, most of which are hydrocarbons.
- [ ] That crude oil is formed from the dead remains of plankton and other plants and animals.
- [ ] That the hydrocarbons in crude oil are mainly alkanes.
- [ ] How crude oil can be separated into fractions using fractional distillation.

Uses of Crude Oil

- [ ] That fuels and feedstocks for the petrochemical industry are produced from crude oil fractions.
- [ ] That diesel oil, petrol, kerosene, heavy fuel oil and LPG come from crude oil and are used as fuels.
- [ ] That carbon compounds can form a wide variety of groups known as homologous series.
- [ ] That the petrochemical industry produces many materials which are useful in modern life such as polymers, detergents, solvents and lubricants.

Cracking Crude Oil

- [ ] That cracking breaks down long-chain hydrocarbons into shorter, more useful hydrocarbons.
- [ ] That some of the products that are made when long-chain molecules are cracked are useful as fuels, while others are useful as raw materials for making other substances, such as plastics.
- [ ] That cracking is a thermal decomposition reaction (i.e. molecules break down when they're heated).
- [ ] How hydrocarbons can be cracked using a catalyst or using steam and very high temperatures.
- [ ] That cracking can be used to produce alkanes and alkenes.
- [ ] How to balance equations for cracking if you know the formulas for the products and reactants.

Exam-style Questions

1   Many modern cars use petrol as their fuel source.
Petrol is produced from crude oil by a process known as fractional distillation.

    1.1   Describe the process of fractional distillation.

(4 marks)

    1.2   Petrol is removed from near the top of the fractionating column.
What does this tell you about the hydrocarbons that make up petrol?

(1 mark)

    1.3   Petrol often contains heptane (C_7H_{16}).
Write a balanced symbol equation for the complete combustion of heptane.

(3 marks)

2   Alkanes are a type of saturated hydrocarbon.

    2.1   What is the general formula of the alkanes?

(1 mark)

This table contains information about some common alkanes.

Alkane	Formula	Length of carbon chain
Propane	C_3H_8	3
Heptane	C_7H_{16}	7
Decane	$C_{10}H_{22}$	10

    2.2   Which of the alkanes in the table is likely to be the least flammable?
Explain your answer.

(2 marks)

    2.3   Which of the alkanes in the table would be most suitable to use in bottled gas?
Explain your answer.

(3 marks)

3   Ethene (C_2H_4) is an alkene that's used as a starting material
in the production of polymers.

    3.1   Ethene can be formed from the thermal decomposition (cracking) of octane (C_8H_{18}).
An alkane is also formed in this reaction. Give the formula of the alkane.

(1 mark)

    3.2   Give the balanced equation for the reaction in 3.1.

(1 mark)

    3.3   Describe the reaction conditions of **one** method to carry out the reaction in 3.1.

(2 marks)

    3.4   Describe a test you could use to distinguish between ethene and the alkane.

(3 marks)

Learning Objectives:

- Know that in chemistry, a pure substance only contains one element or compound, and how this differs from the meaning of purity in everyday language.
- Understand that the boiling and melting points of pure substances are at specific temperatures.
- Be able to tell whether or not a substance is pure based on its melting and boiling points.
- Know that a formulation is a mixture with exact amounts of components made for a specific function.
- Know that each component in a formulation is there for a specific reason.
- Know that formulations include paints, cleaning agents, medicines, alloys, fertilisers, fuels and foods.
- Be able to use given information to identify if a substance is a formulation.

Specification References
5.8.1.1, 5.8.1.2

1. Purity and Formulations

Purity is really important in chemistry. Chemists are always trying to find new ways to produce products which are as pure as possible, but it can be tricky.

What is a pure substance?

Usually, when you refer to a substance as being pure you mean that nothing has been added to it, so it's in its natural state. For example, pure milk or beeswax. But if something is described as a pure substance in chemistry it means it only contains one compound or element throughout — it's not mixed with anything else.

Testing for purity

A chemically pure substance will boil or melt at a specific temperature. This means you can test the purity of a sample by measuring its melting or boiling point and comparing it with the melting or boiling point of the pure substance (which you can find from a data book). Impurities in your sample will:

- Lower the melting point and increase the melting range of your substance.
- Increase the boiling point and may result in a sample boiling over a range of temperatures.

Example

The table below shows melting point and boiling point data of two prepared samples of copper chloride (A and B), along with the boiling and melting points of pure copper chloride.

	Melting point (°C)	Boiling point (°C)
Sample A	494	995
Sample B	475	1000-1005
Pure copper chloride	498	993

The melting points of both Samples A and B are less than the pure copper chloride sample, suggesting that the samples are not completely pure. The boiling points are both higher than the pure substance with Sample B melting over a range of temperatures. Again, this suggests that neither sample is pure.

Sample A's melting and boiling points are closer to those of the pure substance, which suggests that Sample A is more pure than Sample B.

Formulations

Formulations are useful mixtures with a precise purpose that are made by following a 'formula' (a recipe). Each component in a formulation is present in a measured quantity, and contributes to the properties of the formulation so that it meets its required function.

Tip: A formulation is a mixture but not all mixtures are formulations. To be a formulation, a mixture has to be a useful product, have been made with a precise purpose in mind and have its components present in particular, carefully measured quantities.

Example

Paint is a formulation composed of four components:

- Pigment — gives the paint colour, for example titanium oxide is used as a pigment in white paints.

- Solvent — used to dissolve the other components and alter the viscosity.

- Binder — forms a film that holds the pigment in place after it's been painted on.

- Additives — added to further change the physical and chemical properties of the paint.

Depending on the purpose of the paint, the chemicals used and their amounts will be changed so the paint produced is right for the job.

Exam Tip
You could be asked to identify whether or not something is a formulation in your exam. So make sure you know what makes a formulation a formulation.

Formulations are really important in the pharmaceutical industry. For example, by altering the formulation of a pill, chemists can make sure it delivers the drug to the correct part of the body at the right concentration, that it's consumable and has a long enough shelf-life.

Formulations can be found in cleaning products, fuels, cosmetics, fertilisers, metal alloys and even food and drink.

When you buy a product, you might find that it has information about its composition on the packaging. For example, the ratio or percentage of each component. This tells you that the product's a formulation. It also lets you choose a formulation with the right composition for your particular use.

Practice Questions — Fact Recall

Q1 What is the definition of a pure substance in chemistry?

Q2 What effect will impurities have on the melting point of a sample?

Q3 What is a formulation?

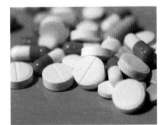

Figure 1: The majority of drugs are formulations.

Practice Questions — Application

Q1 A student describes 100% beeswax as a chemically pure substance. Suggest, with reasoning, whether the student is correct or not.

Q2 The melting point of a sample of paracetamol with 98% purity was measured as being between 164-168 °C. The melting point of pure paracetamol is 169 °C and the boiling point is 420 °C.

   a) Suggest how the melting point of a sample with 95% purity would be different from the melting point of the sample with 98% purity.

   b) Suggest how the boiling point of both impure samples would vary compared to pure paracetamol.

Tip: The percentage purity of a sample is the percentage of the sample that is the intended chemical. So if a sample of calcium carbonate has a purity of 95% it means that 95% of the sample is actually calcium carbonate, the remaining 5% is made up of other chemicals.

2. Analysing Paper Chromatography

You met chromatography on page 35. But here's a bit more info on it...

- Know that chromatography can be used to separate and identify substances.
- Know that all types of chromatography have a mobile and a stationary phase.
- Know that, during chromatography, different substances in a mixture may separate based on how long they spend in the mobile or stationary phase.
- Be able to explain how paper chromatography works.
- Understand that a pure substance will only ever form one spot during paper chromatography, regardless of the solvent.
- Know that the ratio between the distance the dissolved substance travels and the distance travelled by the solvent is called the R_f value.
- Know that you can use R_f values to identify the components of a mixture by comparing them with a reference compound.
- Understand that the R_f value of a substance depends on the solvent.
- Be able to interpret chromatograms and calculate R_f values to an appropriate number of significant figures (Required Practical 12).

Specification Reference
5.8.1.3

Theory of Chromatography

Chromatography is an analytical method used to separate the substances in a mixture. You can then use it to identify the substances. There are different types of chromatography, but they all have two 'phases':

- A **mobile phase** — where the molecules can move. This is a liquid or gas.
- A **stationary phase** — where the molecules can't move. This can be a solid or a really thick liquid.

During a chromatography experiment, the substances in the sample constantly move between the mobile and the stationary phases — an equilibrium is formed between the two phases. The mobile phase moves through the stationary phase, and anything dissolved in the mobile phase moves with it. How quickly a chemical moves depends on how it's 'distributed' between the two phases — whether it spends more time in the mobile or stationary phase.

The components in a mixture will normally separate through the stationary phase, so long as all the components spend different amounts of time in the mobile phase. In paper chromatography, the number of spots formed may change in different solvents. This is because the distribution of some chemicals (how long they spend in each phase) may be the same in some solvents but different in others. A pure substance will only ever form one spot in any solvent as there is only one substance in the sample.

Theory of paper chromatography

During paper chromatography the stationary phase is the chromatography paper (often filter paper) and the mobile phase is the solvent (e.g. ethanol or water). The amount of time the molecules spend in each phase depends on:

1. How soluble they are in the solvent.
2. How attracted they are to the paper.

Molecules with a higher solubility in the solvent, and which are less attracted to the paper, will spend more time in the mobile phase — and they'll be carried further up the paper.

R_f values   REQUIRED PRACTICAL 12

The result of a chromatography experiment is called a chromatogram. Each substance on a chromatogram has an **R_f value**. This is the ratio between the distance travelled by the dissolved substance (from the baseline to the centre of the spot — see Figure 1) and the distance travelled by the solvent. The further through the stationary phase a substance moves, the larger the R_f value. You can calculate R_f values using the formula:

$$R_f \text{ value} = \frac{\text{distance travelled by substance } (B)}{\text{distance travelled by solvent } (A)}$$

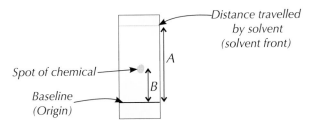

Figure 1: A chromatogram for paper chromatography.

Tip: There's more on how to carry out paper chromatography on page 35. If you do carry one out, then make sure you do a risk assessment first.

Example

A finished chromatogram is shown below. The solvent travelled 7.0 cm up the paper and the substance travelled 2.8 cm.

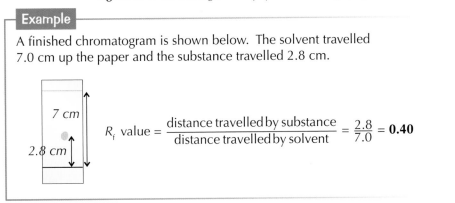

$$R_f \text{ value} = \frac{\text{distance travelled by substance}}{\text{distance travelled by solvent}} = \frac{2.8}{7.0} = \mathbf{0.40}$$

Tip: The chromatogram on the left only shows one spot, so it could be a <u>mixture</u> that hasn't separated in this solvent, or it could be a <u>pure substance</u>.

Tip: To find the distance travelled by the substance you need to measure from the <u>baseline</u> (which should be the centre of the spot of the original mixture) to the <u>centre</u> of the spot of the substance that's separated out.

Identifying substances using chromatography

Chromatography is often carried out to see if a certain substance is present in a mixture. To do this, you run a pure sample of that substance (a reference) alongside the unknown mixture. If the R_f values of the reference and one of the spots in the mixture match, the substance may be present (although you haven't yet proved they're the same).

Example

Chromatography was carried out on a reference dye and an ink at the same time. The chromatogram is shown below. The reference dye is the substance on the left, the ink is the substance on the right.

A = 10.0 cm
B = 4.0 cm
C = 7.0 cm
D = 4.0 cm

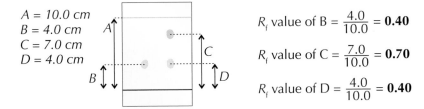

R_f value of B = $\frac{4.0}{10.0}$ = **0.40**

R_f value of C = $\frac{7.0}{10.0}$ = **0.70**

R_f value of D = $\frac{4.0}{10.0}$ = **0.40**

As the R_f values of B and D are the same, you can suggest that the reference dye may be in the ink. However, this isn't proof that B and D are the same substance, as other dyes may have the same R_f value in this solvent.

Tip: Make sure you use a pencil to draw the baseline and solvent front lines — ink might run into the solvent.

Tip: Remember to round your R_f values to the lowest number of significant figures that the distances are measured to. So, for example, if the distance travelled by the substance is given to 2 s.f. and the distance travelled by the solvent is given to 3 s.f., the R_f value needs to be given to 2 s.f..

The R_f value is dependent on the solvent — if you change the solvent the R_f value for a substance will change. You can test both the mixture and the reference in different solvents. If the R_f value of the reference compound matches the R_f value of one of the spots in the mixture in all the solvents, then it's likely the reference compound is present in the mixture. If the spots in the mixture and the spot in the reference only have the same R_f value in some of the solvents, then the reference compound isn't present in the mixture.

Figure 2: *A paper chromatography experiment using water as a solvent (left beaker) and ethanol (right beaker). The dyes have different R_f values due to the different solvents.*

Example

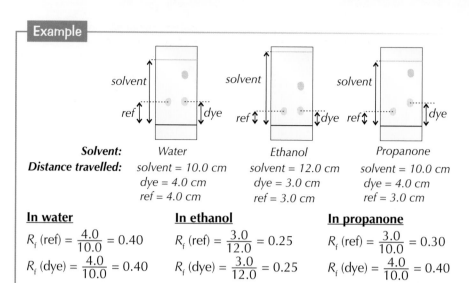

Solvent:	Water	Ethanol	Propanone
Distance travelled:	solvent = 10.0 cm	solvent = 12.0 cm	solvent = 10.0 cm
	dye = 4.0 cm	dye = 3.0 cm	dye = 4.0 cm
	ref = 4.0 cm	ref = 3.0 cm	ref = 3.0 cm

In water

$$R_f \text{ (ref)} = \frac{4.0}{10.0} = 0.40$$

$$R_f \text{ (dye)} = \frac{4.0}{10.0} = 0.40$$

In ethanol

$$R_f \text{ (ref)} = \frac{3.0}{12.0} = 0.25$$

$$R_f \text{ (dye)} = \frac{3.0}{12.0} = 0.25$$

In propanone

$$R_f \text{ (ref)} = \frac{3.0}{10.0} = 0.30$$

$$R_f \text{ (dye)} = \frac{4.0}{10.0} = 0.40$$

The R_f values of the reference and the dye are the same in both water and ethanol. However in propanone, the reference and the dye have different R_f values — this means that they are not the same substance and the reference dye isn't in the ink.

Practice Questions — Fact Recall

Q1 In chromatography, what's the name of the phase which can't move?

Q2 What conditions affect how long molecules are in the mobile phase?

Practice Questions — Application

Q1 On a chromatogram, a solvent travelled 12.3 cm and a substance travelled 6.9 cm. Calculate the R_f value of the substance.

Q2 A red spot and a blue spot are on a chromatogram. The R_f value of the red substance is 0.77, the blue substance has an R_f value of 0.52.

a) Which substance has travelled furthest up the chromatogram?

b) Which substance spent the most time in the mobile phase?

Q3 A student used paper chromatography to analyse a substance in 5 different solvents. In each solvent only one spot appeared. The R_f value of the spot was different in each solvent.

a) Make a prediction about the purity of this substance.

b) Give reasons why the R_f value of the spots were different.

Q4 A student analysed a chromatogram of a mixture containing three substances. A red spot was 3.5 cm from the baseline, a purple spot was 4.7 cm from the baseline and a yellow spot had travelled 5.3 cm. The solvent had travelled 8.3 cm.

a) Calculate the R_f values of the red, purple and yellow substances.

b) The student thinks that the purple substance is methyl violet. Suggest how she could investigate whether she is correct.

Exam Tip
R_f values are <u>always</u> less than 1. So if you get an answer that's greater than 1 you need to go back and do the calculation again — you'll have made a mistake somewhere.

3. Tests for Common Gases

Learning Objective:

- Know how to carry out tests for chlorine, oxygen, hydrogen and carbon dioxide and be able to identify positive results.

Specification Reference 5.8.2

Many reactions you'll come across release gases as a product. Identifying these gases can be a useful way of telling if a particular reaction occurred.

Test for chlorine

Chlorine (Cl_2) bleaches damp litmus paper, turning it white (it may turn red for a moment first though — that's because a solution of chlorine is acidic.)

Chlorine gas

Damp litmus paper turning white when in contact with chlorine.

Figure 1: *Testing for chlorine gas.*

Tip: Make sure you wear appropriate safety protection and carry out a risk assessment before doing any of these tests.

Test for oxygen

To test for oxygen, put a glowing splint inside a test tube containing the gas. If oxygen is present it will relight the glowing splint — see Figure 2.

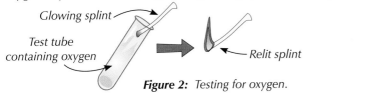

Glowing splint

Test tube containing oxygen

Relit splint

Figure 2: *Testing for oxygen.*

Test for hydrogen

If you hold a lit splint at the open end of a test tube containing hydrogen, you'll get a "squeaky pop". (The noise comes from the hydrogen burning quickly with the oxygen in the air to form H_2O.)

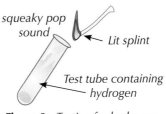

squeaky pop sound

Lit splint

Test tube containing hydrogen

Figure 3: *Testing for hydrogen.*

Figure 4: *A lit splint being used to test whether or not the gas produced by a reaction is hydrogen.*

Test for carbon dioxide

If you make a solution of calcium hydroxide in water (called limewater) and bubble gas through it, the solution will turn cloudy if there's carbon dioxide in the gas. The cloudiness is caused by the formation of calcium carbonate.

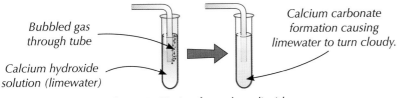

Bubbled gas through tube

Calcium hydroxide solution (limewater)

Calcium carbonate formation causing limewater to turn cloudy.

Figure 5: *Testing for carbon dioxide.*

Practice Questions — Application

Q1 The thermal decomposition of calcium carbonate results in the production of carbon dioxide and calcium oxide. Describe how you could test that this reaction was occurring.

Q2 A student places a glowing splint into a test tube containing a gas. The splint relights. Suggest the identity of the gas in the test tube.

Figure 6: *A test tube containing limewater. It has turned cloudy due to the presence of CO_2 in the gas being bubbled through it.*

Topic Checklist — Make sure you know...

Purity and Formulations

☐ That in everyday language, a pure substance is something that's had nothing added to it, but that in chemistry a pure substance only contains one compound or element.

☐ That a pure compound has specific melting and boiling points.

☐ That a formulation is a useful mixture with exact amounts of components each with a specific function.

☐ That formulations include paints, cleaning agents, medicines, alloys, fertilisers, fuels and foods.

Analysing Paper Chromatography

☐ That chromatography is used as an analytical and separation technique.

☐ That chromatography always includes a mobile and a stationary phase.

☐ How substances are separated based on how long they spend in the mobile or stationary phase.

☐ That during paper chromatography a pure substance will only ever produce one spot on the chromatogram in any solvent.

☐ That the R_f value is the ratio between the distance that a dissolved substance travels and the distance travelled by the solvent.

☐ How to calculate the R_f value of a spot on a chromatogram to an appropriate number of significant figures.

☐ That R_f values can be used to analyse the components of a mixture by comparison with the R_f values of known compounds.

☐ That R_f values change depending on the solvent.

Tests for Common Gases

☐ How to test for chlorine.

☐ How to test for oxygen.

☐ How to test for hydrogen.

☐ How to test for carbon dioxide.

Exam-style Questions

1   A chemist has samples of four different substances — A, B, C and D. A and B are
gases, C is a liquid and D is a solid.

1.1   The chemist carries out some tests to identify what the gases are.
The results are shown in **Table 1**.

Table 1

Test	Result with A	Result with B
Damp litmus paper is placed in the sample	Litmus paper turns white.	No effect.
A glowing splint is placed in the sample	No effect.	No effect.
A lit splint is held above the sample	No effect.	A popping noise is produced.

Identify substances A and B.

(2 marks)

1.2   The chemist knows the identity of substance D and wants to test how pure her sample
is by investigating its melting point. Outline how the chemist could do this.

(2 marks)

1.3   She also knows the identity of substance C. Suggest how she could investigate the
purity of substance C. How would she know if the sample wasn't very pure?

(2 marks)

2   A chemist carried out paper chromatography on a sample of a reaction mixture
following completion of the reaction. The chromatogram is shown below.

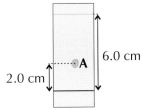

2.1   Calculate the R_f value for the spot, A.

(1 mark)

2.2   Paper chromatography was carried out again but in a different solvent. This time two
spots were produced. What does this suggest about the reaction mixture?

(1 mark)

2.3   Describe how R_f values found in the two different solvents could be used to identify
the components of the reaction mixture.

(2 marks)

Learning Objectives:

- Know that the composition of the atmosphere hasn't changed much in the last 200 million years.

- Know the composition of the atmosphere, including the relative abundances of nitrogen and oxygen.

- Know that one theory suggests that volcanic activity released the gases that formed the early atmosphere (which was mainly carbon dioxide) and also water vapour which condensed to form oceans.

- Know how the level of carbon dioxide in the atmosphere decreased and the level of nitrogen increased.

- Know that coal and limestone are both sedimentary rocks, and how they formed.

- Know how crude oil and natural gas formed.

- Know how the level of oxygen in the atmosphere increased.

- Be able to write the equation for photosynthesis.

- Understand why it is hard to prove theories about how the atmosphere evolved.

- Be able to interpret evidence and evaluate different theories about how the atmosphere evolved.

Specification Reference
5.9.1

1. Evolution of the Atmosphere

The Earth's atmosphere is really important — without it, life as we know it wouldn't have evolved. This is the story of how the atmosphere was formed.

The atmosphere today

The Earth's **atmosphere** has been roughly as it is now for the last 200 million years or so. The main gases in the atmosphere are nitrogen and oxygen. Nitrogen is by far the most abundant gas — about four-fifths (80%) of the atmosphere is nitrogen. About one-fifth (20%) of the atmosphere is oxygen. There are also small amounts of other gases. These include carbon dioxide, water vapour and noble gases (see page 64).

Formation of the early atmosphere and oceans

The Earth's surface was originally molten for many millions of years. It was so hot that any atmosphere just dispersed into space. Eventually things cooled down a bit and a thin crust formed, but volcanoes kept erupting.

There was intense volcanic activity for the first billion years after the Earth was formed, and the volcanoes gave out lots of gas. Scientists think that these gases went on to form the early atmosphere and the oceans. There are lots of different theories, but the most popular theory suggests that the early atmosphere was probably mostly carbon dioxide (CO_2), with virtually no oxygen (O_2). This is quite like the atmospheres of Mars and Venus today. Volcanic activity probably also released nitrogen, which built up in the atmosphere over time, as well as water vapour, and small amounts of methane (CH_4) and ammonia (NH_3).

As the Earth cooled, the water vapour in the atmosphere condensed, forming the oceans.

Decreasing the amount of carbon dioxide

Although the early atmosphere was mostly carbon dioxide, it didn't stay that way for long. Most of the carbon dioxide was gradually removed from the atmosphere. This happened in a number of ways.

Absorption by the oceans

The oceans are a natural store of carbon dioxide. When the oceans formed, a lot of the carbon dioxide from the atmosphere dissolved into them. This dissolved carbon dioxide then went through a series of reactions to form carbonate precipitates that formed sediments on the seabed. When marine animals evolved, their shells and skeletons contained carbonates from the oceans which became trapped when they died (see next page).

Absorption by plants and algae

Green plants and algae evolved over most of the Earth. Algae evolved first — about 2.7 billion years ago. Then over the next billion years or so, green plants also evolved. They absorbed some of the carbon dioxide in the atmosphere and used it for a process called photosynthesis (see below).

Locking away the carbon

When plants, plankton and marine animals die in the oceans, they sink to the seabed and, over time, get buried under layers of sediment. Over millions of years, they become compressed and form sedimentary rocks, oil and gas — trapping the carbon within them and helping to keep carbon dioxide levels in the atmosphere reduced.

Things like coal, crude oil and natural gas that are made by this process are called 'fossil fuels'. Crude oil and natural gas are formed from deposits of plankton and form reservoirs under the seabed. Coal is a sedimentary rock made from thick plant deposits.

Limestone is also a sedimentary rock. It's mostly made of calcium carbonate deposits from the shells and skeletons of marine organisms. A lot of the carbon from the carbon dioxide in the early atmosphere is now locked away in limestones.

Tip: There's more about the formation and separation of crude oil on pages 191-192.

Figure 1: *Limestone containing the fossilised remains of early marine organisms.*

Increasing the amount of oxygen

As well as absorbing the carbon dioxide in the atmosphere, green plants and algae produced oxygen by photosynthesis — this is when plants use light to convert carbon dioxide and water into sugars:

$$\text{carbon dioxide} + \text{water} \xrightarrow{\text{light}} \text{glucose} + \text{oxygen}$$

$$6CO_2 + 6H_2O \xrightarrow{\text{light}} C_6H_{12}O_6 + 6O_2$$

As oxygen levels built up in the atmosphere over time, more complex life (like animals) could evolve. Eventually, about 200 million years ago, the atmosphere reached a composition similar to what it is today.

Exam Tip
Make sure you learn the word equation and the symbol equation for photosynthesis. You could be asked about either in the exam.

Evidence for the evolution of the atmosphere

The problem with coming up with a theory for how the atmosphere evolved is the time scale over which it happened. The atmosphere evolved over about 4.6 billion years, so there's very little evidence left that scientists can use to work out what the atmosphere was originally like, and how it changed to become what it is today.

This means that there are lots of theories about how the atmosphere evolved — the one you've read about is just one of them.

Even though there are no records of what the atmosphere used to be like, there are things scientists can study to try and work out how it evolved.

Tip: Theories about how the atmosphere evolved have changed as new evidence has been found and as scientists have been able to produce better models to predict how the composition might have changed.

Tip: Looking at data and coming up with a hypothesis that seems to explain that data is an important part of Working Scientifically.

WORKING SCIENTIFICALLY

Examples

- **Evidence from volcanoes:** The gases released by volcanoes today are likely to be similar to those produced when volcanoes were erupting billions of years ago. So this gives evidence about what gases were present in the early atmosphere.

- **Evidence from other planets:** The atmospheres of planets where there isn't life, such as Mars and Venus, can be used to predict what Earth's atmosphere might have been like before life evolved.

- **Evidence from rocks:** Certain rocks, called 'red beds' contain lots of iron oxide. The iron oxide in these red beds could only have formed when there was enough oxygen in the atmosphere to react with the iron. So the age of red beds can be used to predict the point at which oxygen levels reached a certain level in the atmosphere.

- **Evidence from living things:** Some simple organisms, such as early bacteria, don't rely on reactions that use oxygen to release energy. Instead they use other gases, such as carbon dioxide. Fossils of these bacteria have been found which are older than fossils of creatures that depend on oxygen. This implies that life first evolved without the need for oxygen, so there wasn't much oxygen in the early atmosphere.

Practice Questions — Fact Recall

Q1 What are the approximate percentages of nitrogen and oxygen in the Earth's atmosphere today?

Q2 Describe the likely composition of the Earth's early atmosphere.

Q3 Why did the evolution of green plants and algae lead to a decrease in the concentration of carbon dioxide in the atmosphere?

Q4 What type of rock is limestone, and how is it formed?

Practice Question — Application

Q1 This graph shows how the composition of gases in the atmosphere may have changed over the last 4.5 billion years.

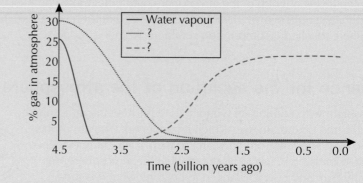

a) Describe and explain the change in the concentration of water vapour in the atmosphere between 4.5 and 4 billion years ago.

b) The other two lines on the graph are not labelled. Suggest which gases these lines represent, giving reasons for your answers.

2. Greenhouse Gases & Climate Change

Some of the gases in the atmosphere help to keep Earth warm, which is great. But if their concentrations get too high, they can cause the climate to change.

What are greenhouse gases?

Greenhouse gases like carbon dioxide, methane and water vapour act like an insulating layer in the Earth's atmosphere — this, amongst other factors, keeps the Earth warm enough to support life. Here's how it works...

All particles absorb certain frequencies of radiation. The sun emits short wavelength radiation which passes through the Earth's atmosphere, as it isn't absorbed by greenhouse gases. The short wavelength radiation reaches the Earth's surface, is absorbed, and then re-emitted as long wavelength radiation. This radiation is absorbed by greenhouse gases in the atmosphere. The greenhouse gases then re-radiate it in all directions — including back towards the Earth. The longwave radiation is thermal radiation, so it results in the warming of the surface of the Earth. This is the **greenhouse effect**.

Short wavelength radiation from the Sun.

Some long wavelength (thermal) radiation emitted by the Earth is absorbed by greenhouse gases and re-radiated in all directions.

Some long wavelength radiation emitted by the Earth escapes.

Figure 1: The greenhouse effect.

Human activity and greenhouse gases

Over the last 150 years or so, the world's human population has shot up and we've become more industrialised. Both of these factors mean that we've been burning more and more fossil fuels. And this means that carbon, that was 'locked up' in the fuels, has been released into the atmosphere. We've also been chopping down forests which used to absorb carbon dioxide by photosynthesis. So, overall, we're adding more carbon dioxide to the atmosphere and less is being removed from it.

The increasing global population also means more food needs to be produced, and this has led to methane levels rising. For example, cows produce large amounts of methane (from both ends) and paddy fields, in which rice is grown, kick out a fair bit of it too. More people also means more waste is produced, much of which ends up in landfill sites. Some of this waste breaks down and releases carbon dioxide and methane.

It's thought that these human activities, as well as others, have caused a rise in greenhouse gas concentrations in the atmosphere. This enhances the greenhouse effect as more thermal radiation is absorbed and radiated back towards Earth, which causes Earth to get warmer — this is **global warming**.

Learning Objectives:

- Know that greenhouse gases help to keep Earth warm enough for life and be able to describe how they work.
- Know that methane, carbon dioxide and water vapour are greenhouse gases.
- Be able to give examples of human activities that increase the levels of greenhouse gases in the atmosphere.
- Know that many scientists believe that increases in the temperature of the Earth are linked to human activities, and that this will cause climate change.
- Be able to evaluate given evidence about climate change and describe possible uncertainties in the evidence.
- Understand why it is difficult to model and predict climate change.
- Be able to describe why peer review and communication of results is important.
- Be able to describe some of the possible consequences of climate change, and be able to discuss the scale and risk of these consequences.

Specification References 5.9.2.1-5.9.2.3

Figure 2: Forests being cut down (deforestation) contributes to the increased level of carbon dioxide in the atmosphere.

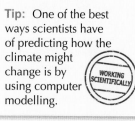

Tip: One of the best ways scientists have of predicting how the climate might change is by using computer modelling.

Tip: Don't get confused. Global warming and climate change aren't the same thing — global warming is a type of climate change.

Figure 3: The change in global sea levels between 1992 and 2014. Areas in blue show where sea levels have gone down. Areas in orange and red show where sea levels have risen.

Carbon dioxide and global warming

Recently, the average temperature at the Earth's surface has been increasing. Even though the Earth's temperature varies naturally, most scientists agree that the extra greenhouse gases from human activity are causing an increase in temperature and that this will lead to **climate change**. Evidence for this has been peer-reviewed (see page 2), so we know that the information out there is reliable.

Unfortunately, it's hard to fully understand the Earth's climate — it's complex, and there are many variables, so it's very hard to make a model that isn't oversimplified. This has led to speculation about what is causing climate change and what impact it might have. This speculation happens a lot in the media — where stories may be biased or only give some of the information.

In general, the more data that's been collected about an aspect of global warming, and the more variables that have been taken into account when designing models, the better quality the predictions will be.

Consequences of climate change

Even though the Earth's climate is complex and difficult to predict, it's still important to try and make predictions about the consequences of climate change. This is so that policy-makers can make decisions now about how to try and prevent climate change, or how to adapt to the consequences of it.

Examples

- An increase in global temperature could lead to polar ice caps and glaciers melting, causing a rise in sea levels, increased flooding in coastal areas and coastal erosion.

- Changes in rainfall patterns (the amount, timing and distribution) may cause some regions to get too much or too little water. This, along with changes in temperature, may affect the ability of certain regions to produce food.

- The frequency and severity of storms may also increase.

- Changes in temperature and the amount of water available in a habitat may affect wild species, leading to differences in their distribution.

Climate change is something that could affect everyone on the planet, so it's important that scientists communicate new evidence to a wide range of people, including governments and the general public. Once people are informed they can decide how to act in response to climate change.

Assessing the risks of climate change

The risks posed by different types of climate change aren't all equal. Here are some things that policy-makers need to consider:

- **How many people might be affected:** Some changes will affect fewer people than others. For example, people living inland are unlikely to be affected by coastal erosion. However, if the climate in a region that's important for global food production changes so that crops can no longer be grown, millions of people may be affected.

- **What impact the change could have:** Some changes have short-term impacts. For example, more severe blizzards may disrupt transport links, but things will return to normal once the snow melts again. However, some things aren't so reversible. For example, rising sea levels could permanently flood towns or cities close to the sea.

> **Tip:** There's more about assessing risks on pages 7-8.

Practice Questions — Fact Recall

Q1 Explain how greenhouse gases help to keep the Earth warm.

Q2 State two ways that human activity is leading to an increase in methane in the atmosphere.

Q3 Explain why there are uncertainties in predictions made about climate change.

Q4 a) What is global warming?

b) Global warming may lead to climate change.
   Suggest one consequence of climate change.

Q5 State two things policy-makers should think about when assessing the risks of a potential change in the climate.

Learning Objectives:
- Know what a carbon footprint is.
- Be able to describe actions that can be taken to reduce carbon footprints.
- Be able to describe some of the reasons why actions to reduce carbon footprints may be limited.

Specification Reference
5.9.2.4

3. Carbon Footprints

Carbon footprints sound jazzy, but they're just a measure of the greenhouse gas emissions caused by something. So not that jazzy, but very useful.

What are carbon footprints?

Carbon footprints are basically a measure of the amount of carbon dioxide and other greenhouse gases that are released over the full life cycle of something. That can be a service (e.g. the school bus), an event (e.g. the Olympics), a product (e.g. a toastie maker) — almost anything.

Measuring the total carbon footprint of something can be really hard, though — or even impossible. That's because there are so many different factors to consider. For example, you would have to count the emissions released from sourcing all the parts of your toastie maker, and in making it, not to mention the emissions produced when you actually use it and finally dispose of it.

Still, a rough calculation can give a good idea of what the worst emitters are, so that people can avoid them in the future.

Tip: Carbon footprints might sound like they only measure carbon dioxide emissions, but don't forget they include other greenhouse gases, like methane, as well.

Reducing carbon footprints

You can try to reduce a carbon footprint. Many methods involve finding ways to reduce emissions of carbon dioxide or methane.

- Lots of carbon dioxide emissions come from burning fossil fuels, so one way to reduce emissions is to use renewable energy sources or nuclear energy instead. Another way is to develop more efficient processes that use less energy, so less fossil fuels need to be burnt. Processes that produce less waste could cut greenhouse gas emissions, as some waste decomposes to produce methane gas.

- To encourage people to reduce emissions, governments could tax companies or individuals based on the amount of greenhouse gases they emit. They could also put a cap on emissions of all greenhouse gases that companies make — then sell licences for emissions up to that cap.

> **Examples**
>
> - In the UK, some businesses have to pay tax on the amount of waste they send to landfill.
> - Bills that businesses pay for things such as electricity, natural gas and coal are taxed, in order to encourage them to use more energy-efficient processes.

- There's also technology that captures the carbon dioxide produced by burning fossil fuels before it's released into the atmosphere — it can then be stored deep underground in cracks in the rock such as old oil wells. This is known as carbon capture and storage.

Problems with reducing carbon footprints

It's easy enough saying that we should cut emissions, but actually doing it — that's a different story. For a start, there's a lot of work still to be done on alternative technologies that result in lower carbon dioxide emissions.

A lot of governments are also worried that introducing taxes or caps on greenhouse gas emissions could reduce the economic growth of communities. This is particularly important for countries that are still developing. Because not everyone is willing to make changes, it's hard to make international agreements to reduce emissions. Most countries don't want to sacrifice their economic development if they think that others won't do the same. It's the same for companies too — reducing their carbon footprint can be costly and can lead to reduced profits.

Individuals can reduce their carbon footprint by making changes to their lifestyles. For example, cycling or walking instead of driving, or using more energy efficient appliances will help to reduce greenhouse gas emissions. But it's hard to get people to make changes — they may not want to and there often isn't enough education about why the changes are necessary and how to make them.

Tip: When making decisions, there's more to consider than just scientific evidence. Social, economic and ethical reasoning all play a part as well.

Practice Questions — Fact Recall

Q1 What is a carbon footprint?

Q2 State two things a business could do to reduce its greenhouse gas emissions.

Q3 One way of reducing carbon footprints is by carbon capture and storage. Explain how this works.

Practice Question — Application

Q1 A government is deciding whether or not to introduce a tax on electricity produced by coal-fired power stations.

   a) Explain why this tax may reduce carbon footprints.

   b) Give a reason why the government may decide not to introduce the tax.

Tip: Coal-fired power stations produce a huge amount of carbon dioxide.

Learning Objectives:

- Know that the combustion of fuels produces water and carbon dioxide.

- Be able to describe how carbon monoxide, carbon particles (soot) and unburnt hydrocarbons can be produced when fuels are burned.

- Be able to describe some of the problems associated with particulates in the air.

- Understand why carbon monoxide is toxic and why it is difficult to detect.

- Know that fuels such as coal may contain sulfur as well as carbon and hydrogen.

- Be able to describe how sulfur dioxide and nitrogen oxides can be produced when fuels are burned.

- Be able to use the composition of a fuel to predict what will be produced when it is burned.

- Be able to describe some of the problems caused by sulfur dioxide and oxides of nitrogen, including respiratory problems and acid rain.

**Specification References
5.9.3.1, 5.9.3.2**

4. Air Pollution

Greenhouse gases aren't the only things produced by human activity that are damaging our environment. Burning fossil fuels produces other nasties, too...

Products of combustion

Fossil fuels, such as crude oil and coal, contain hydrocarbons (molecules made up of carbon and hydrogen only). During combustion, the carbon and hydrogen in these compounds are oxidised so that carbon dioxide and water vapour are released into the atmosphere.

When there's plenty of oxygen, all the carbon in the fuel is oxidised to carbon dioxide — this is called complete combustion (see page 189). If there's not enough oxygen, some of the carbon in the fuel isn't completely oxidised — this is called incomplete combustion. Under these conditions, solid particles (called particulates) of soot (carbon) and unburnt fuel are released and carbon monoxide can be produced as well as carbon dioxide and water.

If a fuel contains sulfur impurities, the sulfur will be oxidised to produce sulfur dioxide when the fuel is burnt. Oxides of nitrogen will also form if the fuel burns at a high temperature, for example in internal combustion engines of cars. This is because at very high temperatures, nitrogen and oxygen in the air react with one another.

Problems caused by the products of combustion

Problems with carbon particulates

Particulates in the air can cause all sorts of problems. If particulates are inhaled, they can get stuck in the lungs and cause damage. This can then lead to respiratory problems. They're also bad for the environment — they reflect sunlight back into space and help to produce more clouds. This means that less light reaches the Earth — causing **global dimming**.

Problems with carbon monoxide

It's not just particulates from incomplete combustion that cause problems. Carbon monoxide is pretty nasty too. Carbon monoxide is really dangerous because it can stop your blood from doing its proper job of carrying oxygen around the body. It does this by binding to the haemoglobin in your blood that normally carries oxygen — so less oxygen is able to be transported round your body. A lack of oxygen in the blood can lead to fainting, a coma or even death. Carbon monoxide doesn't have any colour or smell, so it's very hard to detect. This makes it even more dangerous.

Acid rain

When sulfur dioxide or oxides of nitrogen mix with the water in the clouds, they react with water to form sulfuric acid or nitric acid. This then falls as acid rain (see Figure 1).

Tip: Oxides of nitrogen include nitrogen oxide (NO) and nitrogen dioxide (NO_2).

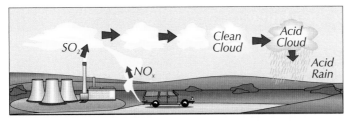

Figure 1: The formation of acid rain.

Acid rain causes lakes to become acidic and many plants and animals die as a result. Acid rain also kills trees (see Figure 2), damages limestone buildings and ruins some stone statues (see Figure 3). Links between acid rain and human health problems have also been suggested.

Breathing problems

Sulfur dioxide and nitrogen oxides don't only cause acid rain — they can also be bad for human health. This is because they cause respiratory problems if they're breathed in.

Practice Questions — Fact Recall

Q1 a) What two products are formed when a hydrocarbon fuel is completely combusted?

b) What other substances may be released if a hydrocarbon fuel undergoes incomplete combustion?

Q2 What gas other than carbon dioxide and water vapour will be formed if a fuel containing sulfur impurities is burnt in plenty of oxygen?

Q3 Under what conditions will nitrogen oxides form when a hydrocarbon fuel is burned?

Q4 a) Name two gases that can cause acid rain.

b) Give two ways in which acid rain can damage the environment.

Practice Questions — Application

Q1 A study by scientists at a local weather station has shown that over the last 50 years, the amount of sunlight reaching the weather station has decreased. Suggest a possible explanation for this finding.

Q2 The composition of two fuels is shown below:

Fuel A: 80% carbon, 12% hydrogen, 8% sulfur

Fuel B: 72% carbon, 10% hydrogen, 18% sulfur

Which fuel would be the better choice to use in a car in order to reduce the chance of acid rain? Give a reason for your answer.

Tip: You can test for sulfur impurities in a fuel by bubbling the gases from combustion through a solution containing Universal indicator. If the fuel contains sulfur, the gases will contain sulfur dioxide which will react with the water to form sulfuric acid. This will turn the Universal indicator red.

Figure 2: Trees that have been killed by acid rain.

Figure 3: A statue that has been damaged by acid rain.

Tip: Incomplete combustion can also be called partial combustion.

Exam Tip
You can tell from what's in a fuel what pollutants could be produced when it's burned. If it only contains carbon and hydrogen, carbon dioxide, carbon particles, carbon monoxide and oxides of nitrogen could be made. If it also contains sulfur, you could get sulfur dioxide as well.

Topic Checklist — Make sure you know...

Evolution of the Atmosphere

☐ That Earth's atmosphere contains roughly 80% nitrogen and 20% oxygen, and has had this composition for approximately 200 million years.

☐ That Earth's early atmosphere was probably formed from gases released from volcanoes, and was made up mainly of carbon dioxide, as well as water vapour, nitrogen, methane and ammonia.

☐ That the oceans formed when water vapour condensed from the atmosphere.

☐ How the level of carbon dioxide in the atmosphere decreased.

☐ How sedimentary rocks and fossil fuels formed, and how they 'lock away' carbon.

☐ That photosynthesis by plants increased the level of oxygen in the atmosphere, and the equation for this reaction.

☐ That it's difficult to know for sure how the atmosphere evolved, as the time scale was so long.

Greenhouse Gases & Climate Change

☐ How greenhouse gases such as carbon dioxide, methane and water vapour keep Earth warm.

☐ Examples of human activities that are leading to an increase in the amounts of carbon dioxide and methane in the atmosphere, and that these are causing the Earth to get warmer.

☐ How the climate might change if Earth's temperature increases.

☐ How to evaluate evidence about climate change, and discuss possible uncertainties in the evidence.

Carbon Footprints

☐ That a carbon footprint is a measure of the amount of greenhouse gases that something produces.

☐ Ways that carbon footprints can be reduced.

☐ Why governments, businesses or individuals may be unwilling to reduce their carbon footprint.

Air Pollution

☐ That most fuels contain hydrogen and carbon, and that some may contain sulfur impurities.

☐ That all combustion reactions produce carbon dioxide and water and that incomplete combustion of fuels can also produce carbon monoxide and solid particulates.

☐ That the combustion of fuels containing sulfur impurities can produce sulfur dioxide.

☐ That the high temperatures involved in combustion reactions can cause nitrogen and oxygen from the air to react and produce oxides of nitrogen.

☐ That carbon monoxide is a toxic gas which is difficult to detect and stops the body from transporting oxygen properly, and that carbon particulates can cause breathing problems and global dimming.

☐ The problems caused by sulfur dioxide and oxides of nitrogen.

Exam-style Questions

1   The composition of the Earth's atmosphere has changed a lot over the last 4.5 billion years.

1.1   Name the gas that is most abundant in our atmosphere today.

(1 mark)

1.2   Where did the gases that formed the early atmosphere come from?

(1 mark)

Scientists think that the most abundant gas in the atmosphere 4.5 billion years ago was carbon dioxide. Now, there is very little carbon dioxide in our atmosphere.

1.3   Give two reasons why the concentration of carbon dioxide in the atmosphere decreased to the level that it is at today.

(2 marks)

1.4   The burning of fossil fuels is now causing the concentration of carbon dioxide in the atmosphere to rise again. Give one environmental impact that an increased level of carbon dioxide in the atmosphere may cause.

(1 mark)

2   A cattle farm wishes to reduce its carbon footprint.

2.1   The biggest contributor to the carbon footprint of the farm is methane gas. Suggest why this is.

(1 mark)

2.2   Suggest two things the farm could do to reduce its carbon footprint.

(2 marks)

2.3   Other farms in the area are not trying to reduce their carbon footprints. Explain why this might disadvantage the original farm.

(1 mark)

2.4   The farm has a generator that runs off a hydrocarbon fuel. The farmer notices that a layer of soot has formed around the generator. Explain how this soot might have formed, and how soot formed in this way can affect health and the environment if it gets into the atmosphere.

(3 marks)

2.5   The process that causes soot to form can also result in the production of a harmful gas. State what this gas is and explain why it can be harmful to health.

(2 marks)

1. Resources and Sustainability

Learning Objectives:
- Know what natural resources are used for and know that some have been replaced by synthetic alternatives or enhanced by agriculture.
- Know what renewable and finite resources are and be able to use data to determine whether a resource is finite or renewable.
- Know what sustainable development is and how chemistry can improve sustainability.
- Know that many everyday products are made from finite resources and understand the environmental impacts of extracting and processing these resources.
- Know that lots of the energy used to extract and process raw materials comes from finite resources.
- Know how the sustainability of finite resources can be improved.
- H Know that there are a limited supply of copper-rich ores and be able to describe methods of extracting copper from low-grade ores, such as bioleaching and phytomining and analyse them given information.

Specification References
5.10.1.1, 5.10.1.4,
5.10.2.2

Natural resources are what keeps mankind going. There are loads of different types of resources providing energy, shelter and food.

Natural resources

Natural resources form without human input. They include anything that comes from the earth, sea or air. We use them to provide energy for things like heating or travelling, as well as for building materials and food. For example, wind is a natural resource used to generate electricity by wind turbines and metals mined from the ground can be used to make metallic objects. Some of these natural products can be replaced by synthetic products.

> **Examples**
>
> - Rubber is extracted from the sap of a tree, however man-made polymers have now been made which can replace rubber in uses such as tyres.
>
> - Wood has been replaced by plastics in many applications. For example, laminate flooring is composed of a polymer resin and a man-made wood composite. Window frames are now mainly made from uPVC (a polymer).
>
> - Cork is produced from the bark of a tree and can be used as a wine stopper. Synthetic corks, made of plastics, are now often used in place of natural cork to prevent tainting of the wine by a chemical found in the bark.

Agriculture provides conditions where natural resources can be enhanced for our needs. For example, the development of fertilisers has meant we can produce a high yield of crops.

Renewable and finite (non-renewable) resources

Renewable resources can be re-formed at a similar rate to, or faster than, we use them. For example, timber is a renewable resource as trees can be planted following a harvest and only take a few years to regrow. Other examples of renewable resources include vegetable crops and sustainably caught fish.

Finite (non-renewable) resources can't be formed quickly enough to be considered replaceable. Finite resources include fossil fuels and nuclear fuels such as uranium and plutonium. Minerals and metals found in ores in the earth are also non-renewable materials. After they've been extracted, many finite resources undergo man-made processes to provide fuels and materials necessary for modern life. For example, fractional distillation (see p.191) is used to produce usable products such as petrol from crude oil, and metal ores are reduced to produce a pure metal (see p.137-138).

Interpreting resource use

You may be asked to interpret information about a resource from information in a graph, chart or table.

Example

The table below shows information for two resources, coal and timber. You can use the information in the table, and your own knowledge of renewable resources to distinguish which is which.

	Energy density (MJ/m³)	Time it takes to form
Resource 1	7 600 – 11 400	10 years
Resource 2	23 000 – 26 000	10^6 years

The time is takes for Resource 1 to form is 10^5 times shorter than Resource 2 and on a human time frame. This suggests that Resource 2 is a non-renewable resource. Resource 1 is also a far less energetic fuel than Resource 2, so is more likely to be timber than coal.

Resource 1 is timber and Resource 2 is coal.

> **Tip:** 10^6 is a shorthand way of showing 1 000 000. This is because $10^6 = 10 \times 10 \times 10 \times 10 \times 10 \times 10 =$ 1 000 000.

Sustainable development

Sustainable development is an approach to development that takes account of the needs of present society while not damaging the lives of future generations.

Finite resources and sustainability

Many modern materials are made from raw, finite resources, for example most plastics, metals and building materials.

As finite resources run out it's unsustainable to keep using them. Furthermore, extracting resources can be unsustainable due to the amount of energy used and waste produced. Processing the resources into useful materials, such as glass or bricks, can be unsustainable too, as the processes often use energy that's made from finite resources. So people have to balance the social, economic and environmental effects of extracting finite resources.

Example

Mining metal ores is good because useful products can be made. It also provides local people with jobs and brings money into the area. However, mining ores is bad for the environment as it uses loads of energy, scars the landscape, produces lots of waste and destroys habitats.

One way of reducing the use of finite resources is for people to use less. This doesn't just reduce the use of that resource but also anything needed to produce it. Recycling often uses far less energy than is required to extract finite resources and helps stop the raw material from being used up. Reusing an object saves even more energy as no processing is required.

> **Tip:** There's more about reusing and recycling on page 222.

Chemistry and sustainability

We can't stop using finite resources altogether, but chemists can develop and adapt processes in industry and agriculture so that we use lower amounts of finite resources and reduce damage to the environment. For example, chemists have developed catalysts that reduce the amount of energy required for certain industrial processes.

Sustainability of copper   Higher

The supply of copper-rich ores is limited and the demand for copper is growing — this could lead to shortages in the future. To help with this, scientists are developing new ways of extracting copper from low-grade ores (ores that only contain small amounts of copper) or from the waste that is produced when copper is extracted. Using traditional methods to extract copper from these low-grade ores is expensive. Examples of new methods to extract copper from low-grade ores are **bioleaching** and **phytomining**.

Bioleaching

Bioleaching uses bacteria which convert copper compounds in the ore into soluble copper compounds, separating out the copper from the ore in the process. The leachate (the solution produced by the process) contains copper ions, which can be extracted, for example by electrolysis or displacement with a more reactive metal. Scrap iron is often used to displace copper from these solutions as it's cheap and reduces the amount of scrap iron going to landfill.

> **Tip:** There's more information about electrolysis (p.145-146) and displacement (p.135-136) in Topic 4.

Phytomining

Phytomining involves growing plants in soil that contains copper. The plants can't use or get rid of the copper so it gradually builds up in the leaves. The plants can be harvested, dried and burned in a furnace. The ash contains copper compounds from which copper can be extracted by electrolysis or displacement using scrap iron.

> **Tip:** H The ash produced by phytomining contains a higher concentration of copper ions than the soil the plants were grown in so it can be extracted in reasonable quantities.

Bioleaching and phytomining — pros and cons

Traditional methods of copper mining are pretty damaging to the environment. These new methods of extraction are cheap and have a much smaller environmental impact. For example, they require less energy which is good for the environment because energy use often contributes to climate change and other environmental problems. The low-grade ores used don't need to be mined in the same ways as high-grade ores, which protects habitats as large amounts of earth don't need to be dug up, shifted and disposed of in order to obtain the ores. The disadvantage of these new extraction methods is that they're slow. For example, in phytomining it takes a long time for plants to grow and take up copper.

> **Tip:** H Bioleaching and phytomining can be used to extract other metals as well as copper.

Practice Questions — Fact Recall

Q1   Suggest a natural resource which has been replaced by a synthetic alternative.

Q2   What is the definition of a renewable resource?

Q3   Give an example of a finite resource.

Q4   Give one social or economic benefit of mining metals.

Q5   Give two ways recycling helps to reduce the use of finite resources.

Q6   Suggest one way that chemistry contributes to sustainable development.

Q7   The extraction of copper from low-grade ores using bacteria is known as bioleaching. The leachate solution produced from the process contains soluble copper compounds.

   a) The copper can be extracted from the solution by adding scrap iron. What type of reaction does this involve?

   b) Give a benefit of using scrap iron in this reaction.

Figure 1: *Bioleaching of copper sulfide ores at a copper mine.*

Practice Question — Application

Q1   The graph below shows the demand and total supply of two natural resources during a year.

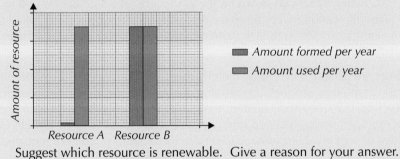

■ *Amount formed per year*
■ *Amount used per year*

Suggest which resource is renewable. Give a reason for your answer.

Learning Objectives:
- Know what it means to reuse or recycle a product.
- Know the advantages of recycling and reusing products.
- Know how metals can be recycled.
- Know how glass can be reused or recycled.
- Be able to analyse methods to reduce the use of resources given information.

Specification Reference
5.10.2.2

2. Reuse and Recycling

As many of the materials we use are from finite resources, finding ways to reduce our consumption of them is important to improving sustainability.

What are reuse and recycling?

Reusing a product can mean using it more than once for the same purpose or putting a used product to a new purpose. For example, glass milk bottles get reused. Recycling involves using waste materials to make new products. For example, yoghurt pots can be melted down and the plastic used to make other products.

Recycling metals

It's important to recycle metals. Here are some reasons why:

- Recycling metals only uses a small fraction of the energy needed to mine and extract new metal. For example, recycling copper takes 15% of the energy that's needed to mine and extract new copper. This is good for the environment because using energy usually has negative environmental impacts. Using less energy also helps to conserve fossil fuels — this is important as they are a finite resource which is running out.

- Energy doesn't come cheap, so recycling saves money too.

- There's a finite amount of each metal in the Earth. Recycling conserves these resources.

- Recycling metal cuts down on the amount of rubbish that gets sent to landfill. Landfill takes up space and pollutes the surroundings. If all the aluminium cans in the UK were recycled, there'd be 14 million fewer dustbins to empty each year.

Tip: Recycling of most materials results in a reduction of waste, fewer finite resources being used and a lower environmental impact due to lower energy consumption.

Metals are usually recycled by melting them and then casting them into the shape of the new product. Depending on what the metal will be used for after recycling, the amount of separation required for recyclable metals can change. For example, waste steel and iron can be kept together as they can both be added to iron in a blast furnace to reduce the amount of iron ore required.

Tip: A blast furnace is used to extract iron from its ore at a high temperature using carbon.

Glass recycling

Reusing or recycling glass can help sustainability by reducing the amount of energy needed to make new glass products, and also the amount of waste created when used glass is thrown away. Glass bottles can often be reused without reshaping. Other forms of glass can't be reused so they're recycled instead. Usually the glass is separated by colour and chemical composition before being recycled. The glass is crushed and then melted to be reshaped for use in glass products such as bottles or jars. It might also be used for a different purpose such as insulating glass wool for wall insulation in homes.

Practice Questions — Fact Recall

Q1 Give two advantages of recycling metals.

Q2 Give an example of a product that can be made from recycled glass bottles.

3. Life Cycle Assessments

Life cycle assessments are becoming increasingly popular with manufacturers as a way to measure the effects of a new product on the environment.

Stages in a life cycle assessment

Life cycle assessments (LCAs) assess the environmental impact of the entire lifetime of a product. The stages of the lifetime of a product can be seen as:

- Getting the raw materials
- Manufacturing and packaging
- Using the product
- Product disposal

At each stage certain factors need to be considered, including the amount of energy that is needed, how much water and other resources are used, the amount of pollution produced, how much waste is formed and how this waste is disposed of.

Getting the raw materials

Extracting raw materials needed for a product can damage the local environment, e.g. mining metals. Extraction can also result in pollution due to the amount of energy needed.

The transportation of raw materials to where they are used in manufacturing can result in greenhouse gas emissions from the combustion of fossil fuels.

Raw materials often need to be processed to extract the desired materials and this often needs large amounts of energy. E.g. extracting metals from ores or fractional distillation of crude oil. There are often large amounts of waste associated with these processes which need to be disposed of.

Manufacturing and packaging

Manufacturing products and their packaging can use a lot of energy resources and can also cause a lot of pollution, e.g. harmful fumes such as carbon monoxide or hydrogen chloride.

The chemical reactions used to make compounds from their raw materials can produce waste products. Some waste can be turned into other useful chemicals, reducing the amount that ends up polluting the environment.

Using the product

The use of a product can damage the environment.

> **Example**
>
> Burning fuels releases greenhouse gases and other harmful substances. Fertilisers can leach into streams and rivers causing damage to ecosystems.

How long a product is used for or how many uses it gets is also a factor considered by LCAs — products that need lots of energy to produce, but are used for ages, may mean less waste and raw materials needed in the long run.

Learning Objectives:

- Know what a life cycle assessment (LCA) is.
- Know what stages of a product's life need to be considered to conduct an LCA.
- Be able to use an LCA to interpret information about the environmental impact of a product.
- Know that some environmental impacts can be quantified but some impacts require judgements, meaning LCAs aren't completely objective.
- Understand that some LCAs may be selective and why these LCAs might be misleading.
- Know how to carry out and compare simple LCAs for bags made of paper and plastic.

Specification Reference 5.10.2.1

Exam Tip
In the exam you may be asked to evaluate the use of different materials for a particular product, using an LCA.

Tip: The environmental impact of transport of materials and the product needs to be considered at each stage of an LCA.

Product disposal

Energy is used to transport waste to landfill, which causes pollutants to be released into the atmosphere. The waste kept in landfill takes up space and can pollute land and water, e.g. if paint peels off a product and gets into rivers. If the material is biodegradable, the space taken up by landfill may only be temporary. However, non-biodegradable materials, such as many plastics, may take up to a thousand years to degrade.

Another way to dispose of products is incineration. This is when waste is burnt at very high temperatures. This cuts down on waste going to landfill and can be used to generate electricity but can cause air pollution.

If all or part of the product can be recycled or reused, that will reduce the amount of waste going to landfill.

Tip: Products that can be made using recycled materials will need fewer raw materials to be manufactured, which improves their life cycle assessment.

Evaluating life cycle assessments

Life cycle assessments can be used to evaluate different products and allow decisions to be made on which product has the least environmental impact.

Exam Tip
You may be asked to interpret LCAs that are based on data only, or that include judgements based on opinion.

Example

A company is carrying out a life cycle assessment to work out which car, A, B or C, it should make. Using the data in the table, explain which car the company should produce to minimise the environmental impact.

Car	A	B	C
CO_2 emissions (tonnes)	17	21	34
Waste solid produced (kg)	10 720	5900	15 010
Water used (m^3)	8.2	6.0	17
Expected lifespan of product (years)	11	17	12

- Car A produces the least CO_2 but produces the second highest amount of waste solids and uses the second highest amount of water. It also has the shortest life span.

- Car B produces more CO_2 than car A, but produces by far the least waste solid, uses the least water and also has the longest life span. On balance, this looks a better choice than car A.

- Car C produces the most CO_2, the most waste solid uses the most water, and has almost as short a life span as car A. This looks like the worst choice. So, on balance, car B looks like the one that will have the least environmental impact.

Problems with life cycle assessments

The use of energy, some natural resources and the amount of certain types of waste produced by a product over its lifetime can be easily quantified. But the effect of some pollutants is harder to give a numerical value to. E.g. it's difficult to apply a value to the negative visual effects of plastic bags in the environment compared to paper ones. So, producing an LCA is not a fully objective method as it takes into account the values of the person carrying out the assessment. This means LCAs can be biased.

Tip: <u>Quantified</u> means to give a numerical value to something.

Selective LCAs only show some of the impacts of a product on the environment. These can also be biased as they can be written to deliberately support the claims of a company, e.g. in order to give them positive advertising.

Tip: Selective LCAs are also known as abbreviated LCAs.

Life cycle assessments for shopping bags

You can conduct simple life cycle assessments comparing plastic and paper shopping bags.

Life Cycle Assessment Stage	Plastic Bag	Paper Bag
Raw Materials	Crude oil	Timber
Manufacturing and Packaging	The compounds needed to make the plastic are extracted from crude oil by fractional distillation, followed by cracking and then polymerisation. Waste is reduced as the other fractions of crude oil have other uses.	Pulped timber is processed using lots of energy. Lots of waste is made.
Using the Product	Can be reused. Can be used for other things as well as shopping, for example bin liners.	Usually only used once.
Product Disposal	Recyclable but not biodegradable and will take up space in landfill and pollute land.	Biodegradable, non-toxic and can be recycled.

Figure 1: Life cycle assessments for a plastic bag and a paper bag.

Figure 2: A paper bag carrying groceries.

Life cycle assessments have shown that even though plastic bags aren't biodegradable, they take less energy to make and have a longer lifespan than paper bags, so they may be less harmful to the environment.

Practice Questions — Application

Q1 A student suggests that life cycle assessments are not objective. Discuss whether he is correct.

Q2 A furniture firm carried out a life cycle assessment to decide whether to make tables out of wood or plastic.

Stage	Wooden Table	Plastic Table
Raw Materials	Timber	Crude oil
Manufacturing and Packaging	Wood is cut and treated using low energy processes.	Fractional distillation, cracking and then polymerisation. Manufacture process uses a high amount of energy.

a) Using the information in table above, explain which table has a smaller environmental impact.

b) Suggest why the information in the table isn't enough to make a full decision on which material has a smaller environmental impact.

Learning Objectives:
- Know what potable water is.
- Know the difference between potable water and pure water.
- Know that how potable water is produced varies depending on location.
- Know that water in the UK generally comes from fresh water sources supplied by rainfall.
- Be able to describe how fresh water is treated to make it potable.
- Know that in dry places, desalination of salt water is used to produce potable water by distillation or processes using membranes.
- Know that desalination of salt water requires lots of energy.
- Be able to analyse and purify water samples (Required Practical 13).

Specification Reference 5.10.1.2

4. Potable Water

Water is vital to life, that's why having potable (drinkable) water for humans is essential. How water is made safe to drink depends upon where you live...

What is potable water?

Potable water is water that's been treated or is naturally safe for humans to drink — it's essential for life. Chemists wouldn't call it pure, though. Pure water only contains H_2O molecules whereas potable water can contain lots of other dissolved substances. The important thing is that the levels of dissolved salts aren't too high, that it has a pH between 6.5 and 8.5 and that there aren't any dangerous bacteria or other microbes swimming around in it.

How potable water is produced in a specific place depends upon on a number of factors. The climate, landscape and cost all play a part in finding ways to obtain drinking water.

Fresh water

Fresh water is water that doesn't have much dissolved in it. Rainwater, a type of fresh water, can either be collected as surface water (in lakes, rivers and reservoirs) or as groundwater (in rocks called aquifers that trap water underground).

In the UK, the vast majority of our water comes from fresh water sources. The source of fresh water chosen used depends on location. Surface water tends to dry up first, so in warm areas, e.g. the south-east, most of the domestic water supply comes from groundwater.

Treatment of fresh water

Even though it only has low levels of dissolved substances, water from fresh water sources still needs to be treated to make it safe before it can be used. This process includes:

1. Filtration — a wire mesh screens out large twigs etc, and then gravel and sand beds filter out any solid bits.

2. Sterilisation — the water is sterilised to kill any harmful bacteria or microbes. This can be done by bubbling chlorine gas through it or by using ozone or ultraviolet light.

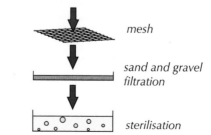

mesh

sand and gravel filtration

sterilisation

Figure 1: *A diagram showing the three main steps of water treatment.*

Tip: Chemicals can also be added to the water supply, such as fluoride (which is good for teeth). This is controversial, because people aren't given any choice over whether they consume them or not.

Sea water

In some dry countries, e.g. Kuwait, there's not enough surface water or ground water so instead sea water must be treated by desalination to provide potable water. Desalination of sea water can be done via distillation or by processes that use membranes — like reverse osmosis.

During reverse osmosis, salty water is passed through a membrane that only allows water molecules to pass through. Ions and larger molecules are trapped by the membrane and so separated from the water.

Both distillation and reverse osmosis need loads of energy, so they're really expensive and not used if there are other sources available.

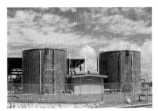

Figure 2: *A desalination plant in Sydney, Australia.*

How to test and distil salt water

Before water can be drunk it must be tested to make sure it's safe. If the water contains high levels of salts it needs to be distilled before it's considered safe to drink. You can carry out testing and distillation in the lab.

First, test the pH of the water using a pH meter. If the pH is too high or too low, you'll need to neutralise it. You do this by adding some acid (if the sample's alkaline) or some alkali (if the sample's acidic) until the pH is 7.

To distil the water, pour the salty water into a distillation apparatus, like the one on p.40. Heat the flask from below. The water will boil and form steam, leaving any dissolved salts in the flask. The steam will condense back to liquid water in the condenser and can be collected as it runs out.

Retest the pH of the water with a pH meter to check it's neutral (has a pH of 7). You can tell whether there were salts in your initial sample by looking to see whether there are any crystals in the round bottomed flask once the water's been distilled.

Figure 3: *A reverse osmosis desalination plant in Israel.*

> **Tip:** Make sure you carry out a risk assessment before carrying out any practical work.

> **Tip:** For more on distillation turn to page 40.

Practice Questions — Fact Recall

Q1   What is potable water?

Q2   State a sterilising agent used in the treatment of fresh water.

Practice Questions — Application

Q1   A student claims that tap water is pure water. Is she correct? Explain your answer.

Q2   Describe the differences in the techniques used to produce potable water in the UK compared to a hot dry country.

- Know that domestic and agricultural waste water is treated to remove organic matter and harmful microbes before being released into the environment.
- Know that industrial waste water may need to have organic matter and harmful chemicals removed during treatment.
- Know that screening, sedimentation, aerobic digestion and anaerobic digestion are stages in sewage treatment.
- Know that treated sewage can be recycled as potable water in areas where fresh water is scarce.
- Be able to describe the relative ease of getting potable water from ground, waste and salt water.

Specification Reference 5.10.1.3

Figure 1: *Sedimentation tanks at a water treatment plant.*

Tip: <u>Aerobic</u> just means with oxygen, whereas <u>anaerobic</u> means without oxygen.

5. Waste Water Treatment

We use water for lots of different purposes but once we've used it we need to make sure it is safe before releasing it back into the natural environment.

Sources of waste water

In the home, we use water for lots of different things — like having a bath, going to the toilet, doing the washing-up, etc. When you flush this water down the drain, it goes into the sewers and towards sewage treatment plants. Agricultural systems also produce a lot of waste water including run-off from fields, which may contain chemicals from fertilisers, and slurry from animal farms. Sewage from domestic or agricultural sources has to be treated to remove any organic matter and harmful microbes before it can be put back into fresh water sources like rivers or lakes. Otherwise it could pollute them and pose health risks.

Industrial processes also produce a lot of waste water that has to be collected and treated. As well as organic matter, industrial waste water can contain harmful chemicals — so it has to undergo additional stages of treatment before it's safe to release into the environment.

Stages of waste water treatment

Screening

Before being treated the sewage is screened — this involves removing any large bits of material (like twigs or plastic bags) as well as any grit.

Sedimentation

The screened waste is allowed to stand in a settlement tank and undergoes sedimentation — the heavier suspended solids sink to the bottom to produce sludge while the less dense effluent floats on the top.

Aerobic digestion

The effluent in the settlement tank is removed and treated by biological aerobic digestion. This is when air is pumped through the water to encourage aerobic bacteria to break down any organic matter — including other microbes in the water.

Anaerobic digestion

The sludge from the bottom of the settlement tank is also removed and transferred into large tanks. Here it gets broken down by bacteria in a process called anaerobic digestion. Anaerobic digestion breaks down the organic matter in the sludge, releasing methane gas in the process. The methane gas can be used as an energy source and the remaining digested waste can be used as a fertiliser.

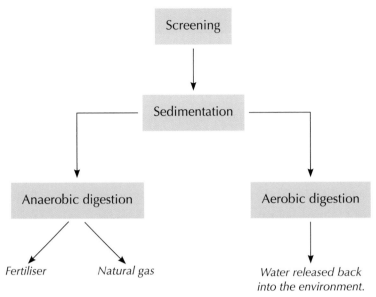

Figure 2: A flow chart showing the stages in sewage treatment.

Figure 3: Anaerobic biodigesters, at a sewage treatment plant in Manchester.

For waste water containing toxic substances, additional stages of treatment may involve adding chemicals (e.g. to precipitate metals), UV radiation or using membranes.

Potable water from waste water

Potable water can be retrieved from waste water using these processes, and could be a viable alternative in areas where there's not much fresh water. For example, Singapore is treating waste water and recycling it back into drinking supplies. Sewage treatment requires more processes than treating fresh water but uses less energy than the desalination of salt water. However, people don't like the idea of drinking water that used to be sewage.

> **Tip:** Most treated waste water is released back into the sea or rivers.

Practice Questions — Fact Recall

Q1 State two types of contaminants that may be present in agricultural waste water.

Q2 State two types of contaminants that may be present in waste water from industrial processes and need to be removed before the water can be released back into the environment.

Q3 Describe what happens during the following stages of waste water treatment.

a) Screening

b) Sedimentation

Q4 State one advantage and one disadvantage of producing potable water from waste water compared to fresh water and sea water.

Topic Checklist — Make sure you know...

Resources and Sustainability

☐ That humans use natural resources for energy, building materials and food but some have been replaced by synthetic alternatives or enhanced by agriculture.

☐ That resources which can replaced at the same, or a faster rate than they are being used are known as renewable resources.

☐ That resources which are being used at a faster rate than they being replenished, so will run out one day, are known as finite resources.

☐ How to interpret graphs, table and charts to work out whether a resource is renewable or finite.

☐ That sustainable development is development that meets the needs of present society while taking into account the needs of future generations.

☐ That many products we use are made from finite resource and that processing and extracting these materials has an environmental impact.

☐ That recycling, reusing and reducing consumption of materials made from finite resources all improve sustainability.

☐ That chemistry can be used to adapt and develop industrial and agricultural processes to contribute to sustainability.

☐ H That supplies of copper-rich ores are limited and traditional extraction techniques are damaging to the environment.

☐ H That new methods of extracting copper from low-grade ores and waste from traditional extraction include bioleaching and phytomining.

Reusing and Recycling

☐ What recycling means and what reusing a product means.

☐ Know the environmental advantages of recycling or reusing a product.

☐ Know how metals and glass are recycled and how glass is reused.

Life Cycle Assessments

☐ What life cycle assessments are and what stages of a product's life they consider.

☐ How to interpret the environmental impact of a product using a life cycle assessment.

☐ That only certain environmental impacts can be quantified as some rely on opinions.

☐ What selective life cycle assessments are and how they may be used to support a company's claims.

☐ How to carry out and compare simple life cycle assessments for bags made out of paper and plastic.

Potable Water

☐ What potable water is and how it is different from pure water.

☐ That in the UK, potable water generally comes from fresh water sources.

cont...

☐ That fresh water is treated by filtration followed by sterilisation.

☐ That in dry places, desalination of salt water can be used to produce potable water by distillation or processes using membranes, and that these processes require lots of energy.

☐ How to analyse and purify water samples.

Waste Water Treatment

☐ That organic matter and harmful microbes need to be removed from agricultural and domestic waste water, and that organic waste and harmful chemicals need to be removed from industrial waste water before the water is released back into the environment.

☐ That sewage treatment includes screening, sedimentation, aerobic digestion and anaerobic digestion.

☐ That waste water can be treated and recycled for use as potable water and how this compares to treating fresh water and salt water.

Exam-style Questions

1 A drinks company conducts two Life Cycle Assessments (LCAs). One is for a drinks bottle made of a material derived from plants. The other is for a drinks bottle made from a polymer derived from crude oil.

   1.1 Suggest **one** way that the extraction and processing of the bottles made from the plant-based material would be more sustainable than the polymer bottle.

(1 mark)

   1.2 Suggest how the sustainability of the polymer bottle could be improved by the consumer.

(1 mark)

   1.3 The drinks company did not consider the manufacturing stage of the production of the bottles. Suggest why this limits any conclusions that could be drawn from the LCA.

(1 mark)

2 This question is on potable water and water treatment.

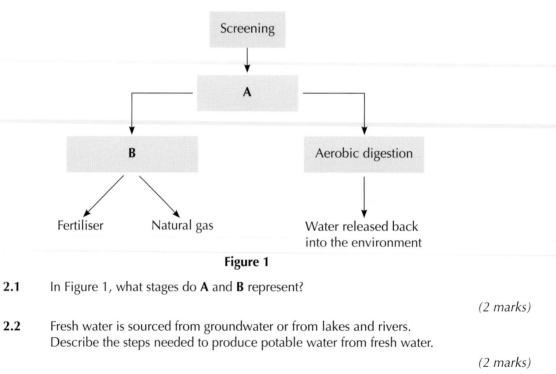

Figure 1

   2.1 In Figure 1, what stages do **A** and **B** represent?

(2 marks)

   2.2 Fresh water is sourced from groundwater or from lakes and rivers.
Describe the steps needed to produce potable water from fresh water.

(2 marks)

   2.3 In certain countries where fresh water is scarce, treated waste water is recycled to produce potable water. Suggest one other possible method of producing water in countries without enough fresh water.

(1 mark)

1. Drawing Equipment

For the chemistry part of GCSE Combined Science, you'll have to do at least six practicals, called Required Practical Activities. You'll also need to know how to use various pieces of apparatus and carry out different scientific techniques. And not only do you need to carry out the practicals and techniques, you could also be asked about them in the exams. Luckily, all the chemistry Required Practical Activities are covered in this book, and the next few pages cover some of the other techniques that you'll need to know about.

Scientific drawings

When you're writing out a method for your experiment, it's always a good idea to draw a labelled diagram showing how your apparatus will be set up. The easiest way to do this is to use a scientific drawing, where each piece of apparatus is drawn as if you're looking at its cross-section. Some basic pieces of equipment that you're likely to need to draw are shown in Figures 1 and 2.

> **Tip:** The Required Practical Activities in this book are marked with a big stamp like this...
>
> REQUIRED PRACTICAL **1**
>
> The practicals that you do in class might be slightly different to the ones in this book (as it's up to your teacher exactly what practicals you do), but they'll cover the same principles and techniques.

> **Tip:** In the scientific drawing of a cell, the longer line is the positive side, and the shorter line is negative.

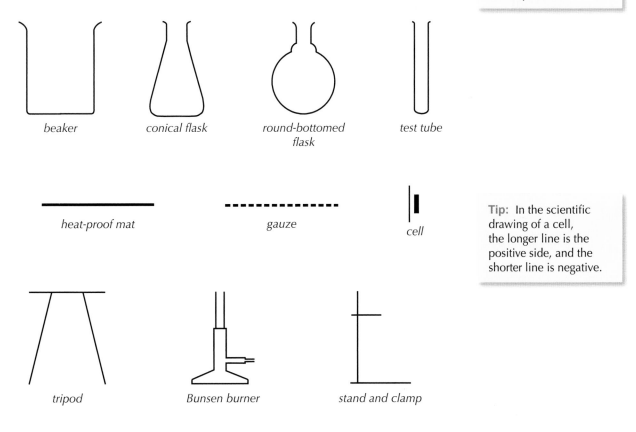

Figure 1: *Scientific diagrams of some basic laboratory equipment.*

Tip: There's more information on using pipettes and measuring cylinders on pages 235-236.

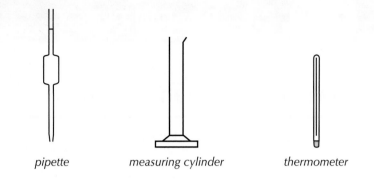

pipette   *measuring cylinder*   *thermometer*

Figure 2: *Scientific diagrams of some more basic laboratory equipment.*

Exam Tip
Always make sure the set-up is drawn correctly in your diagrams. This might mean making sure your diagram shows a closed system if you're collecting a gas, making sure any thermometers are positioned at the right point for where you're measuring the temperatures, or making sure that any equipment with a water flow shows it going in the right direction.

None of the pieces of glassware (such as the conical flask) shown in Figure 1 have been drawn with tops. If you see this, it means that the equipment is open to the air, so things can get in and out. For experiments where the equipment needs to be sealed, make sure that you draw a bung in the top of the flask.

Example

To measure the volume of gas given off in a reaction, the equipment needs to be sealed so no gas can escape, as shown in Figure 3.

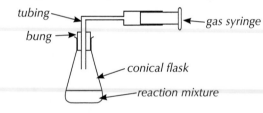

tubing — *gas syringe*
bung —
conical flask
reaction mixture

Figure 3: *Equipment for measuring the volume of gas produced by a reaction.*

2. Measuring Substances

The results of an experiment won't be any good if you don't know how to measure and record things properly. Some of this may seem obvious, but measuring things carefully is key to getting good results.

Measuring the mass of solids

You weigh solids using a balance. To do this you should put the container you are weighing your substance into on the balance, and make sure the balance is set to exactly zero. Then, start weighing out your substance. Once you've measured a quantity of a substance you need to be careful you don't lose any. In particular, think about how to minimise losses if you're transferring the solid from the measuring equipment into another container. For example, if you're dissolving the solid in a solvent to make a solution, you could wash any remaining solid into the new container using the solvent. Or you could reweigh the weighing container after you've transferred the solid so you can work out exactly how much you added to your experiment. The mass you transferred is just the difference between the mass of the weighing container before you transferred the solid, and its mass afterwards.

> **Tip:** If you don't set your mass balance to exactly zero, your results will have 'zero errors' (see page 13).

Measuring the volumes of liquids

There are a few methods you might use to measure the volume of a liquid. Whichever method you use, always read the volume from the bottom of the meniscus (the curved upper surface of the liquid) when it's at eye level (see Figure 1).

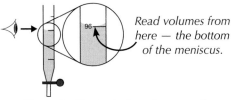

Read volumes from here — the bottom of the meniscus.

Figure 1: *The technique for correctly measuring the volume of a liquid.*

Measuring cylinders

Measuring cylinders are the most common way to measure out a liquid. They come in all different sizes. Make sure you choose one that's the right size for the measurement you want to make. It's no good using a huge 1000 cm³ cylinder to measure out 2 cm³ of a liquid — the graduations will be too big, and you'll end up with massive errors. It'd be much better to use one that measures up to 10 cm³.

Pipettes

Pipettes are long, narrow tubes that are used to suck up an accurate volume of liquid and transfer it to another container. They are often calibrated to allow for the fact that the last drop of liquid stays in the pipette when the liquid is ejected. This reduces transfer errors.

To use a pipette, you'll need to attach a pipette filler to the top. This could be a plastic tube with a wheel that you turn to draw liquid into the pipette (see Figure 2). To release the liquid, either turn the wheel in the opposite direction, or press the quick release lever on the side. Alternatively, it could be a rubber ball with three valves. To use it, press the top valve and squeeze air out of the rubber ball. Then press the valve just below the rubber ball to suck liquid into the pipette. To release liquid, press the valve on the side-arm.

> **Tip:** You could use a pipette to accurately measure out a volume of solution to use in a rate of reaction experiment (see pages 176-177).

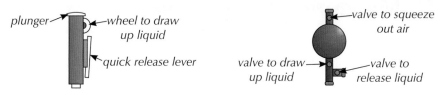

Figure 2: *Different pipette fillers.*

Dropping pipettes

If you only want a couple of drops of liquid and don't need it to be accurately measured, you can use a dropping pipette to transfer it. For example, you'd use a dropping pipette to add indicator to a liquid or solution to test its pH (see page 124).

Figure 3: *A dropping pipette being used to add Universal indicator to an acid.*

Measuring the volumes of gases

There are times when you might want to collect the gas produced by a reaction. When you're measuring a gas, your equipment has to be sealed or gas will escape and your results won't be accurate. You should take all your measurements at the same temperature and pressure, as both these factors affect the volume of a gas. Here are a couple of methods you could use:

Gas syringes

Tip: Gas syringes can be used to follow the rate of a reaction (see page 169-170).

The most accurate way to measure the volume of a gas is with a gas syringe. You should use a gas syringe that's the right size. Before you use the syringe, you should make sure it's completely sealed and that the plunger moves smoothly.

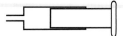

Figure 4: *A scientific diagram of a gas syringe.*

Collecting gases over water

You can collect gases by displacing water from a measuring cylinder. To do this, you should first fill a measuring cylinder with water, and carefully place it upside down in a container of water. Record the initial level of the water in the measuring cylinder. Then position a delivery tube coming from the reaction vessel so that it's inside the measuring cylinder, pointing upwards. Any gas that's produced will pass through the delivery tube and into the measuring cylinder. As the gas enters the measuring cylinder, the water is pushed out. Record the level of water in the measuring cylinder. You can calculate the volume of gas produced by subtracting the final volume of liquid in the measuring cylinder from the initial volume.

Figure 5: *Collecting the gas produced in a reaction by displacing water from a test tube.*

This method is less accurate than using a gas syringe to measure the volume of gas produced. This is because some gases can dissolve in water, so less gas ends up in the measuring cylinder than is actually produced.

If just want to collect a sample to test (and don't need to measure a volume), you can collect it over water as above using a test tube. Once the test tube is full of gas, you can stopper it and store the gas for later.

Measuring temperature

You can use a thermometer to measure the temperature of a substance. Always wait for the temperature to stabilise before taking an initial reading and if you're using a thermometer with a scale, read off your measurement at eye level to make sure it's accurate. Think about where you need to take your measurement from — if you're measuring the temperature of a liquid, the bulb of the thermometer should be submerged in the liquid. If you're measuring the temperature of a gas as it evaporates from a liquid during distillation, then the bulb of your thermometer should be at the outlet of the distillation apparatus (see Figure 6). This is so you know the temperature being measured is the same as the temperature of the substance that is being distilled.

Measuring time

You should use a stopwatch to time experiments. These measure to the nearest 0.1 s so are pretty sensitive. Make sure you start and stop the stopwatch at exactly the right time. For example, if you're investigating the rate of an experiment, you should start timing the moment you mix the reagents and start the reaction. If you're measuring the time taken for a precipitate to form, you should stop timing the moment the reaction goes cloudy.

Measuring pH

You need to be able to decide the best method for measuring pH, depending on what your experiment is. There are two methods you might come across.

Indicators

Indicators are dyes that change colour depending on the pH. You use them by adding a couple of drops of the indicator to the solution you're interested in.

Universal indicator is a mixture of indicators that changes colour gradually as pH changes. It doesn't show a sudden colour change. It's useful for estimating the pH of a solution based on its colour.

Indicators can be soaked into paper and strips of this paper can be used for testing pH. If you use a dropping pipette to spot a small amount of a solution onto some indicator paper, it will change colour depending on the pH of the solution. Indicator paper is useful when you don't want to change the colour of all of the substance. You can also hold a piece of damp indicator paper in a gas sample to test the pH of the solution it forms.

> **Examples**
>
> - Litmus paper is red in acidic conditions and blue in basic conditions.
> - Universal indicator paper can be used to estimate pH based on its colour. It's blue or purple in alkaline conditions, green in neutral conditions and yellow, orange or red in acidic conditions.

pH probes

A pH meter is an electronic gadget that can be used to give a precise and accurate value for the pH of a solution. They're made up of a probe attached to a digital display. You put the probe in the solution you're measuring and read the pH off the display.

Tip: Measuring temperature accurately is important for investigating how different factors affect the temperature change of a reaction (see p.153).

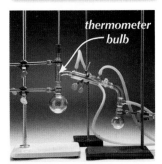

thermometer bulb

Figure 6: *Distillation apparatus. The bulb of the thermometer is level with the outlet to the condenser.*

Tip: There's more about distillation on pages 40-41.

Exam Tip
In the exam, you may have to read a method or look at a diagram of equipment and work out whether an experiment would be valid. Experiments can only be valid if everything's been measured correctly, so make sure you know these measuring techniques.

3. Handling and Mixing Substances

Tip: Being able to plan and carry out experiments safely is a key part of Working Scientifically.

So now you know how to measure things carefully. But that's not the end, I'm afraid. In order to carry out an experiment safely, you also need to know how to handle and mix substances properly. And that's what this page is on.

Handling chemicals

There are lots of hazards in science experiments, so before you start any experiment, you should read any safety precautions to do with your method or the chemicals you're using.

The substances used in chemical reactions are often hazardous. For example, they might catch fire easily (they're flammable), or they might irritate or burn your skin if you come into contact with them. Whenever you're doing an experiment, you should wear a lab coat, safety goggles and gloves. Always be careful that the chemicals you're using aren't flammable before you go lighting any Bunsen burners, and make sure you're working in an area that's well ventilated.

Tip: There's more about safety in experiments on pages 7-8.

If you're doing an experiment that might produce nasty gases (such as chlorine), you should carry out the experiment in a fume hood so that the gas can't escape out into the room you're working in.

Never directly touch any chemicals (even if you're wearing gloves). Use a spatula to transfer solids between containers. Carefully pour liquids between different containers, using a funnel to avoid spillages, and make sure you transfer things below eye level. For example, if you're filling a measuring cylinder, you should place it securely on a surface so that the opening is below your eyes, rather than reaching up to fill it. This reduces the risk of splashing chemicals into your eyes.

Figure 1: Dissolving copper sulfate in water to make a solution.

Mixing chemicals

Be careful when you're mixing chemicals, as a reaction might occur.

Examples

- If you're diluting a liquid, add the concentrated substance to the water (not the other way around) or the mixture could get very hot.

- To dissolve a solid, you should always add the solid to the liquid. Then, to mix the substances properly, you should either use a glass stirrer, or put a bung in the top of the container and carefully invert it a few times. If you're using the second method, make sure the substances don't react to form a gas, or the pressure will build up in the container and the bung could fly off the top.

- If you're carrying out a reaction that involves a catalyst, you should mix the reactants first and then add the catalyst.

4. Heating Substances

If you need to heat a substance, you can't always just hold it over a Bunsen burner until it's the right temperature. The way you heat something depends on how flammable it is and how accurate its final temperature needs to be.

Bunsen burners

Bunsen burners are good for heating things quickly. You can easily adjust how strongly they're heating. But you need to be careful not to use them if you're heating flammable compounds as the flame means the substance would be at risk of catching fire.

To use a Bunsen burner, you should first connect it to a gas tap, and check that the hole is closed. Place it on a heatproof mat. Next, light a splint and hold it over the Bunsen burner. Now, turn on the gas. The Bunsen burner should light with a yellow flame. The more open the hole is, the more strongly the Bunsen burner will heat your substance. Open the hole to the amount you want. As you open the hole more, the flame should turn more blue. Heat things just above the blue cone, as this is the hottest part of the flame.

Tip: Some things take a long time to cool down, and you can't necessarily tell by looking whether they're hot or cold. So, after heating equipment, you should always handle it with tongs so you don't get burnt.

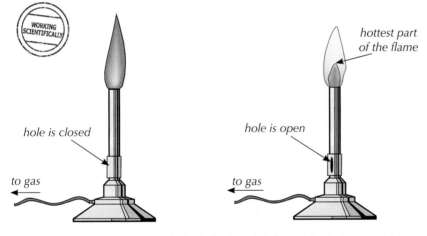

Figure 1: *A Bunsen burner with the hole closed (left) and the hole open (right).*

If your Bunsen burner is alight but not heating anything, make sure you close the hole so that the flame becomes yellow and clearly visible. If you're heating something so that the container (e.g. a test tube) is in the flame, you should hold the vessel at the top, furthest away from the substance (and so the flame) using a pair of tongs. If you're heating something over the flame (e.g. an evaporating dish), you should put a tripod and gauze over the Bunsen burner before you light it, and place the vessel on this.

Tip: Many organic substances, such as alkanes, are very flammable, so you shouldn't heat them with a Bunsen burner.

Example

If you wanted to distil pure water from salt water, you could use a Bunsen burner to heat the salt water.

Figure 2: *An electric heater.*

Electric heaters

Electric heaters are often made up of a dish of metal that can be heated to a particular temperature. The reaction vessel goes on top of the hot plate (see Figure 2). The mixture is only heated from below, so you'll usually have to stir the reaction mixture to make sure it's heated evenly.

Electric heaters don't have a flame, so can be used to safely heat flammable substances. It's also easy to control how strongly they heat. And unlike water baths (see below), they can heat things to above 100 °C.

| Example |

If you wanted to distil a flammable mixture, you couldn't use a Bunsen burner. An electric heater could be used instead.

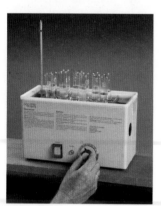

Figure 3: *A water bath.*

Water baths

A water bath is a container filled with water that can be heated to a particular temperature. To use one, start by setting the temperature on the water bath, and allow the water to heat up. Place the container with the substance you want to heat in the water bath using a pair of tongs. The level of the water outside the container should be just above the level of the substance inside the vessel. The substance will then heat up until it reaches the same temperature as the water.

As the substance in the container is surrounded by water, the heating is very even. Water boils at 100 °C though, so you can't use a water bath to heat something to a higher temperature than this — the water won't get hot enough.

| Example |

You could use a water bath to get two liquids or solutions to the same temperature before mixing them. This could be used in an experiment to find the temperature change over the course of a reaction (see pages 153-154).

Maths skills for GCSE Combined Science

Maths is a key part of GCSE Combined Science, so you need to be confident using your maths skills by the time you sit your exams. You'll find loads of examples using maths skills in this book but, to be extra useful, here's a section all about maths to help you out with your chemistry exams. How delightful.

1. Calculations

Calculations are the cornerstone of maths in science. So being able to carry them out carefully is pretty important.

Making estimates

Estimates are useful when it's difficult to be accurate. For example, when you're using something that's hard to measure, or can't be measured directly. Estimates are also useful for checking whether an answer to a calculation is sensible.

Example

During a chromatography experiment, a mixture separates into two spots. Spot A travels 2.4 cm up the filter paper, and spot B travels 1.1 cm. The solvent front travels 5.0 cm. From this data, you can calculate the R_f of spot A is 0.48 and the R_f of spot B is 0.22.

You can check your answer is sensible by doing a quick estimate. The distance travelled by spot A is just over double the distance travelled by spot B. So the R_f of A should be just over double the R_f of B. It is, so there's a good chance that the calculations have been done correctly.

Fractions and decimals

Values that aren't whole numbers can either be written as fractions or as decimals. Decimal numbers are equivalent to a fraction. Here are some common equivalents that could be useful to know.

Examples

$$0.5 = \frac{1}{2} \qquad 0.33... = \frac{1}{3} \qquad 0.25 = \frac{1}{4} \qquad 0.1 = \frac{1}{10}$$

You can do calculations with numbers that contain fractions or decimals.

Example

In a chromatography experiment, the solvent moved 4.2 cm and a spot of substance moved 1.4 cm. The R_f value of the substance is:

$$R_f = \frac{1.4}{4.2} = 0.33 \text{ (or } \frac{1}{3})$$

Exam Tip
Around 20% of the marks in the chemistry exams will depend on your maths skills. That's a lot of marks so it's definitely worth making sure you're up to speed.

Tip: All the examples in this book that include the kind of maths you could get in your exam are clearly marked. You can spot them by the little stamp that says...

Exam Tip
If you've done a calculation in your head, make sure you check it using a calculator. (Unless you're really, really confident that you've got it right.)

Percentages

A percentage is a way of comparing one number to another as a fraction of 100. No matter what you're calculating the percentage of, the method is always the same:

1. Work out the number you're comparing to. Sometimes this may be given to you, but other times you'll have to work it out.

2. Divide your value by the number you're comparing to.

3. Multiply by 100 to get the percentage.

Tip: 'Percent' means 'out of 100'. So, for example, 62% means 62 out of 100. This can also be written as a fraction: $62\% = \frac{62}{100}$

Example

2.0 g of a mixture contains 1.2 g of iron.
What is the percentage mass of iron in the mixture?

Here, you want to work out what the mass of iron is as a percentage of the total mass of the mixture. So the number you're comparing to is 2.0 g.

Divide your value by the number you're comparing to: $1.2 \div 2.0 = 0.60$

Multiply by 100 to get the percentage: $0.60 \times 100 = \mathbf{60\%}$

Ratios

Ratios are a way of comparing quantities. Ratios are usually written like this:

A colon separates one quantity from the other. $x : y$ *x and y stand for the quantities of each thing.*

To write a ratio, first write down the numbers you have of each thing, separated by a colon. Then divide the numbers by the same amount until they're the smallest they can be whilst still being whole numbers.

Tip: Working out the ratio of substances in equations can be really useful for working out the amount of product formed from a given amount of reactant, or vice versa (see page 111).

Example

Give the ratio of oxygen to water in the following reaction in its simplest form: $C_5H_{12} + 8O_2 \rightarrow 5CO_2 + 6H_2O.$

From the equation, there are 8 molecules of oxygen for every 6 molecules of water. So the ratio can be written as 8 : 6.

Both numbers are divisible by 2, so the simplest form of the ratio is **4 : 3**.

Standard form

You might need to use or understand numbers written in standard form. Standard form must always look like this:

Tip: '*A*' can be 1 or any number <u>up to</u> 10 but it can't <u>be</u> 10.

This number must always be between 1 and 10. ➔ $A \times 10^n$ ◄ *This number is the number of places the decimal point moves.*

Standard form is used for writing very big or very small numbers in a more convenient way.

Tip: If the power that 10 is raised to is a positive number, the number is bigger than 10. If it's a negative number, the number is smaller than 1.

Examples

- There are 602 000 000 000 000 000 000 000 particles in a mole. It's much quicker to write this as 6.02×10^{23}.

- A magnesium atom has an atomic radius of 0.00000000015 m. In standard form, that's 1.5×10^{-10} m.

You can write numbers out in full rather than in standard form by moving the decimal point. Which direction to move the decimal point, and how many places to move it depends on 'n'. If 'n' is positive, the decimal point moves to the right. If 'n' is negative, the decimal point moves to the left.

Examples

Here's how to write out 9.3×10^4 in full.

- The decimal point needs to move to the right because 'n' is a positive number (4).

- Then count the number of places the decimal point has to move to the right. In this example it's four:

$$9.3 \times 10^4 = 9\overset{1\ 2\ 3\ 4}{3\,0\,0\,0.}$$

- So 9.3×10^4 is the same as 93 000.

Here's how to write out 5.6×10^{-5} in full.

- 'n' is a negative number (−5) so the decimal point needs to move to the left.

- Count five places to the left.

$$5.6 \times 10^{-5} = \overset{5\ 4\ 3\ 2\ 1}{.0\,0\,0\,0\,5}\,6$$

- So 5.6×10^{-5} is the same as 0.000056.

Tip: You can use the 'Exp' button on your calculator to type something in standard form. So if, for example, you wanted to type in 2×10^7, you'd type in: '2' 'Exp' '7'. Some calculators may have a different button that does the same job, for example it could say 'EE' or '× 10^x'.

You can do calculations with numbers that are in standard form.

Example

Atoms have a radius of about 1×10^{-10} m. Nuclei have a radius of about 1×10^{-14} m. Approximately how many times bigger than a nucleus is an atom?

To work this out, you just have to divide the approximate radius of an atom by the approximate radius of a nucleus.

$(1 \times 10^{-10}) \div (1 \times 10^{-14}) = \mathbf{1 \times 10^4}$

So the radius of an atom is approximately 1×10^4 (or 10 000) times bigger than the radius of a nucleus.

Figure 1: *The 'Exp' or '×10^x' button is used to input standard form on calculators.*

2. Equations

There are lots of equations to get your head around in GCSE Combined Science. Knowing how to use them properly is really important.

Substituting values into equations

There are a few equations you need to learn for your chemistry exams. They link together certain quantities, such as concentration, mass and volume, or moles, mass and relative mass. To use an equation, just substitute the numbers from the question into the correct part of the equation and calculate the answer.

Exam Tip
You won't necessarily be given equations in the exam, so make sure you learn the ones in this book.

Example

During the first 30 seconds of a reaction, 0.69 g of a gas was produced. Calculate the mean rate of reaction during this time.

The formula to use is: $\text{mean rate of reaction} = \dfrac{\text{quantity of product formed}}{\text{time}}$

In this scenario, the amount of product formed is 0.69 g of gas, and the time is 30 seconds.

So, $\text{mean rate of reaction} = \dfrac{0.69}{30} = \textbf{0.023 g/s}$

If you're unsure what the units of your final answer should be, you can work them out by substituting the units of the values you did have into the equation. Whatever you've done with the numbers, you do the same with the units.

Example

In the example above, the quantity of product formed was in g, and time was in s.

The units of rate $= \dfrac{\text{units of quantity of product formed}}{\text{units of time}} = \dfrac{g}{s} = \textbf{g/s}$

When you're substituting values into an equation, always double check that they've got the right units. Sometimes the values you need to put into an equation may have different units to the values you're given, so you may need to convert between units (see pages 18-19 for more on this).

Tip: The <u>subject</u> of an equation is the thing that's on its own on one side of the equals sign. It should be the thing you want to calculate.

Rearranging formulas

You'll often need to change the subject of an equation. To do this, you'll need to rearrange it. The crucial thing to remember here is that whatever you do to one side of the equation you need to do exactly the same to the other side.

Example

Rearrange the following equation to make the mass of solute the subject:

$$\text{concentration (g/dm}^3) = \frac{\text{mass of solute (g)}}{\text{volume of solution (dm}^3)}$$

1. Multiply both sides by the volume of solution:

$$\text{concentration} \times \text{volume of solution} = \frac{\text{mass of solute}}{\text{volume of solution}} \times \text{volume of solution}$$

2. You can cancel out 'volume of solution' on the right hand side:

$$\text{concentration} \times \text{volume of solution} = \frac{\text{mass of solute}}{\cancel{\text{volume of solution}}} \times \cancel{\text{volume of solution}}$$

3. Which leaves: **concentration × volume of solution = mass of solute**

Exam Tip
Write down all the steps if you're rearranging an equation, so that you can check that your method is correct.

Formula triangles

Formula triangles are really useful tools for changing the subject of an equation. If three things are related by an equation like this:

$$a = b \times c \qquad \text{or like this:} \qquad b = \frac{a}{c}$$

...then you can put them into a formula triangle. The components that are multiplied together go on the bottom of the triangle. Any components that are divided go on the top. To use the formula triangle to write out a formula just cover up the component that you want to make the subject, and write down what's left.

Example

The equation 'number of moles = mass ÷ M_r' can be put into this formula triangle:

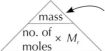

Mass is divided by M_r in the equation, so it must go on the top of the formula triangle.

If you want to make 'mass' the subject of the equation, just cover it up in the triangle and you're left with 'number of moles' next to 'M_r'. This means the number of moles needs to be multiplied by M_r. So mass = number of moles × M_r.

Exam Tip
If you're struggling to rearrange an equation in the exam, it might be useful to work out the formula triangle and use that to help you.

Symbols

You need to know the symbols used to show mathematical relationships. You'll have seen many of these before but here's a quick refresher:

Symbol	Meaning
<	less than
<<	much less than
>	greater than
>>	much greater than

Symbol	Meaning
=	equal to
∝	proportional to
~	approximately

Tip: For the greater than or less than symbols, remember that the wider end always points to the bigger number.

3. Handling Data and Graphs

How to process data from experiments is covered on pages 14-17, but here's a quick round-up of the key points.

Significant figures

The first significant figure of a number is the first digit that isn't zero. Every digit after that is significant (even if it's zero). When doing calculations, you should always try to round your answer to the lowest number of significant figures of the data you used to calculate your answer. When you're carrying out long calculations, try not to round until you get your final answer, or it might be less accurate.

Tip: The mean is the average of your data, whilst the range tells you how spread out the data is. There's more about calculating these values on page 14.

Tables, graphs and charts

The easiest way to collect data is in a table. Tables should have clearly labelled headers, and you should always make sure you've drawn enough columns for the number of measurements you're going to take. It can also be useful to include columns for calculating the **mean** or **range** of repeated experiments.

Whilst tables are great for collecting data, they're not great for spotting trends in data. To do this, you'll need to draw a graph or chart. The type of graph you draw will depend on the type of data you have. If it's split into categories, a bar chart may be the way to go. If both the variables you're plotting are continuous, then you should plot a graph. There's lots more about drawing graphs and charts on pages 16-17.

The straight line equation

If you draw a graph and the line of best fit is a straight line, then the line can be represented by the equation:

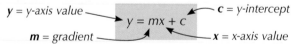

$$y = mx + c$$

y = y-axis value c = y-intercept m = gradient x = x-axis value

The y-intercept is the point at which the line crosses the y-axis. If the straight line passes through the origin of the graph, then the y-intercept is just zero.

Gradients

Tip: The units of the gradient are '(units of y)/(units of x)'.

The **gradient** (slope) of a graph tells you how quickly the dependent variable changes as you change the independent variable. It is calculated using:

$$\text{gradient} = \frac{\text{change in } y}{\text{change in } x}$$

Tip: There's lots more about finding the gradients of lines on graphs on pages 173-174.

Finding the gradient of a straight line graph is fairly simple. You just pick two points on the line that are easy to read and a good distance apart. Draw a line down from one of the points and a line across from the other to make a triangle. The line drawn down the side of the triangle is the change in y and the line across the bottom is the change in x.

For a curved graph, the gradient is always changing. So it's a bit more complicated to calculate the gradient at a single point.

To find the gradient of a curve at a point, you need to draw a **tangent** to the curve at that point. A tangent is a straight line that touches the curve at that point, but doesn't cross it. Then you just find the gradient of the tangent in the same way as before.

Figure 2: Finding the tangent to a curve.

Figure 1: The rate of a reaction where a gas is produced is equal to the gradient of a graph of mass against time.

Finding the intercept of a graph

The *y*-intercept of a graph is the point at which the line of best fit crosses the *y*-axis. The *x*-intercept is the point at which the line of best fit crosses the *x*-axis.

MATHS SKILLS

Example

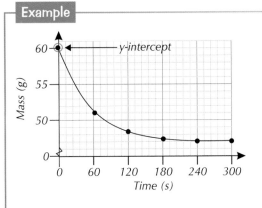

On a graph showing how the mass of a reaction flask changes over the course of a reaction that produces a gas, the *y*-intercept is equal to the initial mass of the flask.

The initial mass of the reaction flask was **60 g**.

4. Geometry

Time for a look at some 2D and 3D shapes now. They may not be the most obvious things you need to learn about for a chemistry exam, but need to learn them you do — you never know when this information could be useful.

2D shapes

Make sure you remember how to calculate the areas of triangles and squares.

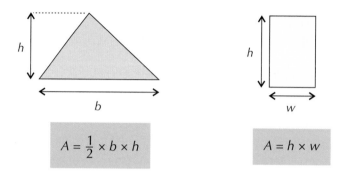

$$A = \frac{1}{2} \times b \times h$$

$$A = h \times w$$

Figure 1: *The equations used to calculate the areas of triangles and rectangles.*

3D shapes

Tip: Make sure you don't forget to add <u>all</u> <u>six</u> sides together when finding the surface area of a cube or cuboid.

If you need to work out the surface area of a 3D shape, you just need to add up the areas of all the 2D faces of the shape. So, for example, if you need to work out the surface area of a cuboid, you just find the area of all the rectangular faces of the cuboid and then add them together.

Make sure you remember how to calculate the volume of a cuboid:

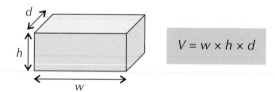

$$V = w \times h \times d$$

Figure 2: *The equation used to calculate the volume of a cuboid.*

Example

Tip: If the lengths were in m, then the volume would have been in m³.

A block of copper is shown. Calculate the volume of the copper.

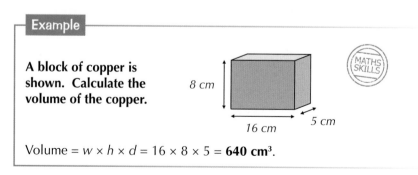

Volume = $w \times h \times d$ = 16 × 8 × 5 = **640 cm³**.

1. The Exams

Unfortunately, to get your GCSEs in Combined Science you'll need to sit some exams. And that's what these pages are about — what to expect in your exams.

Assessment for GCSE Combined Science

To get your GCSEs in Combined Science you'll have to do some exams that test your science knowledge, your understanding of the Required Practical Activities and how comfortable you are with Working Scientifically. You'll also be tested on your maths skills.

All the chemistry content that you need to know is in this book. The chemistry Required Practical Activities are covered and clearly labelled, examples that use maths skills are marked up, and there are even dedicated sections on Working Scientifically (p.2-21), Practical Skills (p.233-240) and Maths Skills (p.241-248). You'll also need to know all the biology and physics content, which isn't covered in this book.

The exams

You'll sit six separate exams at the end of your course — two for each of biology, chemistry and physics.

In the chemistry exams, you'll be tested on maths skills in at least 20% of the marks, and could be asked questions on the Required Practical Activities and Working Scientifically requirements in either exam. You're allowed to use a calculator in all of your GCSE Combined Science exams, so make sure you've got one.

The structure of the chemistry exams is shown below:

> **Exam Tip**
> Make sure you have a good read through these pages. It might not seem all that important now but you don't want to get any surprises just before an exam.

> **Exam Tip**
> As well as a calculator, you should make sure you've got a ruler for both exams. And don't forget the basics — a couple of black pens and sharp pencils.

> **Exam Tip**
> You're expected to know the basic concepts of chemistry in both papers.

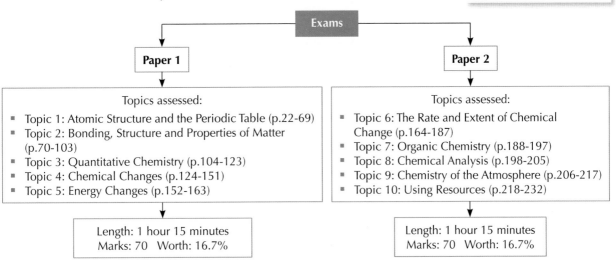

Exams

Paper 1

Topics assessed:
- Topic 1: Atomic Structure and the Periodic Table (p.22-69)
- Topic 2: Bonding, Structure and Properties of Matter (p.70-103)
- Topic 3: Quantitative Chemistry (p.104-123)
- Topic 4: Chemical Changes (p.124-151)
- Topic 5: Energy Changes (p.152-163)

Length: 1 hour 15 minutes
Marks: 70   Worth: 16.7%

Paper 2

Topics assessed:
- Topic 6: The Rate and Extent of Chemical Change (p.164-187)
- Topic 7: Organic Chemistry (p.188-197)
- Topic 8: Chemical Analysis (p.198-205)
- Topic 9: Chemistry of the Atmosphere (p.206-217)
- Topic 10: Using Resources (p.218-232)

Length: 1 hour 15 minutes
Marks: 70   Worth: 16.7%

2. Exam Technique

Figure 1: *An exam hall of doom... It's really just a hall with some chairs and tables in it. Not so scary, after all.*

Knowing the science is vitally important when it comes to passing your exams. But having good exam technique will also help. So here are some handy hints on how to squeeze every mark you possibly can out of those examiners.

Time management

Good time management is one of the most important exam skills to have — you need to think about how much time to spend on each question. Check out the length of your exams (you'll find them on page 249 and on the front of your exam papers). These timings give you about 1 minute per mark. Try to stick to this to give yourself the best chance to get as many marks as possible.

Don't spend ages struggling with a question if you're finding it hard to answer — move on. You can come back to it later when you've bagged loads of other marks elsewhere. Also, you might find that some questions need a lot of work for only a few marks, while others are much quicker — so if you're short of time, answer the quick and easy questions first.

Exam Tip
You shouldn't really be spending more time on a 1 mark question than on a 4 mark question. Use the marks available as a rough guide for how long each question should take to answer.

> **Example**
>
> The questions below are both worth the same number of marks but require different amounts of work.
>
> **1.1**   What is the chemical symbol for sodium?
>
> *(1 mark)*
>
> **2.1**   Balance the equation shown below for the reaction between carbon monoxide and oxygen.
>
> $$......CO \quad + \quad ......O_2 \quad \rightarrow \quad ......CO_2$$
>
> *(1 mark)*
>
> Question 1.1 only asks you to write down the symbol for sodium — if you can remember this then it shouldn't take you too long.
>
> Question 2.1 asks you to balance an equation — this may take you longer than writing down a symbol, especially if you have to have a few goes at it before finding the answer.
>
> So, if you're running out of time it makes sense to do questions like 1.1 first and come back to 2.1 if you've got time at the end.

Exam Tip
Don't forget to go back and do any questions that you left the first time round — you don't want to miss out on marks because you forgot to do the question.

Reading the question

You've probably heard it a million times before, but make sure you always read the whole question carefully. It can be easy to look at a question and read what you're expecting to see rather than what it's actually asking you. Read it through before you start answering, and read it again when you've finished, to make sure your answer is sensible and matches up to what the question is asking.

Remember to pay attention to the marks available too. They can often give you a sense how much work is needed to answer the question. If it's just a 1 mark question, it'll often only need a single word or phrase as an answer, or a very simple calculation. Questions with 4, 5 and 6 marks are likely to be longer questions, which need to be clearly structured and may involve writing a short paragraph or a more complicated calculation.

Making educated guesses

Make sure you answer all the questions that you can — don't leave any blank if you can avoid it. If a question asks you to tick a box, circle a word or draw lines between boxes, you should never, ever leave it blank, even if you're short on time. It only takes a second or two to answer these questions, and even if you're not absolutely sure what the answer is you can have a good guess.

Exam Tip
If you're asked, for example, to tick one box, make sure you only tick one. If you tick more than one, you won't get the marks even if some of your answers are correct.

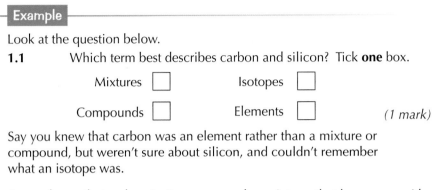

> **Example**
>
> Look at the question below.
>
> **1.1**   Which term best describes carbon and silicon? Tick **one** box.
>
> Mixtures ☐   Isotopes ☐
>
> Compounds ☐   Elements ☐   *(1 mark)*
>
> Say you knew that carbon was an element rather than a mixture or compound, but weren't sure about silicon, and couldn't remember what an isotope was.
>
> As you know that carbon isn't a compound or mixture, that leaves you with a possible answer of 'isotope' or 'element'. If you're not sure which it is, just have a guess. You won't lose any marks if you get it wrong and there's a 50% chance that you'll get it right.

Calculations

Questions that involve a calculation can seem a bit scary. But they're really not that bad. At least 20% of the total marks for GCSE Combined Science will come from questions that test your maths skills, however, so make sure you've brushed up on them before the exam.

When you're doing calculations the most important thing to remember is to show your working. It only takes a few seconds more to write down what's in your head and it'll stop you from making silly errors and losing out on easy marks. You won't get a mark for a wrong answer but you could get marks for the method you used to work out the answer.

Diagrams

You may be asked to draw a diagram or a graph in your exams. Whatever the diagram is, make sure it's really clear, and draw it large enough to show all the details (but make sure that you stay within the space given for that answer).

If you've drawn a diagram incorrectly, don't scribble part of it out and try to fix it — it'll look messy and be hard for the examiner to figure out what you're trying to show. Cross the whole thing out and start again. And always double check that you've included all the things that you should have done.

Exam Tip
Take a sharp pencil with you into the exams to draw diagrams with. Also take a rubber and a pencil sharpener.

Periodic table

You'll be given a copy of the periodic table in the exams. It contains lots of information about the different elements. For example, it tells you what period and group elements are in, as well as their relative atomic masses and atomic numbers. If you're unsure about some data for an element, check the periodic table, just in case it has the information you need.

3. Question Types

If all questions were the same, exams would be mightily boring. So really, it's quite handy that there are lots of different question types. Here are just a few...

Command words

Command words are just the bits of a question that tell you what to do. You'll find answering exam questions much easier if you understand exactly what they mean, so here's a brief summary of the most common ones:

Exam Tip
When you're reading an exam question, you might find it helpful to underline the command words. It can help you work out what type of answer to give.

Exam Tip
It's easy to get <u>describe</u> and <u>explain</u> mixed up, but they're quite different. For example, if you're asked to describe some data, just state the overall pattern or trend. If you're asked to explain data, you'll need to <u>give reasons</u> for the trend.

Command word:	What to do:
Give / Name / Identify / State / Write down	Give a brief one or two word answer, or a short sentence.
Define	Give the meaning of something.
Choose	Select your answer from a range of options.
Complete	Write your answer in the space given. This could be a gap in a sentence or table, or you might have to finish a diagram.
Describe	Write about what something's like, e.g. describe the trend in a set of results.
Suggest / Predict	Use your scientific knowledge to work out what the answer might be.
Determine	Use the data or information you've been given to reach your answer.
Explain	Clarify a point, or give the reasons why something happens. The points in your answer need to be linked together, so you should include words like because, so, therefore, due to, etc.
Calculate / Work out	Use the numbers in the question to work out an answer.
Show	Give clear evidence, and state a conclusion which this evidence supports.
Compare	Give the similarities and differences between two things.
Evaluate	Give the arguments both for and against an issue, or the advantages and disadvantages of something. You may also need to give an overall judgement.
Sketch	Draw without a lot of detail, e.g. for a graph you just need the general shape and correct axes.

Some questions will also ask you to answer 'using the information provided' (e.g. a graph, table or passage of text) — if so, you must refer to the information you've been given or you won't get the marks. You'll often need to use information or diagrams that are provided for you when answering questions with command words such as 'measure' or 'plot'.

Levels of response questions

Some questions are designed to assess your ability to present and explain scientific ideas in a logical and coherent way, as well as your scientific knowledge. These questions often link together different topics, and are worth more marks than most other question types. You'll be told which questions these are on the front of your exam paper.

This type of question is marked using a 'levels of response' mark scheme. Your answer is given a level depending on the number of marks available and its overall quality and scientific content. Here's an idea of how the levels may work out for a 6 mark question:

Example

Level 0

A Level 0 answer has no relevant information, and makes no attempt to answer the question. It receives no marks.

Level 1

A Level 1 answer usually makes one or two correct statements, but does not fully answer the question. For instance, when asked to describe and explain the differences between two materials, it might state one or two correct properties of the materials, but not explain them or attempt to compare the two. These answers receive 1 or 2 marks.

Level 2

A Level 2 answer usually makes a number of correct statements, with explanation, but falls short of fully answering the question. It may miss a step, omit an important fact, or not be organised as logically as it should be. These answers receive 3 or 4 marks.

Level 3

A Level 3 answer will answer the question fully, in a logical fashion. It will make a number of points that are explained and related back to the question. Any conclusions it makes will be supported by evidence in the answer. These answers receive 5 or 6 marks.

Make sure you answer the question fully, and cover all points indicated in the question. You also need to organise your answer clearly — the points you make need to be in a logical order. Use specialist scientific vocabulary whenever you can. For example, if you're talking about electrolysis, you need to use scientific terms like 'electrodes' and 'oxidation'. Obviously you need to use these terms correctly — it's no good using the words if you don't know what they actually mean.

Exam Tip
It might be useful to write a quick plan of your answer in the spare space of your paper. This can help you get your thoughts in order, so you can write a logical, coherent answer. But remember to cross your plan out after you've written your answer so it doesn't get marked.

Exam Tip
Make sure your writing is legible — you don't want to lose marks just because the examiner couldn't read your handwriting.

Exam Tip
Make sure your writing style is appropriate for an exam. You need to write in full sentences and use fairly formal language.

Required Practical Activities

Exam Tip
There are Required Practical Activities for biology and physics too. They're <u>not</u> covered in this book.

The Required Practical Activities for GCSE Combined Science include six specific chemistry experiments that you need to carry out during your lessons. They cover a range of scientific techniques. You'll be asked about some of these experiments in your exams. The questions might cover slightly different experiments to the ones you've done in class, but the techniques will be the same, and any extra information you need will be given to you in the questions. There are a lot of different types of question you could be asked on these experiments. Here are some basic areas they might ask you about:

- Carrying out the experiment — e.g. planning or describing a method, describing how to take measurements or use apparatus.

- Risk assessment — e.g. identifying or explaining hazards associated with the experiment, or safety precautions which should be taken.

- Understanding variables — e.g. identifying control, dependent and independent variables.

- Data handling — e.g. plotting graphs or doing calculations using some sample results provided.

- Analysing results — e.g. making conclusions based on sample results.

- Evaluating the experiment — e.g. making judgements on the quality of results, identifying where mistakes may have been made in the method, suggesting improvements to the experiment.

Exam Tip
The Required Practical Activity questions are likely to have some overlap with Working Scientifically, so make sure you've brushed up on pages 2-21.

Answers

Topic 1 — Atomic Structure and the Periodic Table

Topic 1a — Atoms, Elements, Compounds and Mixtures

1. Atoms

Page 23 — Fact Recall Questions

Q1 E.g. atoms have a small nucleus surrounded by electrons. The nucleus is in the middle of the atom and contains protons and neutrons. The electrons occupy shells around the nucleus.

Q2 The nucleus is about 1/10 000 the size of the atom.

Q3 a) +1 b) 0 c) −1

Q4 1

Q5 They have the same number of protons as electrons and protons and electrons have opposite charges of the same size, so cancel each other out.

Page 23 — Application Questions

Q1 9

Q2 47

Q3 34

2. Elements

Page 26 — Fact Recall Questions

Q1 An element is a substance containing only one type of atom.

Q2 a) The number of protons in the atom.
   b) The total number of neutrons and protons in the atom.

Q3 By subtracting the atomic number from the mass number.

Q4 True

Page 26 — Application Questions

Q1 $^{63}_{29}Cu$

Copper has 29 protons so has an atomic number of 29.
Mass number = number of protons + number of neutrons
$$= 29 + 34 = 63$$

Q2 $75 − 33 = \mathbf{42}$

Q3 a) 8 protons, $16 − 8 = \mathbf{8}$ neutrons
   b) 13 protons, $27 − 13 = \mathbf{14}$ neutrons
   c) 23 protons, $51 − 23 = \mathbf{28}$ neutrons
   d) 47 protons, $108 − 47 = \mathbf{61}$ neutrons

3. Isotopes

Page 28 — Fact Recall Questions

Q1 Isotopes are different forms of the same element, which have the same number of protons but a different number of neutrons.

Q2 An average mass of an element, taking into account the different masses of the isotopes, along with their relative abundances.

Page 28 — Application Questions

Q1 **A** is the isotope.
   You know A is the isotope because it has the same number of protons (17) but a different number of neutrons (20 as opposed to 18).

Q2 Copper has more than one isotope and the relative atomic mass is an average that takes into account the different masses of these isotopes.

Q3 relative atomic mass $= \dfrac{(92.5 \times 7) + (7.5 \times 6)}{92.5 + 7.5}$

$= \dfrac{647.5 + 45}{100} = \dfrac{692.5}{100} = 6.925 = \mathbf{6.9}$

Q4 abundance of $^{11}B = 100 − 19.9 = 80.1\%$

relative atomic mass $= \dfrac{(19.9 \times 10) + (80.1 \times 11)}{100}$

$= \dfrac{199 + 881.1}{100} = \dfrac{1080.1}{100} = 10.801 = \mathbf{10.8}$

4. Compounds

Page 30 — Fact Recall Questions

Q1 Compounds are substances formed from two or more elements, the atoms of which are bonded together in fixed proportions throughout the compound.

Q2 positive ions

Q3 covalent bonding

Page 30 — Application Questions

Q1 Carbon and oxygen.

Q2 1 H atom + 1 N atom + 3 O atoms = **5 atoms**

Q3 **D**

   D is a compound because it contains atoms of different elements chemically joined together. A and C only contain atoms of one element, so can't be compounds. B contains atoms of different elements, but there are no bonds between the atoms.

5. Chemical Equations

Page 33 — Application Questions

Q1 a) Iron sulfate and copper.
   b) Copper sulfate and iron.
   c) copper sulfate + iron → iron sulfate + copper

Q2 sodium hydroxide + hydrochloric acid → sodium chloride + water

Q3 a) $Cl_2 + 2KBr \rightarrow Br_2 + 2KCl$
   b) $2HCl + Mg \rightarrow MgCl_2 + H_2$
   c) $C_3H_8 + 5O_2 \rightarrow 3CO_2 + 4H_2O$
   d) $Fe_2O_3 + 3CO \rightarrow 2Fe + 3CO_2$

6. Mixtures

Page 34 — Fact Recall Questions

Q1 A mixture is substance which consists of two or more elements or compounds which aren't joined together by chemical bonds.

Q2 The properties of a mixture are a mixture of the properties of its components.

Q3 Any three from: e.g. chromatography, filtration, crystallisation, simple distillation, fractional distillation.

7. Paper Chromatography

Page 36 — Fact Recall Questions
Q1 Because the ink might be washed away by the solvent.
Q2 To stop the solvent evaporating.
Q3 A chromatogram.
Q4 You could spot all the inks separately at different points along the base line on the same piece of filter paper.

Page 36 — Application Questions
Q1 Only one of the inks is soluble in water. The other one isn't so doesn't separate out. The student could use another solvent e.g ethanol.
Q2 **C**: Three or more. There are 3 spots so there must be at least 3 dyes. But if two different dyes have travelled similar distances, their spots could have joined together. So there could be more than 3 dyes.

8. More Separating Techniques

Page 39 — Fact Recall Questions
Q1 E.g. filtration
Q2 E.g. an evaporating dish, a tripod, a Bunsen burner and a gauze mat.
Q3 Drying the crystals.

Page 39 — Application Questions
Q1 E.g. fold a filter paper into a cone shape and place it into a filter funnel sitting in a container. Pour the mixture containing water and silver bromide into the funnel lined by the filter paper. The silver bromide will remain on the filter paper and the water will pass through the filter paper into the container below.
Q2 Crystallisation, because it does not use high temperatures so the sodium nitrate will not decompose.
Q3 a) lead bromide
   b) sodium sulfate

9. Distillation

Page 41 — Application Questions
Q1 a) The boiling points of ethanol and propanol are too close together for simple distillation to separate them successfully.
   b) fractional distillation
Q2 propanoic acid
Q3 Place the mixture in a round-bottomed flask attached to a fractionating column attached to a condenser. Heat the mixture until the thermometer reaches 65 °C. At this point the vapour of the first fraction, methanol will reach the top of the column, form a liquid in the condenser and can be collected. Increase the temperature to 78 °C. The ethanol fraction will reach the top of the column and can be collected. The final fraction, propanol, can be collected at the end of the condenser when the temperaure reaches 97 °C.

10. The History of the Atom

Page 43 — Fact Recall Questions
Q1 John Dalton
Q2 James Chadwick

Page 43 — Application Questions
Q1 a) They fired positively charged alpha particles at a thin gold film. Most of the particles passed straight through, and a small number were deflected backwards.
   b) If the plum pudding model was right, the particles would have passed straight through or been slightly deflected, but they wouldn't have been deflected backwards.
Q2 a) He suggested that the electrons stayed in shells (energy levels) a fixed distance away from the nucleus.
   b) It was taken seriously because experimental evidence supported his theory.

11. Electronic Structure

Page 45 — Fact Recall Questions
Q1 An energy level.
Q2 2 electrons
Q3 8 electrons
Q4 8 electrons
Q5 The one closest to the nucleus. / The one with lowest energy level.

Page 45 — Application Questions
Q1 Neon
Q2 Carbon
Q3 Sulfur
Q4

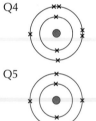

Q5

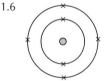

Q6 2, 8, 5
Q7 2, 8, 2

Pages 48-49 — Atoms, Elements, Compounds and Mixtures
Exam-style Questions
1.1 elements *(1 mark)*
1.2 compounds *(1 mark)*
1.3 carbon monoxide + oxygen → carbon dioxide *(1 mark)*
1.4 $2CO + O_2 + 2CO_2$ *(1 mark)*
1.5 Two molecules of carbon monoxide *(1 mark)* react with one molecule of oxygen *(1 mark)* to form two molecules of carbon dioxide *(1 mark)*.
1.6

(1 mark for drawing six electrons, 1 mark for placing two in the first shell and four in the second shell.)

It doesn't matter if the electrons are paired in your diagram or not, you would still get the marks.
1.7 6 *(1 mark)*. This is because it contains 6 protons which each have a positive charge of 1 *(1 mark)*.

2.1

Atomic number	17
Mass number	37
Number of protons	17
Number of electrons	17
Number of neutrons	20

(1 mark for each correct answer)

2.2 E.g. they are isotopes *(1 mark)*.
2.3 It is a mixture as the dissolved components and water are not chemically bonded to each other *(1 mark)*.
2.4 2,8,7 *(1 mark)*
2.5

(1 mark for drawing 11 electrons, 1 mark for placing two in the first shell, 8 in the second shell and 1 in the third.)

It doesn't matter if the electrons are paired in your diagram or not, you would still get the marks.

2.6 Any two from: E.g. evaporation / crystallisation / distillation *(1 mark for each correct answer)*
3.1 A nucleus with a positive charge *(1 mark)* where most of the mass is concentrated *(1 mark)* surrounded by a 'cloud' of negative electrons *(1 mark)*.
3.2 E.g. the plum pudding model has a ball of positive charge with electrons stuck in it *(1 mark)* as opposed to the nucleus holding the positive charge in the nuclear model *(1 mark)*.
3.3 Previously electrons were thought of as a 'cloud', but following Bohr's work they were thought to be in shells *(1 mark)* a fixed distance from the nucleus *(1 mark)*.

Topic 1b — The Periodic Table

1. Development of the Periodic Table
Page 51 — Fact Recall Questions
Q1 In order of increasing relative atomic mass.
Q2 Any one from: E.g. early periodic tables were not complete / elements were placed in the wrong group with elements with different properties.
Q3 He arranged the elements in order of atomic mass but changed the order if the properties of the elements meant it should be switched. He left gaps so that the elements were arranged in groups with similar properties allowing space for undiscovered elements.
Q4 E.g. isotopes of an element were found which have different atomic masses but have the same chemical properties as each other so occupy the same position in the periodic table. / New elements were discovered that fitted into the gaps in Mendeleev's table and their properties fitted with Mendeleev's predictions.

2. The Modern Periodic Table
Page 53 — Fact Recall Questions
Q1 In order of increasing atomic number.
Q2 a) The number of electron shells.
    b) The number of electrons in the outer shell.
Q3 1
Q4 Because they have the same number of electrons in their outer shell.

Page 53 — Application Questions
Q1 3
Q2 2+. Magnesium is in the same group as calcium (two electrons in it's outer shell) so is likely to also form a 2+ ion.

3. Metals and Non-metals
Page 55 — Fact Recall Questions
Q1 positive ions/cations
Q2 negative ions/anions
Q3 metals
Q4 a) Metals tend not to have very many electrons in their outer shell or their outer electrons are a long way away from the nucleus so don't feel much attraction (or both). Either of these effects will mean that not much energy is needed to remove all the outer electrons, meaning metals form positive ions easily.
    b) Non-metals tend to have lots of electrons to remove from their outer shell or the outer electrons are close to the nucleus so feel a strong attraction (or both). Either of these effects means lots of energy is needed to remove all the outer electrons and so non-metals don't form positive ions easily.
Q5 E.g. metals tend to be strong, malleable, good conductors of heat and electricity and have high boiling and melting points. Non-metals tend to be dull, more brittle, have lower melting and boiling points than metals, don't normally conduct electricity and often have low density compared to metals.

4. Group 1 — The Alkali Metals
Page 59 — Fact Recall Questions
Q1 Group 1
Q2 low density
Q3 Reactivity increases down Group 1.
Q4 a) ionic bonds
    b) Any two from: e.g. they are white / they are solids / they are soluble / they dissolve in water to give colourless solutions.
Q5 a) alkali metal + water → metal hydroxide + hydrogen
    b) alkaline
Q6 alkali metal + chlorine → metal chloride
Q7 potassium superoxide and potassium peroxide

Page 60 — Application Questions
Q1 a) potassium   b) rubidium
Q2 a) lithium   b) potassium
Q3 an ionic compound
    The alkali metals always form ionic compounds when they react with non-metals.
Q4 a) $2Li_{(s)} + 2H_2O_{(l)} \rightarrow 2LiOH_{(aq)} + H_{2(g)}$
    b) $2Na_{(s)} + Cl_{2(g)} \rightarrow 2NaCl_{(s)}$
    c) $Rb_{(s)} + O_{2(g)} \rightarrow RbO_{2(s)}$

5. Group 7 — The Halogens
Page 63 — Fact Recall Questions
Q1 two
Q2 At the top of Group 7.
Q3 As you go down Group 7, the increased atomic
    radius as you go down the group means there is
    less attraction between the outer electron shell and
    the nucleus. As the halogens generally react by
    gaining electrons in their highest electron shell, this
    decreasing attraction means that elements lower
    in the group are less likely to gain an electron so
    reactivity decreases down the group.
Q4 The melting points of the halogens increase as you
    move down Group 7.
Q5 1– / –1
Q6 ionic bonding

Page 63 — Application Questions
Q1 a) chlorine   b) fluorine
Q2 a) iodine   b) bromine
Q3 a) yes   b) no
    c) no   d) yes
Q4 a) $Cl_{2(g)} + 2KI_{(aq)} \rightarrow I_{2(aq)} + 2KCl_{(aq)}$
    b) $Br_{2(g)} + 2NaI_{(aq)} \rightarrow I_{2(aq)} + 2NaBr_{(aq)}$

6. Group 0 — The Noble Gases
Page 65 — Fact Recall Questions
Q1 the noble gases
Q2 They increase.

Page 65 — Application Questions
Q1 a) 8
    b) Argon has a full outer shell of electrons so doesn't
       need to gain or lose electrons to become more
       stable. This means that it's inert.
Q2 Krypton will be a a gas at this temperature. Krypton
    is further up Group 0 and therefore will have a lower
    boiling point meaning it will be a gas at the boiling
    point of xenon.

Pages 68-69 — The Periodic Table
Exam-style Questions
1.1 Any one from: E.g. Mendeleev left gaps for
     undiscovered elements / he placed elements
     according to properties as well as relative atomic
     mass *(1 mark)*.
1.2 Elements are arranged in order of atomic number/
     proton number, not relative atomic mass *(1 mark)*.
2.1 6 *(1 mark)*
     The number of electrons in the outer shell of an element is
     the same as its group number in the periodic table.
2.2 4 *(1 mark)*
     The number of occupied shells in an element is the same as
     the period number in the periodic table.
2.3 Sulfur and selenium are in the same group *(1 mark)*
     so will react similarly as they have the same number
     of electrons in their outer shell *(1 mark)*.
3.1 Metals typically react to form positive ions *(1 mark)*,
     whereas non-metals react to form negative ions or
     covalent compounds *(1 mark)*.

3.2 fluorine *(1 mark)*
     Boiling point increases down Group 7, so an element with
     a lower boiling point than chlorine must be above chlorine
     in Group 7. Fluorine is the only element above chlorine in
     Group 7 so the answer must be fluorine.
3.3 A displacement reaction would not occur *(1 mark)*
     because chlorine is more reactive than bromine
     (1 mark).
4.1 Potassium will be more reactive *(1 mark)*. This is
     because atoms get larger down the group/the outer
     electron is further from the nucleus *(1 mark)*, so the
     forces attracting electrons are weaker *(1 mark)* and
     therefore outer electrons are lost more easily making
     them more reactive *(1 mark)*.
4.2 hydrogen *(1 mark)*
4.3 A metal hydroxide is formed in the reaction *(1 mark)*,
     which dissolves in the water to give an alkaline
     solution *(1 mark)*.
4.4 +1 *(1 mark)*
4.5 E.g. boiling point of potassium =
        (boiling point of sodium + boiling point of
        rubidium) ÷ 2 = (883 + 688) ÷ 2 = **786 °C**
        (1 mark)
     Any answer within the range of 700-850 °C would get the
     mark.
     E.g. melting point of rudbidium =
        (melting point of potassium + melting point of
        caesium) ÷ 2 = (63 + 28) ÷ 2 = **46 °C** *(1 mark)*
     Any answer in the range between 35-55 would get the
     mark.
5.1 Group 7 *(1 mark)*
5.2 Chlorine and bromine both have the same number of
     electrons in their outer shell / both have 7 electrons in
     their outer shell *(1 mark)*.
5.3 E.g. bubble chlorine through a solution of magnesium
     bromide *(1 mark)*. The chlorine will displace the
     bromide to form magnesium chloride (and bromine)
     (1 mark).
5.4 Argon has a full outer shell of electrons / a stable
     arrangement of electrons *(1 mark)* so is inert *(1 mark)*.

Topic 2 — Bonding, Structure and the Properties of Matter

Topic 2a — Bonding and Structure

1. Ions

Page 71 — Fact Recall Questions
Q1 Charged particles formed when electrons are lost or gained by an atom or molecule.
Q2 Metals form positive ions. Non-metals form negative ions.
Q3 +2

2. Ionic Bonding

Page 74 — Fact Recall Questions
Q1 Ionic bonding is the strong electrostatic attraction that holds oppositely charged ions together in an ionic lattice.
Q2 A metal and a non-metal.
Q3 a)

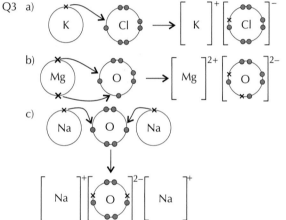

You may have shown all the inner shells of electrons in your answer — that's fine.

Page 74 — Application Questions
Q1 a) E.g. potassium has one electron in its outer shell and iodine has seven electrons in its outer shell. When they react, the electron in the outer shell of the potassium atom is transferred to the iodine atom. A positively charged potassium ion and a negatively charged iodide ion are formed. They both have full outer shells of electrons.
    b) Like iodine, fluorine is in Group 7 of the periodic table. This means they both have seven electrons in their outer shell and need one more to get a full outer shell. They can both get this electron from a potassium atom.
Q2

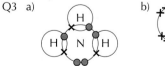

You are still correct if you include the inner shells in your diagram.
Q3 **C**

3. Ionic Compounds

Page 77 — Fact Recall Questions
Q1 giant ionic lattice
Q2 a) Advantage: e.g. you can see the electron transfer.
      Disadvantage: any one of e.g. they don't show the lattice structure / the relative sizes of the ions / how the ions are arranged.
    b) Advantage: e.g. they show the regular pattern of ions / they show relative sizes of ions.
      Disadvantage: e.g. you can only see the outer layer of the lattice.
    c) Advantage: any one from e.g. they show that the crystal extends further than what is shown / show the regular pattern in an ionic lattice / how all the ions are arranged.
      Disadvantage: any one of e.g. they suggest that there are gaps between the ions / sometimes ions not shown to scale.
Q3

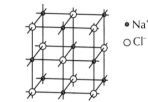

Q4 Identify the ions in the compound. Find their charges using their periodic table group numbers. Decide how many of each ion are needed to balance the positive and negative charges to make the overall charge zero. Write the formula using these numbers, putting the metal first.
Q5 High melting point, soluble in water, conduct electricity when molten or dissolved, but not when solid.

Page 77 — Application Questions
Q1 a) giant ionic lattice
    b) Magnesium forms 2+ ions and iodine forms 1− ions. So to balance the charges, two iodide ions are needed for each magnesium ion. So the formula is MgI_2.
Q2 Caesium forms 1+ ions and chlorine forms 1− ions. So to balance the charges, one caesium ion is needed for each chloride ion. So the formula is $CsCl$.
Q3 B
    Potassium chloride is formed from a metal and a non-metal, so must be ionic. Ionic compounds have high melting points and don't conduct electricity when solid.

4. Covalent Bonding

Page 80 — Fact Recall Questions
Q1 non-metal atoms
Q2 Two pairs of electrons shared between two atoms.
Q3 a)   b)

Q4 By single straight lines.

Q5 a) Advantage: e.g. they show which atom the electrons in each bond come from.
Disadvantage: e.g. they don't show the shape of the molecule / they don't show the relative sizes of the atoms.
b) Advantage: e.g. they show the shape of the molecule.
Disadvantage: e.g. they can be confusing for large molecules / they don't show where the electrons in the bonds have come from.

Page 80 — Application Questions
Q1 Molecule A: $O=C=O$
Molecule B: $Br-Br$
Molecule C: $H-P-H$ with H below P
Q2 No, you wouldn't expect it to be covalent. Lithium is a metal and covalent bonds form between two non-metals.
Q3 a) H_2O_2 b) NH_3 c) CH_3Cl

5. Simple Molecular Substances
Page 84 — Fact Recall Questions
Q1 A molecule made up of only a few atoms held together by covalent bonds.
Q2 a) hydrogen chloride
b) water
Q3 a)

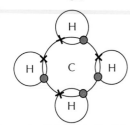

b)

c)

Q4 $N\equiv N$
Q5 Only the weak intermolecular forces that exist between the molecules need to be overcome in order to melt the substance. This doesn't take much energy so the melting points are low.
Q6 No. There are no charged particles.

Page 84 — Application Questions
Q1 'A' has seven electrons in its third shell, so needs one more to have a full outer shell. Hydrogen has one electron in its outer shell, so needs one more to have a full outer shell. Hydrogen and element A both share one of their electrons so that both atoms have a full outer shell, forming a single covalent bond.
Q2 Sulfur will have a higher melting point than phosphorus. This is because it contains bigger molecules so the intermolecular forces between them will be stronger and more energy is required to overcome them.

6. Larger Covalent Substances
Page 86 — Fact Recall Questions
Q1 A substance consisting of lots of long molecules made of repeating sections. The atoms are joined by covalent bonds.
Q2 a) B, C, A
b) In simple molecular substances, only the weak intermolecular forces must be overcome to melt the substance. In polymers, it's still only the intermolecular forces that need to be overcome, but these are stronger than those between simple molecules (due to molecular size). To melt a giant covalent substance you need to break the covalent bonds, which takes a lot of energy.

Page 86 — Application Questions
Q1

$$\left(\begin{array}{cc} X & Y \\ | & | \\ -C-C- \\ | & | \\ Y & X \end{array} \right)_n$$

$(C_2X_2Y_2)_n$

Q2 A = poly(ethene) (melting point between the other two), B = diamond (highest melting point), C = oxygen (lowest melting point).
Q3 $(C_3H_6)_n$

7. Allotropes of Carbon
Page 89 — Fact Recall Questions
Q1 B and C
Q2 Diamond. It has no free electrons or ions.
Q3 Graphene is a sheet of carbon atoms joined together in hexagons. It's basically a single layer of graphite.
Q4 B
Q5 Fullerenes are hollow molecules made of carbon atoms arranged in rings.
Q6 C_{60}
Q7 Any two from e.g. good conductors / very strong / large surface area / good lubricants / high length to diameter ratio
Q8 Any three from e.g. in medicine to deliver drugs / as industrial catalysts / as lubricants / in strengthening materials / in electronics.

Page 89 — Application Question
Q1 Ammonia — Doesn't conduct electricity.
Melting point = –78 °C
Graphite — Conducts electricity.
Melting point = 3500 °C
Diamond — Doesn't conduct electricity.
Melting point = 3500 °C

8. Metallic Bonding
Page 91 — Fact Recall Questions
Q1 A giant structure with the atoms held in a regular arrangement by a sea of delocalised electrons.
Q2 electrostatic
Q3 The layers of atoms are able to easily slide over each other.
Q4 The electrons are free to move so carry thermal energy through the structure.

Q5 Different elements have different sized atoms. When another element is mixed with a pure metal, the new element atoms distort the layers of metal atoms, making it more difficult for them to slide over each other.

Pages 94-96 — Bonding and Structure Exam-style Questions

1.1
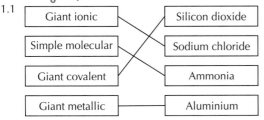

Giant ionic	Silicon dioxide
Simple molecular	Sodium chloride
Giant covalent	Ammonia
Giant metallic	Aluminium

(1 mark for each correct line drawn).

1.2 simple molecular *(1 mark)*
giant metallic *(1 mark)*
giant covalent *(1 mark)*
giant ionic *(1 mark)*

2.1 Covalent bonding *(1 mark)*

2.2 Chlorine is made of simple molecules *(1 mark)* and the intermolecular forces between molecules are weak *(1 mark)*. This means not much energy is needed to overcome them/chlorine has a low boiling point *(1 mark)*.

2.3 Lithium loses one electron *(1 mark)* and chlorine gains one electron *(1 mark)*. Both lithium and chlorine then have a full outer shell of electrons/stable electronic structure *(1 mark)*.

2.4
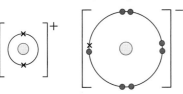

(1 mark for correct electron arrangement for a lithium ion, 1 mark for correct electron arrangement for a chloride ion. 1 mark for both charges shown correctly.)
You'd also get the mark if you drew lithium with no electrons in its outer shell.

2.5 LiCl *(1 mark)*
Lithium loses one electron so has a charge of +1, chlorine gains one electron so has a charge of −1. (+1) + (−1) = 0, so only one of each ion is needed to balance out the charges.

2.6 Lithium chloride is an ionic compound so consists of oppositely charged ions held together by strong electrostatic forces *(1 mark)*. A lot of energy is required to overcome these forces and melt the compound *(1 mark)*.

3.1 When a covalent bond forms, atoms share a pair of electrons *(1 mark)*.

3.2 Carbon atoms have four electrons in their outer shell *(1 mark)*. They need four more electrons to fill it and get the stable electron configuration of a noble gas *(1 mark)*.

3.3 The covalent bonds do not need to be broken for the polymer to melt *(1 mark)*, just the weaker intermolecular forces *(1 mark)*.

3.4 Advantage: E.g. it shows how the atoms are connected clearly, even in a large molecule *(1 mark)*. Disadvantage: Any one from e.g. it doesn't show the shape of the molecule / it doesn't show which atoms the electrons in the covalent bonds have come from *(1 mark)*.

4.1 Their strong covalent bonds must be broken for the substance to melt *(1 mark)*.

4.2 How to grade your answer:
Level 0: There is no relevant information.
        [No marks]
Level 1: There is a brief explanation of the structure of one of the substances. *[1 to 2 marks]*
Level 2: There is some description of the arrangement of atoms or the bonding in both substances, or the arrangement of atoms and the bonding in one substance. *[3 to 4 marks]*
Level 3: There is a clear and detailed explanation of the arrangement of atoms and the bonding in both substances and how this relates to the hardness of diamond and the softness and slipperiness of graphite. *[5 to 6 marks]*

Here are some points your answer may include:
In diamond each carbon atom forms four covalent bonds.
This makes diamond a hard, rigid, giant covalent structure.
In graphite, each carbon atom only forms three covalent bonds.
This results in layers of carbon atoms.
The layers are held together by weak intermolecular forces/aren't covalently bonded to each other.
The layers can slide over each other making graphite soft and slippery.

4.3 graphene

4.4 Any two from e.g. strengthening materials such as tennis racket frames / drug delivery / industrial catalysts / lubricants / electronics *(1 mark for each)*.

5.1 The electrons in the outer shells of silver atoms are delocalised *(1 mark)*, so they are free to move throughout the whole metal, carrying electric charge *(1 mark)*.

5.2 Diagram B — sterling silver is an alloy so contains atoms of different elements *(1 mark)*.

5.3 Sterling silver is harder — in pure silver the atoms are arranged in layers that can slide over each other making the metal soft *(1 mark)*. In sterling silver other atoms have been added that disrupt the layers, preventing them from sliding over each other *(1 mark)*.

Topic 2b — States of Matter

1. States of Matter
Page 99 — Fact Recall Questions
Q1 solid, liquid, gas
Q2 a) solid, liquid
   b) solid
Q3 As the temperature increases the particles making up the solid vibrate more. This causes the solid to expand.
Q4 The gas particles have only a weak force of attraction between them, so they move randomly, filling the whole container. They move in straight lines, continuing until they hit another particle or the walls of the container.
Q5 Any three from: e.g. in reality, the particles aren't solid/inelastic/spheres. / The model doesn't show the forces between the particles. / The distances between the particles aren't necessarily shown to scale.
Q6 (s) = solid, (l) = liquid, (g) = gas, (aq) = aqueous

Page 99 — Application Question
Q1 $Fe_{(s)} + 2HCl_{(aq)} \rightarrow FeCl_{2(aq)} + H_{2(g)}$

2. Changing State
Page 101 — Fact Recall Questions
Q1 melting
Q2 a) When a solid is heated, the particles' energy increases and they vibrate more, which weakens the forces that hold the solid together. Eventually, the particles have enough energy to break free from their positions forming a liquid.
   b) When a gas is cooled, the particles no longer have enough energy to overcome the forces of attraction between them. Eventually, the forces between the particles are strong enough that the gas becomes a liquid.
Q3 Differences in the structures of substances and the bonding within them affect the strength of the forces between the particles. Stronger forces mean higher melting and boiling points.

Page 101 — Application Question
Q1 a) solid   b) liquid
   c) liquid   d) gas

Page 103 — States of Matter
Exam-style Questions
1.1 A = liquid (1 mark), B = solid (1 mark)
1.2 Any one from: the material / the structure of the substance / type of bonds holding it together / the pressure / the temperature (1 mark).
1.3 Freezing (1 mark). The particles' energy decreases. / They move around less (1 mark). There's not enough energy to overcome the attraction between them. / So more bonds form between them (1 mark).
1.4 $Br_{2(l)} \rightarrow Br_{2(s)}$ (1 mark)
2.1 Sulfur (1 mark)
2.2 Chlorine is a gas at 0 °C (1 mark). The forces of attraction between particles are weak (1 mark). The particles are spread out, moving constantly with random motion (1 mark).

2.3 As the gas is cooled, the particles lose energy (1 mark). At −34 °C, the particles no longer have enough energy to overcome the forces of attraction between them, meaning that bonds form (1 mark) and the gas condenses (1 mark). At −102 °C, so many bonds have formed that the particles become held in place (1 mark) and the liquid freezes (1 mark).

Topic 3 — Quantitative Chemistry

1. Relative Formula Mass
Page 105 — Fact Recall Questions
Q1 By adding together the relative atomic masses of all the atoms in the compound.
Q2 % mass =
$$\frac{A_r \times \text{number of atoms of that element}}{M_r \text{ of the compound}} \times 100$$

Page 105 — Application Questions
Q1 a) $2 \times 16 = \mathbf{32}$
   b) $39 + 16 + 1 = \mathbf{56}$
   c) $1 + 14 + (3 \times 16) = \mathbf{63}$
   d) $40 + 12 + (3 \times 16) = \mathbf{100}$
Q2 a) A_r of H = 1
      M_r of HCl = 1 + 35.5 = 36.5
      % mass of hydrogen = $(1 \div 36.5) \times 100 = \mathbf{2.7\%}$
   b) A_r of Al = 27
      M_r of Al_2O_3 = $(2 \times 27) + (3 \times 16) = 102$
      % mass of aluminium = $((2 \times 27) \div 102) \times 100$
      $= \mathbf{53\%}$
   c) A_r of O = 16
      M_r of $Cu(OH)_2$ = $63.5 + (2 \times (16 + 1)) = 97.5$
      % mass of oxygen = $((2 \times 16) \div 97.5) \times 100$
      $= \mathbf{33\%}$
Q3 In 45 g of the mixture there will be $45 \times (40 \div 100)$ = 18 g of magnesium.
   A_r of Mg = 24, A_r of O = 16
   M_r(MgO) = 24 + 16 = 40
   % mass of magnesium in MgO = $(24 \div 40) \times 100 = 60\%$
   Mass of MgO containing 18 g of Mg = $18 \div (60 \div 100) = \mathbf{30\ g}$

2. The Mole
Page 107 — Fact Recall Questions
Q1 6.02×10^{23}
Q2 An amount of a substance that contains 6.02×10^{23} particles.
Q3 number of moles =
$$\frac{\text{mass in g (of element or compound)}}{M_r \text{ (of element or compound) or } A_r \text{ (of element)}}$$

Page 107 — Application Questions
Q1 a) 23 g
   b) 4 g
   c) $2 \times 80 = \mathbf{160\ g}$
   d) $(2 \times 39) + 16 = \mathbf{94\ g}$
Q2 a) A_r of K = 39
      moles = mass $\div A_r$ = $19.5 \div 39 = \mathbf{0.50\ moles}$
   b) M_r of NaCl = 23 + 35.5 = 58.5
      moles = mass $\div M_r$ = $23.4 \div 58.5 = \mathbf{0.400\ moles}$

c) M_r of $SO_2 = 32 + (2 \times 16) = 64$
moles = mass ÷ M_r = 76.8 ÷ 64 = **1.2 moles**
d) M_r of $CuSO_4 = 63.5 + 32 + (4 \times 16) = 159.5$
moles = mass ÷ M_r = 31.9 ÷ 159.5 = **0.200 moles**

Q3 a) A_r of Ni = 59
mass = moles × A_r = 0.80 × 59 = **47 g**
b) M_r of MgO = 24 + 16 = 40
mass = moles × M_r = 0.50 × 40 = **20 g**
c) M_r of $NH_3 = 14 + (3 \times 1) = 17$
mass = moles × M_r = 1.6 × 17 = **27 g**
d) M_r $Ca(OH)_2 = 40 + (2 \times (16 + 1)) = 74$
mass = moles × M_r = 1.40 × 74 = **104 g**

3. Conservation of Mass

Page 110 — Fact Recall Questions

Q1 During a reaction, no atoms are made or destroyed, so the mass of the products is the same as the mass of the reactants.

Q2 The masses will be the same.

Q3 E.g. the reaction between a metal and oxygen in an unsealed container.

Page 110 — Application Questions

Q1 127 + 32 = **159 g**

Q2 68 – 56 = **12 g**

Q3 The mass will decrease.
Metal carbonates thermally decompose to form a metal oxide and carbon dioxide gas. So the carbon dioxide gas will expand out of the unsealed reaction vessel, causing the mass of stuff inside the reaction vessel to decrease.

Q4 Total M_r of reactants = $(2 \times 35.5) + (2 \times (23 + 80))$
= 71 + 206 = 277
Total M_r of products = $(2 \times 80) + (2 \times (23 + 35.5))$
= 160 + 117 = 277
The total M_r on the left-hand side of the equation is equal to the total M_r on the right-hand side, so mass is conserved.

Q5 Before the reaction, calcium is in the reaction vessel, but oxygen is in the air, so the mass of oxygen isn't accounted for. When the oxygen reacts with calcium to form calcium oxide, it becomes contained inside the reaction vessel — so the total mass of the stuff inside the reaction vessel increases.

4. The Mole and Equations

Page 113 — Application Questions

Q1 a) 2   b) 1

Q2 3 mol
The molar ratio of magnesium to magnesium oxide is 1:1, so the number of moles of magnesium that react is the same as the number of moles of magnesium oxide that form.

Q3 0.4 ÷ 2 = **0.2 mol**
The molar ratio of sodium bromide to bromine is 2:1, so half as many moles of bromine will form compared to the moles of sodium bromide that reacted.

Q4 M_r of $O_2 = 2 \times 16 = 32$
M_r of $Na_2O = (2 \times 23) + 16 = 62$
Number of moles of each substance:
Na: $\frac{4.6}{23} = 0.2$ O_2: $\frac{1.6}{32} = 0.05$ Na_2O: $\frac{6.2}{62} = 0.1$
Divide by the smallest number (0.05):
Na: $\frac{0.2}{0.05} = 4.0$ O_2: $\frac{0.05}{0.05} = 1.0$ Na_2O: $\frac{0.1}{0.05} = 2.0$
Balanced equation: $4Na + O_2 \rightarrow 2Na_2O$

Q5 M_r of HCl = 1 + 35.5 = 36.5
M_r of KCl = 39 + 35.5 = 74.5
M_r of $H_2 = 2 \times 1 = 2$
Number of moles of each substance:
K: $\frac{2.34}{39} = 0.060$ HCl: $\frac{2.19}{36.5} = 0.060$
KCl: $\frac{4.47}{74.5} = 0.060$ H_2: $\frac{0.06}{2} = 0.03$
Divide by the smallest number (0.03):
K: $\frac{0.060}{0.03} = 2$ HCl: $\frac{0.060}{0.03} = 2$
KCl: $\frac{0.060}{0.03} = 2$ H_2: $\frac{0.03}{0.03} = 1$
Balanced equation: $2K + 2HCl \rightarrow 2KCl + H_2$

Q6 Number of moles of each substance:
Z: $\frac{1.20}{30} = 0.040$ O_2: $\frac{4.48}{32} = 0.14$
CO_2: $\frac{3.52}{44} = 0.080$ H_2O: $\frac{2.16}{18} = 0.12$
Divide by the smallest number (0.040):
Z: $\frac{0.040}{0.040} = 1.0$ O_2: $\frac{0.14}{0.040} = 3.5$
CO_2: $\frac{0.080}{0.040} = 2.0$ H_2O: $\frac{0.12}{0.040} = 3.0$
Multiply all the values by 2:
Z: 1.0 × 2 = 2 O_2: 3.5 × 2 = 7
CO_2: 2.0 × 2 = 4 H_2O: 3.0 × 2 = 6
Balanced equation: $2Z + 7O_2 \rightarrow 4CO_2 + 6H_2O$
From the equation, you can see that 2 units of Z contain 4 atoms of C and 12 atoms of H. So 1 unit of Z contains 2 atoms of C and 6 atoms of H, making the chemical formula of Z C_2H_6.
Balanced equation: $2C_2H_6 + 7O_2 \rightarrow 4CO_2 + 6H_2O$

5. Limiting Reactants

Page 116 — Fact Recall Questions

Q1 A reactant that's used up completely in a reaction / the reactant that limits the amount of product that's formed.

Q2 in excess

Pages 116-117 — Application Questions

Q1 a) sodium
The sodium all gets used up, so you know it's the limiting reactant.
b) water

Q2 a) The amount of zinc chloride produced would double.
b) 13.0 ÷ 3.25 = 4.00
So the mass of zinc chloride produced = 4.00 × 6.80 = **27.2 g**
c) 1.36 ÷ 6.80 = 0.200
So the amount of zinc that reacts = 0.200 × 3.25 = **0.650 g**

Q3 $2KBr + Cl_2 \rightarrow 2KCl + Br_2$
M_r of KBr = 39 + 80 = 119
M_r of KCl = 39 + 35.5 = 74.5
moles of KBr = 36.2 ÷ 119 = 0.304... mol
2 moles of KBr react to form 2 moles of KCl, so 0.304... mol of KBr reacts to form 0.304... mol of KCl.
mass of KCl = 0.304... × 74.5 = **22.7 g**

Q4 $6HCl + 2Al \rightarrow 2AlCl_3 + 3H_2$
M_r of $HCl = 1 + 35.5 = 36.5$
M_r of $AlCl_3 = 27 + (3 \times 35.5) = 133.5$
moles of $HCl = 15.4 \div 36.5 = 0.421...$ mol
6 moles of HCl reacts to form 2 moles of $AlCl_3$, so
0.421... moles of HCl reacts to form $(0.421 \div 6) \times 2 =$
0.140... mol of $AlCl_3$.
mass of $AlCl_3 = 0.140... \times 133.5 = $ **18.8 g**

Q5 $CaCO_3 + H_2SO_4 \rightarrow CaSO_4 + H_2O + CO_2$
M_r of $CaCO_3 = 40 + 12 + (3 \times 16) = 100$
M_r of $CaSO_4 = 40 + 32 + (4 \times 16) = 136$
moles of $CaCO_3 = 28.5 \div 100 = 0.285$ mol
1 mole of $CaCO_3$ reacts to form 1 mole of $CaSO_4$,
so 0.285 mol of $CaCO_3$ react to form 0.285 mol of
$CaSO_4$.
mass of $CaSO_4 = 0.285 \times 136 = $ **38.8 g**

Q6 $HNO_3 + KOH \rightarrow KNO_3 + H_2O$
M_r of $KOH = 39 + 16 + 1 = 56$
M_r of $KNO_3 = 39 + 14 + (3 \times 16) = 101$
moles of $KNO_3 = 25.0 \div 101 = 0.247...$ mol
1 mole of KNO_3 forms from 1 mole of KOH, so
0.247... mol of KNO_3 form from 0.247... mol of KOH.
mass of $KOH = 0.247... \times 56 = $ **13.9 g**

Q7 $C_2H_4 + H_2O \rightarrow C_2H_6O$
M_r of $C_2H_4 = (2 \times 12) + (4 \times 1) = 28$
M_r of $C_2H_6O = (2 \times 12) + (6 \times 1) + 16 = 46$
moles of $C_2H_6O = 60.0 \div 46 = 1.30...$ mol
1 mole of C_2H_6O forms from 1 mole of C_2H_4, so
1.30... mol of C_2H_6O form from 1.30... mol of C_2H_4.
mass of $C_2H_4 = 1.30... \times 28 = $ **36.5 g**

Q8 $2Fe_2O_3 + 3C \rightarrow 4Fe + 3CO_2$
M_r of $Fe_2O_3 = (2 \times 56) + (3 \times 16) = 160$
A_r of $Fe = 56$
moles of $Fe = 32.0 \div 56 = 0.571...$ mol
4 moles of Fe form from 2 moles of Fe_2O_3, so 0.571...
mol of Fe form from $(0.571... \div 4) \times 2 = 0.285...$ mol
of Fe_2O_3.
mass of $Fe_2O_3 = 0.285... \times 160 = $ **45.7 g**

6. Concentrations

Page 119 — Fact Recall Questions

Q1 The amount of a substance in a certain volume of a
solution.

Q2 concentration (g/dm³) = mass (g) ÷ volume (dm³)

Page 119-120 — Application Questions

Q1 a) concentration = 150 ÷ 3 = **50 g/dm³**
b) concentration = 48 ÷ 0.4 = **120 g/dm³**

Q2 a) volume = 120 ÷ 1000 = 0.120 dm³
concentration = 60 ÷ 0.120 = **500 g/dm³**
b) volume = 8 ÷ 1000 = 0.008 dm³
concentration = 2.4 ÷ 0.008 = **300 g/dm³**

Q3 a) mass = 2.5 × 32 = **80 g**
b) mass = 0.35 × 60 = **21 g**

Q4 a) volume = 80 ÷ 1000 = 0.080 dm³
mass = 0.080 × 200 = **16 g**
b) volume = 15 ÷ 1000 = 0.015 dm³
mass = 0.015 × 120 = **1.8 g**

Q5 a) Solution A
b) 0.2 ÷ 2 = **±0.1 cm³**

Pages 122-123 — Quantitative Chemistry

Exam-style Questions

1.1 $M_r = 63.5 + 16 = $ **79.5** *(1 mark)*

1.2 E.g. there are two copper atoms and two oxygen
atoms on both the left-hand side and the right-hand
side of the equation *(1 mark)*.

1.3 **0.64 g** *(1 mark)*

1.4 Before the reaction, the oxygen gas wasn't contained
inside the reaction container, so its mass wasn't
accounted for in the initial mass *(1 mark)*. After
the reaction, the oxygen was contained within the
copper oxide inside the reaction vessel, so its mass
was included in the total mass of the reaction vessel
(1 mark).

2.1 volume in dm³ = 30 ÷ 1000 = 0.030 dm³ *(1 mark)*
mass = concentration × volume = 150 × 0.030
= **4.5 g** *(1 mark)*

2.2 volume of new solution = 30 + 60 = 90 cm³
volume in dm³ = 90 ÷ 1000 = 0.090 dm³ *(1 mark)*
concentration = mass ÷ volume = 4.5 ÷ 0.090
= **50 g/dm³** *(1 mark)*
*The mass of $MgCl_2$ in the diluted solution is the same as
the mass in the 150 g/dm³ solution.*

3.1 7.0 + 5.5 = **12.5 g** *(1 mark)*

3.2 3 × 7.0 = **21 g** *(1 mark)*

3.3 $M_r(CaCO_3) = 40 + 12 + (3 \times 16) = $ **100** *(1 mark)*
$M_r(CaO) = 40 + 16 = $ **56** *(1 mark)*
$M_r(CO_2) = 12 + (2 \times 16) = $ **44** *(1 mark)*

3.4 Total M_r of reactants = 100
Total M_r of products = 56 + 44 = 100 *(1 mark)*
Total M_r of reactants = Total M_r of reactants, so mass is
conserved *(1 mark)*.

4.1 M_r of $H_2 = 2$, M_r of $O_2 = 32$, M_r of $H_2O = 18$ *(1 mark)*
Number of moles of each substance:
H_2: $\frac{0.5}{2} = 0.25$ O_2: $\frac{4.0}{32} = 0.125$ H_2O: $\frac{4.5}{18} = 0.25$
(1 mark)

Divide by the smallest number (0.125):
H_2: $\frac{0.25}{0.125} = 2.0$ O_2: $\frac{0.125}{0.125} = 1.0$ H_2O: $\frac{0.25}{0.125} = 2.0$
(1 mark)
Balanced equation: $2H_2 + O_2 \rightarrow 2H_2O$ *(1 mark)*

4.2 E.g. it will be used up first *(1 mark)*.

4.3 0.2 ÷ 0.5 = 0.4
So mass of water = 0.4 × 4.5 = **1.8 g** *(1 mark)*

5.1 moles = 4.8 ÷ 24 = **0.20 mol** *(1 mark)*

5.2 1 mole of magnesium reacts to form 1 mole of
magnesium chloride, so 0.20 moles of magnesium
react to form 0.20 moles of magnesium chloride
(1 mark).
M_r of magnesium chloride = 24 + (2 × 35.5) = 95
(1 mark)
mass of magnesium chloride = 0.20 × 95 = **19 g**
(1 mark)

5.3 1 mole of magnesium reacts with 1 mole of zinc
chloride, so 0.20 moles of magnesium react with 0.20
moles of zinc chloride *(1 mark)*.
M_r of zinc chloride = 65 + (2 × 35.5) = 136 *(1 mark)*
mass of zinc chloride to react = 0.20 × 136 = 27.2 g
(1 mark)
mass of zinc chloride remaining = 35 − 27.2 = **7.8 g**
(1 mark)

5.4 The zinc chloride is no longer in excess *(1 mark)* because 4.8 g of magnesium requires 27.2 g of zinc chloride to react completely / 0.20 mol of magnesium needs 0.20 mol of zinc chloride to react completely, and only 0.15 mol are available *(1 mark)*.

6.1 In 30 g of the mixture there will be 30 × (8 ÷ 100) = 2.4 g of bromine *(1 mark)*.
$M_r(CaBr_2) = 40 + (2 × 80) = 200$ *(1 mark)*
% mass of bromine in $CaBr_2 = ((2 × 80) ÷ 200) × 100$
$= (160 ÷ 200) × 100 = 80\%$ *(1 mark)*
Mass of $CaBr_2$ containing 2.4 g of Br = 2.4 ÷ (80 ÷ 100) = **3.0 g** *(1 mark)*

6.2 moles of $CaBr_2$ = 3.0 ÷ 200 = 0.015 mol *(1 mark)*
1 mole of $CaBr_2$ forms from 1 mole of CaI_2 so 0.015 mol of $CaBr_2$ forms from 0.015 mol of CaI_2 *(1 mark)*.
$M_r(CaI_2) = 40 + (2 × 127) = 294$ *(1 mark)*
mass of CaI_2 = 0.015 × 294 = **4.4 g** *(1 mark)*
If you used 1.5 g as your target mass of $CaBr_2$, you should get 2.2 g as your final answer.

Topic 4 — Chemical Changes

1. Acids and Alkalis
Page 126 — Fact Recall Questions
Q1 E.g. pH is a measure of how acidic or alkaline a solution is.
Q2 pH 7
Q3 pHs greater than 7.
Q4 a) H^+ ions   b) OH^- ions
Q5 water/H_2O

Page 126 — Application Questions
Q1 a) acidic   b) alkaline
Q2 a) pH 6   b) blue
For part a), pH 5 is also acceptable.
Q3 a) neutralisation   b) water/H_2O

2. Strong Acids and Weak Acids
Page 129 — Fact Recall Questions
Q1 Strong acids fully ionise/dissociate in an aqueous solution. E.g. hydrochloric acid / sulfuric acid / nitric acid is a strong acid.
Q2 Weak acids partially ionise/dissociate in an aqueous solution. E.g. any carboxylic acid / citric acid / carbonic acid is a weak acid.
Q3 $CH_3COOH \rightleftharpoons H^+ + CH_3COO^-$
Q4 Factor H^+ ion concentration changes by = 10^{-x}
Q5 Acid strength tells you what proportion of acid molecules ionise in water whereas the concentration is a measure of the amount of acid molecules in a given volume of water.

Page 129 — Application Questions
Q1 Hydrochloric acid is a strong acid and therefore fully dissociates meaning there is a high concentration of H^+ ions in solution leading to a low pH. Ethanoic acid is a weak acid and only partially dissociates, so there is a lower concentration of H^+ ions than in a solution of hydrochloric acid of the same concentration. This leads to a higher pH.

Q2 Difference in pH = 7 − 9 = −2
Factor H^+ ion concentration changes by = $10^{-(-2)} = 10^2 = $ **100**
Q3 Difference in pH = 7 − 4 = 3
Factor H^+ ion concentration changes by = $10^{-(3)} = 10^{-3} = $ **0.001**
0.001 can also be shown as $\frac{1}{1000}$.

3. Reactions of Acids
Page 132 — Application Questions
Q1 a) magnesium chloride
   b) $MgCO_3 + 2HCl \rightarrow MgCl_2 + CO_2 + H_2O$
Q2 a) zinc oxide + hydrochloric acid
      $\rightarrow$ zinc chloride + water
   b) E.g. put the hydrochloric acid in a beaker and heat gently. Then add the zinc oxide and stir. Keep adding the zinc oxide until it is in excess. Then filter out the excess zinc oxide to get the salt solution ($ZnCl_2$) using filter paper and a filter funnel. Finally, you can use crystallisation to get pure crystals of $ZnCl_2$ by gently heating and evaporating some of the water from the solution and then leaving the solution to cool so that crystals form. Filter the crystals and dry them.

4. Reactivity of Metals
Page 136 — Fact Recall Questions
Q1 more reactive
Q2 calcium
Q3 metal + acid $\rightarrow$ salt + hydrogen

Page 136 — Application Questions
Q1 $Fe + 2HCl \rightarrow FeCl_2 + H_2$
Q2 a) iron sulfate   b) calcium hydroxide
Q3 a) B, C, A   b) hydrogen
Q4 a) zinc + iron(II) sulfate $\rightarrow$ zinc sulfate + iron
   b) Copper is less reactive than iron and therefore will not displace it in a compound.

5. Metal Oxides and Redox
Page 138 — Fact Recall Questions
Q1 e.g. gold
Q2 Oxidation is the gain of oxygen by an element or compound.
Q3 It becomes a metal oxide.
Q4 Reduction is the loss of oxygen by an element or compound.

Page 138 — Application Questions
Q1 a) Reduction with carbon.
   b) Electrolysis.
   c) Reduction with carbon.
   d) Electrolysis.
Q2 Lithium is more reactive than carbon and therefore cannot be reduced by it.

6. Redox Reactions
Page 140 — Fact Recall Questions
Q1 Oxidation is the loss of electrons by a substance.
Q2 Reduction is the gain of electrons by a substance.
Q3 oxidised
Q4 oxidised

Page 140 — Application Questions

Q1 a) $ZnSO_{4(aq)} + Cu_{(s)}$
Don't worry if you didn't use state symbols.
  b) oxidised
  c) $Zn_{(s)} + Cu^{2+}_{(aq)} \rightarrow Zn^{2+} + Cu_{(s)}$
Q2 a) Because the metal atoms lose electrons, so are oxidised, and at the same time the hydrogen ions from the acid gain electrons, so are reduced.
  b) $Mg_{(s)} + 2H^+_{(aq)} \rightarrow Mg^{2+}_{(aq)} + H_{2(g)}$

7. Electrolysis

Page 141 — Fact Recall Questions

Q1 They contain free ions which can carry a charge.
Q2 cations/positive ions / metal ions.

Page 143 — Application Questions

Q1 a) (molten) zinc chloride
  b) the positive electrode/the anode
  c) The chloride ions lose one electron each (they are oxidised) and form chlorine molecules.
  d) They are reduced.
Q2 a) $2Br^- \rightarrow Br_2 + 2e^- / 2Br^- - 2e^- \rightarrow Br_2$
     $2H^+ + 2e^- \rightarrow H_2$
  b) $Cu^{2+} + 2e^- \rightarrow Cu$
     $2O^{2-} \rightarrow O_2 + 4e^- / 2O^{2-} - 4e^- \rightarrow O_2$

8. Electrolysis of Metal Ores

Page 144 — Fact Recall Questions

Q1 It allows the aluminium oxide to be melted at a lower temperature, which saves energy, making the process cheaper, easier and more sustainable.
Q2 The oxygen that is produced at the positive electrode reacts with the carbon in the electrode to form carbon dioxide. This means the positive electrodes get 'eaten away' over time.

9. Electrolysis of Aqueous Solutions

Page 147 — Fact Recall Questions

Q1 The reactivity of the elements involved.
Q2 no
Q3 bromine

Page 147 — Application Questions

Q1 Calcium is more reactive than hydrogen so the calcium ions will stay in solution.
Q2 Hydrogen/ H_2 and oxygen/O_2. Hydrogen is produced at the negative electrode because zinc is more reactive than hydrogen. Oxygen is produced at the positive electrode because the solution doesn't contain any halide ions.
Q3 a) E.g. the student should get two inert electrodes and clean the surfaces of them using emery paper. The electrodes should then be placed into a beaker filled with sodium bromide solution and position them so they are inside inverted test tubes containing the sodium bromide solution. The electrodes could then be attached to a d.c. power supply and electrolysis carried out. The gas discharged at each electrode will be collected by the test tube and then tested. Chlorine can then be tested by using damp limus paper. If chlorine

gas is present the litmus paper will bleach and turn white. Hydrogen gas can be tested for by using a lighted splint that will make a 'squeaky pop' noise if hydrogen is present.
  b) Yes the student is correct. Magnesium metal is more reactive than hydrogen so will be discharged at the negative electrode. As chloride ions are present, chlorine will be discharged at the positive electrode.
Q4 anode: $4OH^- \rightarrow O_2 + 2H_2O + 4e^-$
    cathode: $2H^+ + 2e^- \rightarrow H_2$

Pages 150-151 — Chemical Changes
Exam-style Questions

1.1 B *(1 mark)*
1.2 B *(1 mark)*
1.3 A *(1 mark)*
2.1 A *(1 mark)*
2.2 E.g. Niall could add universal indicator to the solution. When the indicator turns green this shows that the solution has become neutral and the reaction has finished / He could use a pH meter to measure when the pH was 7 *(1 mark for a correct method of testing pH, 1 mark for the correct observation)*.
2.3 $H^+_{(aq)} + OH^-_{(aq)} \rightarrow H_2O_{(l)}$
    (1 mark for correct equation, 1 mark for correct state symbols)
3.1 acid + metal oxide $\rightarrow$ salt + water
    (1 mark for each correct product).
3.2 A neutralisation reaction / a redox reaction *(1 mark)*.
4.1 Ethanoic acid partially ionises in solution *(1 mark)*.
4.2 hydrochloric acid *(1 mark)*
4.3 sulfuric acid *(1 mark)*
5.1 magnesium + copper sulfate
    $\rightarrow$ magnesium sulfate + copper
    (1 mark)
5.2 Oxidised: magnesium/Mg *(1 mark)*
    Reduced: copper ions/Cu^{2+} *(1 mark)*
5.3 $Mg_{(s)} + Cu^{2+}_{(aq)} \rightarrow Mg^{2+}_{(aq)} + Cu_{(s)}$
    (1 marks for correct reactants and products, 1 mark for correctly balanced equation, 1 mark for correct state symbols)
5.4 Yes *(1 mark)*.
    Iron is more reactive than copper / iron is more easily oxidised *(1 mark)*.
5.5 When magnesium reacts with hydrochloric acid it is oxidised to magnesium ions *(1 mark)*. The hydrogen ions are reduced to form hydrogen gas *(1 mark)*.
    Ionic equation: $2H^+ + Mg \rightarrow H_2 + Mg^{2+}$
    (1 mark for correct equation, 1 mark for balancing reactants and products)
6.1 Copper chloride solution *(1 mark)*.
6.2 water *(1 mark)*
6.3 Each copper ion gains two electrons/is reduced *(1 mark)* and becomes a neutral copper atom *(1 mark)*.
6.4 $2Cl^- \rightarrow Cl_2 + 2e^-$ *(1 mark)*
6.5 $Cu^{2+} + 2e^- \rightarrow Cu$ *(1 mark for the correct species on the left and right hand side of the equation, 1 mark for balancing)*

Topic 5 — Energy Changes

1. Energy Transfer in Reactions

Page 154 — Fact Recall Questions

Q1 It stays the same.

Q2 a) An exothermic reaction is a reaction that transfers energy to the surroundings.

b) E.g. combustion / neutralisation / some oxidation reactions.

Q3 a) Because endothermic reactions absorb energy from the surroundings.

b) E.g. endothermic reactions are used in some sports injury packs.

Q4 a) E.g. measure out both solutions and record their temperature. Check that they are the same temperature. Pour both solutions into a polystyrene cup and stir well. Observe the temperature of the mixture and record the highest temperature it reaches.

b) E.g. energy being lost to the surroundings.

2. Reaction Profiles

Page 156 — Fact Recall Questions

Q1 E.g.

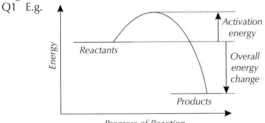

Q2 The minimum amount of energy the reactant particles need when they collide with each other in order to react.

Page 156 — Application Questions

Q1 a) exothermic   b) endothermic

Q2 **C**

3. Energy in Reactions

Page 160 — Fact Recall Questions

Q1 a) endothermic
b) exothermic

Q2 During an exothermic reaction, the energy released in bond formation is greater than the energy used in breaking old bonds. The energy that is left over is released into the surroundings.

Q3 Energy change =
Energy of bond breaking – Energy of bond making

Page 160 — Application Questions

Q1 Energy used in bond breaking =
$(2 \times 436) + 498 = 1370$ kJ/mol
Energy released in bond making =
$(4 \times 464) = 1856$ kJ/mol
Energy change = 1370 – 1856 = **–486 kJ/mol**

Q2 Energy used in bond breaking =
$(2 \times ((3 \times 413) + 358 + 464)) + (3 \times 498)$
= 5616 kJ/mol
Energy released in bond making =
$(2 \times (2 \times 805)) + (4 \times (2 \times 464)) = 6932$ kJ/mol
Energy change = 5616 – 6932 = **–1316 kJ/mol**

Q3 Energy used in bond breaking =
$(4 \times 413) + 612 + 193 = 2457$ kJ/mol
Energy used in bond making =
$348 + (4 \times 413) + (2 \times C–Br) = 2000 + (2 \times C–Br)$
Energy change = 2457 – 2000 – $(2 \times C–Br)$
= –122 kJ/mol
$(2 \times C–Br) = 2457 – 2000 + 122 = 579$
C–Br = 579 ÷ 2 = 289.5 kJ/mol = **290 kJ/mol**

Q4 a) Energy used in bond breaking
= $(4 \times 413) + (4 \times 242) = 2620$ kJ/mol
Energy released in bond making
= $(4 \times 327) + (4 \times 431) = 3032$ kJ/mol
Energy change = 2620 – 3032 = **–412 kJ/mol**

b) Exothermic — the energy change is negative, so energy is being released to the surroundings.

Pages 162-163 — Energy Changes

Exam-style Questions

1.1 The temperature will decrease *(1 mark)*.

1.2 The activation energy *(1 mark)*

1.3 E.g. thermal decomposition / the reaction between citric acid and sodium hydrogen carbonate *(1 mark)*

1.4 Energy change = 1845 – 1590 = **255 kJ/mol** *(1 mark)*

2.1

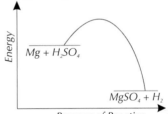

(1 mark for labelling the axes correctly, 1 mark for having the energy of the reactants higher than the energy of the products, 1 mark for drawing a correctly shaped curve)

2.2 To reduce energy loss from the reaction *(1 mark)*.

2.3 To make sure the investigation is valid/a fair test *(1 mark)*.

3.1 The formation of ammonia is exothermic *(1 mark)* because the reactants are at a higher energy on the reaction profile than the products *(1 mark)*.

3.2 Energy used in bond breaking =
$945 + (3 \times 436) = 2253$ kJ/mol *(1 mark)*
Energy released in bond making =
$2 \times (3 \times 391) = 2346$ kJ/mol *(1 mark)*
Energy change = 2253 – 2346 = **–93 kJ/mol** *(1 mark)*

3.3

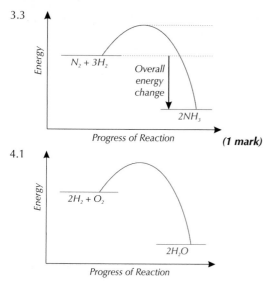

Progress of Reaction

(1 mark)

4.1

Progress of Reaction

(1 mark for labelling the axes correctly, 1 mark for having the energy of the reactants higher than the energy of the products, 1 mark for drawing a correctly shaped curve)

4.2 The overall energy change is negative **(1 mark)**, so less energy is needed to break the bonds in the reactants than is released when the new bonds form **(1 mark)**.

4.3 Energy used in bond breaking:
$(2 \times 436) + 498 = 1370$ kJ mol **(1 mark)**
Energy released in bond making: $4 \times$ H–O
Energy change $= 1370 - (4 \times$ H–O$) = -486$ kJ/mol
$4 \times$ H–O $= 1370 + 486 = 1856$ kJ/mol **(1 mark)**
H–O $= 1856 \div 4 = $ **464 kJ/mol (1 mark)**

4.4 E.g. neutralisation / oxidation **(1 mark)**

Topic 6 — The Rate and Extent of Chemical Change

Topic 6a — Rates of Reaction

1. Rate of Reaction

Page 167 — Fact Recall Questions

Q1 The two particles must collide with sufficient energy.

Q2 Increasing the temperature increases the frequency of collisions because the particles are moving faster. It also increases the energy of the collisions, so more particles collide with enough energy to react.

Q3 If you increase the concentration of the reactants, the particles will be closer together and so collisions between the particles will be more likely. More frequent collisions means a faster rate of reaction.

Q4 A catalyst is a substance that can increase the rate of a reaction without being changed or used up during the reaction.

Q5 They provide an alternative reaction pathway with a lower activation energy.

Q6 A biological catalyst.

Page 167 — Application Question

Q1 a) E.g. going from marble chips to crushed chips to powdered chalk, the surface area of the marble increases and the the rate of the reaction also increases. The larger surface area means that there are more frequent collisions between the reacting particles and so the rate of reaction is faster.

b) The frequency of successful collisions in the reaction with crushed marble chips is double the frequency of sucessful collisions in the reaction with marble chips.

2. Measuring Rates of Reaction

Page 170 — Fact Recall Questions

Q1 mean rate =
$$\frac{\text{quantity of reactant used or product formed}}{\text{time}}$$

Q2 E.g. observe a mark through the solution and time how long it takes for the mark to disappear. The quicker the mark disappears, the quicker the reaction.

Q3 a) E.g. gas syringes are usually quite sensitive and they don't release the gas into the room, which is useful if the gas produced is poisonous. But you can only use this technique to measure the rate if the reaction produces a gas. Also, if the reaction is too vigorous the plunger could blow out of the end of the syringe.

b) E.g. the student could measure the change in mass of the reaction using a mass balance.

Page 170 — Application Questions

Q1 E.g. by directly measuring the amount of carbon dioxide produced over time using a gas syringe. / By measuring the decrease in mass of the reactants as carbon dioxide is given off using a mass balance.
You can use either of these methods for this reaction because one of the products of the reaction is a gas — carbon dioxide. You can tell this from the equation for the reaction that you're given in the question.

Q2 E.g. by putting a mark behind the solution and timing how long it takes for the mark to disappear.
One of the products of this reaction is a solid (Mg(OH)$_2$), which means it will form as a precipitate in the solution.

Q3 4.3 cm^3 $\div$ 5.0 s = **0.86 cm^3/s**

Q4 34.31 g $- 32.63$ g $= 1.68$ g
1.68 g $\div 8.0$ s = **0.21 g/s**

3. Rate of Reaction Graphs

Pages 174-175 — Application Questions

Q1 B, A, C
The tangent with the steepest gradient corresponds to the point on the curve where the rate would be fastest.

Q2 a) **C**
Graph C shows that gas is forming over time and the curve levels off at 200 s, showing that this is the time when the reaction is complete. At this point, 24 cm^3 of gas have been produced.

b) steeper
Both reactions produce the same amount of gas but the second reaction finishes sooner, so will have a faster rate of reaction to begin with.

Q3 Reaction A — reaction A has the steepest curve at the beginning of the reaction. The higher the temperature, the faster the rate of reaction and the steeper the curve.

Q4 a) and b)

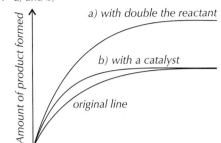

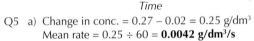

a) with double the reactant

b) with a catalyst

original line

Q5 a) Change in conc. = 0.27 − 0.02 = 0.25 g/dm³
Mean rate = 0.25 ÷ 60 = **0.0042 g/dm³/s**

b)

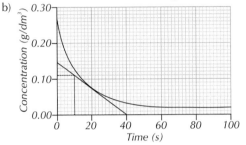

E.g. change in x = 40 − 10 = 30 s
change in y = 0 − 0.11 = −0.11 g/dm³/s
Gradient = change in y ÷ change in x = −0.11 ÷ 30
= −0.0037
Rate = **0.0037 g/dm³/s**

Depending on how you drew your gradient, you may end up with a slightly different value for the rate. But as long as your value is similar, you can still mark it as correct.

4. Reaction Rate Experiments

Page 177 — Fact Recall Questions

Q1 E.g. react hydrochloric acid with magnesium ribbon. Measure the volume of hydrogen produced with a gas syringe / the mass of hydrogen lost with a mass balance. Take readings at regular intervals. Repeat the experiment with different concentrations of hydrochloric acid, keeping the volume of acid and the amount of magnesium the same each time.

Q2 E.g. the reaction between sodium thiosulfate and hydrochloric acid produces a yellow sulfur precipitate. To measure the rate of the reaction you could watch a mark on a piece of paper through the solution and time how long it takes for the mark to disappear.

Page 177 — Application Question

Q1 a) Independent variable: temperature.
Dependent variable: time taken for the reaction mixture to change colour.
b) E.g. the concentrations of the reactants / the volume of the solution / the depth of the solution / the person who decides when the colour change is complete.

c) In order to calculate a mean, which will be more accurate than an individual result.
d) The different scientists might think the colour change is complete at slightly different times, so to make the results precise, the same person should judge each time as their opinion should be consistent.

Pages 179-180 — Rates of Reaction Exam-style Questions

1.1 E.g. measuring the decrease in mass as the CO_2 is given off using a mass balance *(1 mark)*.

1.2 14 minutes *(1 mark)*
You can tell that the reaction finished after 14 minutes because this is how long it took for the graph to level off.

1.3 12 cm³ of CO_2 was produced in the first 2 minutes, so the rate of reaction was 12 ÷ 2 = **6 cm³/min**.
(2 marks for correct answer, otherwise 1 mark for dividing a volume read from the graph by a time read from the graph).

1.4 As the reaction progresses, the reactants get used up, so the concentration of the reactants decreases *(1 mark)*. This means there are fewer collisions between the reacting particles *(1 mark)*.

1.5

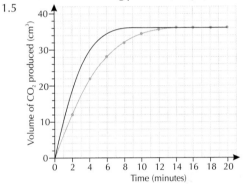

(1 mark for the curve being steeper than the original curve, 1 mark for the curve ending at the same level as the original curve).

The question asked for a sketch, so if you didn't put in the values on the axes, you still get the marks. The important thing here is that the shapes of both curves are correct.

2.1 Hydrochloric acid increases the rate of reaction *(1 mark)* but doesn't appear in the reaction equation *(1 mark)*.

2.2 They provide an alternative reaction pathway *(1 mark)* with a lower activation energy *(1 mark)*.

2.3 E.g.

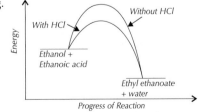

Without HCl

With HCl

Ethanol + Ethanoic acid

Ethyl ethanoate + water

Progress of Reaction

(3 marks — 1 mark for products at lower energy than products, 1 mark for both curves starting and finishing at the same point, 1 mark for reaction with HCl having a smaller initial rise than the reaction without HCl)

2.4 E.g increase the temperature / increase the concentration of ethanol/ethanoic acid *(1 mark)*

3.1 a gas syringe *(1 mark)*

3.2

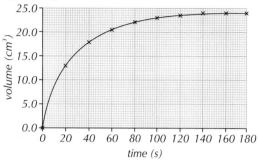

(4 marks — 1 mark for correctly labelled axes, 1 mark for sensible scales on axes, 1 mark for points plotted correctly, 1 mark for line of best fit)

3.3 cm³/s *(1 mark)*

3.4

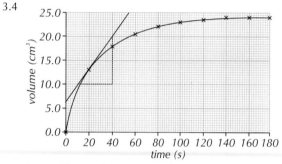

E.g. gradient = change in y ÷ change in x
= (20.0 – 10.0) ÷ (40 – 10) = 10.0 ÷ 30 = **0.33 cm³/s**
(3 marks for rate between 0.25 cm³/s and 0.40 cm³/s, otherwise 1 mark for tangent to curve drawn at 20 s, 1 mark for correct equation used to calculate gradient)

3.5 It halved *(1 mark)*.

Topic 6b — Reversible Reactions

1. Reversible Reactions
Page 183 — Fact Recall Questions
Q1 A reaction where the products of the reaction can themselves react to produce the original reactants

Q2 $A + B \rightleftharpoons C + D$

Q3 It will reach a state of equilibrium.

Q4 The rates of the forward and reverse reactions are the same.

Q5 It will absorb energy.

Page 183 — Application Questions
Q1 $H_{2(g)} + I_{2(g)} \rightleftharpoons 2HI_{(g)}$

Q2 a) E.g. equilibrium is when the forward and backwards reactions are occurring at the same rate.

b) The reverse reaction is exothermic as the forward reaction is endothermic.

2. Le Chatelier's Principle
Page 185 — Fact Recall Questions
Q1 Le Chatelier's principle

Q2 The exothermic reaction.

Q3 E.g. raising the pressure favours the reaction which produces less volume (the fewest number of gas molecules).

Q4 E.g. the system tries to increase the concentration of products by reducing the amount of reactants.

Page 186 — Application Questions
Q1 a) i) The exothermic/reverse reaction.
   ii) $NH_4Cl_{(s)}$/ammonium chloride.
b) i) The endothermic/forward reaction.
   ii) $NH_{3(g)}$/ammonia and $HCl_{(g)}$/hydrogen chloride.

Q2 a) The left side.
b) E.g. the yield of sulfur trioxide (SO_3) increases.
c) E.g. the yield of sulfur trioxide (SO_3) decreases.

Page 187 — Reversible Reactions
Exam-style Questions
1.1 B exothermic *(1 mark)*

1.2 The reaction is reversible *(1 mark)*.

1.3 The reverse reaction is an endothermic reaction *(1 mark)* so the energy from heating converts the solid sodium acetate trihydrate back to sodium acetate trihydrate solution *(1 mark)*.

2.1 A closed system is a system where none of the reactants or products can escape and nothing else can get in *(1 mark)*.

2.2 This would decrease the yield of ethanol *(1 mark)* because increased temperature favours the reverse (endothermic) reaction *(1 mark)*.

2.3 This would increase the yield of ethanol *(1 mark)* because increased pressure favours the reaction that produces fewer molecules of gas (the right-hand side of the equation) *(1 mark)*.

2.4 In a reversible reaction the energy released by the exothermic reaction (production of ethanol) is equal to the energy absorbed by the endothermic reaction (breakdown of ethanol) *(1 mark)*.

Topic 7 — Organic Chemistry

1. Hydrocarbons

Page 190 — Fact Recall Questions

Q1 A hydrocarbon is any molecule that is formed from hydrogen and carbon atoms only.

Q2 propane

Q3 It turns from orange to colourless.

Q4 The shorter the molecules (the shorter the carbon chains) the more flammable the alkane is. / The longer the molecules (the longer the carbon chains) the less flammable the alkane is.

Page 190 — Application Questions

Q1 The general formula of an alkane is C_nH_{2n+2}, so if octane has 8 carbon atoms, it must have $(2 \times 8) + 2 = 18$ hydrogen atoms. So the chemical formula of octane is C_8H_{18}.

Q2 $C_5H_{12} + 8O_2 \rightarrow 5CO_2 + 6H_2O$

Q3 $CH_4 + 2O_2 \rightarrow CO_2 + 2H_2O$

Q4 a) A and C b) C

2. Fractional Distillation of Crude Oil

Page 192 — Fact Recall Questions

Q1 The remains of plants and animals/plankton.

Q2 alkanes

Page 192 — Application Questions

Q1 a) diesel

The fractionating column is hottest at the bottom and coolest at the top, so the fraction with the highest boiling temperature range will be removed at the bottom. This is diesel.

b) 68 °C, petrol

Q2 Tetracontane

3. Uses of Crude Oil

Page 193 — Fact Recall Question

Q1 a) Any one from: e.g. diesel oil / petrol / kerosene / heavy fuel oil / LPG.

b) Any one from: e.g. polymers / solvents / lubricants / detergents.

4. Cracking Crude Oil

Page 195 — Fact Recall Questions

Q1 a) Cracking is the process used to break long-chain hydrocarbons down into smaller ones. It is useful because shorter-chain hydrocarbons are usually more useful than longer-chain hydrocarbons.

b) E.g. fuel and making plastics.

Q2 A thermal decomposition reaction.

Q3 E.g. alkanes and alkenes.

Page 195 — Application Questions

Q1 a) C_3H_6 b) $C_{12}H_{26} \rightarrow C_9H_{20} + C_3H_6$

Q2 a) C_8H_{18} b) e.g. fuel

Page 197 — Organic Chemistry
Exam-style Questions

1.1 The crude oil is heated so that it evaporates *(1 mark)*. The vaporised gases rise up the fractionating column and cool gradually *(1 mark)*. As they cool they condense *(1 mark)*. Different compounds condense at different temperatures and so they are separated *(1 mark)*.

1.2 They have short carbon chains. / They have low boiling points. *(1 mark)*

1.3 $C_7H_{16} + 11O_2 \rightarrow 7CO_2 + 8H_2O$
(3 marks for correct answer, otherwise 1 mark for correct reactants, 1 mark for correct products, 1 mark for balancing the equation).

2.1 C_nH_{2n+2} *(1 mark)*

2.2 Decane *(1 mark)* because it has the longest carbon chains *(1 mark)*.

2.3 Propane *(1 mark)* because it has the shortest carbon chains *(1 mark)* so has the lowest boiling point *(1 mark)*.

3.1 C_6H_{14} *(1 mark)*

3.2 $C_8H_{18} \rightarrow C_6H_{14} + C_2H_4$

3.3 Any one from: e.g. the long-chain hydrocarbons are heated to vaporise them *(1 mark)*. The vapour can then be passed over a powdered catalyst/aluminium oxide causing the long-chain molecules to split apart *(1 mark)*. / The long-chain hydrocarbons are heated to vaporise them *(1 mark)*. The vapour is then mixed with steam and heated to a high temperature causing the long-chain molecules to split apart *(1 mark)*.

3.4 E.g. add a couple of drops of bromine water to each of the substances *(1 mark)*. In the presence of the alkene, the bromine water will change from orange to colourless *(1 mark)*. In the presence of the alkane, the bromine water will stay orange *(1 mark)*.

Topic 8 — Chemical Analysis

1. Purity and Formulations
Page 199 — Fact Recall Questions
Q1 A substance that only contains one compound or element.
Q2 It will lower it.
Q3 A formulation is a useful mixture with a precise purpose made following a formula.

Page 199 — Application Questions
Q1 Beeswax is not considered a pure substance in chemistry as it contains more than one compound/substance.
Q2 a) The sample with 95% purity would have a lower melting point and a larger melting range.
   b) The impure samples would have higher boiling points than pure paracetamol and may boil over a range of temperatures rather than at a particular temperature.

2. Analysing Paper Chromatography
Page 202 — Fact Recall Questions
Q1 stationary phase
Q2 How soluble they are in the solvent and how attracted they are to the paper.

Page 202 — Application Questions
Q1 $6.9 \div 12.3 = $ **0.56**
Q2 a) The red substance.
   b) The red substance.
   The longer a substance spends in the mobile phase the further it will travel up the paper.
Q3 a) It is likely to be pure.
   b) The substance is likely to have different attraction to the solvents / different levels of solubility in the solvents. So it will spend different amounts of time in the mobile phase / will travel further in the mobile phase.
Q4 a) red: $3.5 \div 8.3 = $ **0.42**
      purple: $4.7 \div 8.3 = $ **0.57**
      yellow: $5.3 \div 8.3 = $ **0.64**
   b) E.g. carry out another chromatography experiment using methyl violet as a reference. Repeat the experiment using a number of different solvents. If the purple substance and methyl violet have the same Rf values in all the solvents then it's likely that the substance is methyl violet. If their Rf values are different in any solvents then it's not methyl violet.

3. Tests for Common Gases
Page 203 — Application Questions
Q1 Make a solution of calcium hydroxide in water and bubble any gas produced by the reaction through the solution. The solution will turn cloudy if carbon dioxide is being released from the reaction.
Q2 oxygen

Pages 205 — Chemical Analysis
Exam-style Questions
1.1 A is chlorine *(1 mark)*, B is hydrogen *(1 mark)*.
1.2 She could melt the substance and compare the temperature it melts at with the melting point of the pure substance *(1 mark)*. The lower the melting point is compared to the reference / the wider the melting range of the substance the less pure it is *(1 mark)*.
1.3 She could measure the boiling point of substance C *(1 mark)*. If the sample isn't pure the boiling point will be higher than the boiling point of the pure substance *(1 mark)*. / She could use paper chromatography to test the purity of substance C *(1 mark)*. If the sample is impure it would produce more than one spot in some solvents *(1 mark)*.
2.1 R_f value of A $= \dfrac{2.0}{6.0} = $ **0.33** *(1 mark)*
2.2 That is contains at least two compounds / is not a pure substance *(1 mark)*.
2.3 The R_f values of the different spots for the reaction mixture could be compared to reference R_f values for compounds in both of the solvents used *(1 mark)*. If the R_f values match the reference R_f values in both solvents then it is likely that those compounds are present in the mixture *(1 mark)*.

Topic 9 — Chemistry of the Atmosphere

1. Evolution of the Atmosphere
Page 208 — Fact Recall Questions
Q1 Nitrogen — 80%, oxygen — 20%.
Q2 The early atmosphere was probably mostly carbon dioxide with virtually no oxygen. There may also have been water vapour, nitrogen and small amounts of methane and ammonia.
Q3 Green plants and algae absorb carbon dioxide and use it in photosynthesis.
Q4 It is a sedimentary rock. It forms from the shells and skeletons of marine organisms, which, when they die, fall to the bottom of the ocean where they are covered in layers of sediment. Over millions of years they are compressed to form limestone.

Page 208 — Application Question
Q1 a) The concentration of water vapour in the atmosphere decreased from about 25% 4.5 billion years ago to virtually 0% 4 billion years ago. This is because 4.5 billion years ago the Earth began to cool and the water vapour in the atmosphere condensed to form the Earth's oceans.
   b) E.g. the concentration of carbon dioxide in the early atmosphere was initially high but decreased due to it dissolving in the oceans and being absorbed by plants and algae. So the red/dotted line, which starts high then decreases represents carbon dioxide.
   The concentration of oxygen in the early atmosphere was initially low but increased due to plants and algae producing oxygen during photosynthesis. So the green/dashed line, which starts low and then increases represents oxygen.

2. Greenhouse Gases & Climate Change

Page 211 — Fact Recall Questions

Q1 They absorb long wavelength radiation that gets reflected back off Earth. They then re-radiate this in all directions, including back towards the Earth. This radiation is thermal radiation, so it keeps Earth warm.

Q2 E.g. more food production / waste decomposing in landfill sites.

Q3 The Earth's climate is very complex, so models to predict future climate change are often oversimplified.

Q4 a) An increase in Earth's temperature.
   b) Any one from: e.g. polar ice caps melting / sea levels rising / more flooding / a change in the ability of certain regions to produce food / an increase in the frequency and severity of storms / changes in the distribution of certian wild species / changes in rainfall patterns.

Q5 E.g. how many people might be affected / what impact the change could have.

3. Carbon Footprints

Page 213 — Fact Recall Questions

Q1 A measure of the amount of carbon dioxide and other greenhouse gases that are released over the full life cycle of something.

Q2 Any two from: e.g. use a renewable energy source / nuclear power / use more efficient processes.

Q3 Carbon dioxide produced by burning fossil fuels is captured before it's released into the atmosphere and is stored in cracks deep underground.

Page 213 — Application Question

Q1 a) E.g. introducing a tax on electricity from coal-fired power stations could encourage people to use electricity from other sources that produce less carbon dioxide.
   b) Any one from: e.g. the tax may impact on the economy / if people can't afford to pay the tax, their well-being may be affected.

4. Air Pollution

Page 215 — Fact Recall Questions

Q1 a) Carbon dioxide and water (vapour).
   b) E.g. carbon monoxide, carbon particulates, unburnt fuel

Q2 sulfur dioxide

Q3 A high temperature.

Q4 a) E.g. sulfur dioxide and oxides of nitrogen/nitrogen oxide/nitrogen dioxide
   b) Any two from: e.g. it can cause lakes to become acidic and many plants and animals may die as a result. / It can kill trees. / It can damage limestone buildings or stone statues.

Page 215 — Application Questions

Q1 E.g. the decrease in sunlight could be caused by global dimming which is caused by particles of soot/particulates that are released into the atmosphere when fossil fuels are burned. These particles reflect sunlight back into space or could help produce more clouds that reflect the sunlight back into space.

Q2 Fuel A, as it contains less sulfur, so will release less sulfur dioxide, a cause of acid rain, when it's burnt.

Page 217 — Chemistry of the Atmosphere
Exam-style Questions

1.1 nitrogen *(1 mark)*

1.2 volcanoes *(1 mark)*

1.3 Any two from: e.g. lots of the carbon dioxide was absorbed by the oceans. / Some carbon dioxide was absorbed by plants and algae when they evolved. / The carbon dioxide was locked away in sedimentary rocks/fossil fuels *(1 mark for each correct answer, maximum 2 marks)*.

1.4 E.g. the increased concentrations of carbon dioxide is causing global warming *(1 mark)*.

2.1 Cows produce lots of methane gas *(1 mark)*.

2.2 E.g. use electricity from renewable energy sources / use more efficient processes *(2 marks — 1 mark for each correct answer)*.

2.3 E.g. the profits of the farm could be reduced in comparison to the profits of the surrounding farms *(1 mark)*.

2.4 The soot may have formed from incomplete combustion *(1 mark)*. Soot may cause respiratory problems *(1 mark)* and contribute to global dimming *(1 mark)*.

2.5 Carbon monoxide *(1 mark)* can cause fainting/coma/death *(1 mark)*.

Topic 10 — Using Resources

1. Resources and Sustainability

Page 221 — Fact Recall Questions

Q1 e.g. rubber / wood / cork

Q2 A renewable resource is a resource which can be made at the same or similar rate to how its being used.

Q3 e.g. fossil fuels / nuclear fuels / metal ores

Q4 E.g. Mining metal provides materials to make useful products. / Mining provides local people with jobs. / Mining brings money into the area which means services such as transport and health can be improved.

Q5 It often uses far less energy than is required to extract finite resources and helps stop the raw material from being used up.

Q6 E.g. by developing catalysts that reduce the amount of energy required for industrial chemical processes / by developing new ways of extracting metals from low-grade ores to reduce the demand for high-grade ores.

Q7 a) A displacement reaction.
    b) E.g. scrap iron is very cheap / it reduces the amount of scrap metal going to landfill.

Page 221 — Application Question

Q1 Resource B is renewable. The amount used per year is a similar amount to the amount formed per year so it can be considered replaceable.

2. Reuse and Recycling

Page 222 — Fact Recall Questions

Q1 E.g. it uses a small fraction of energy need to extract new metal / saves money / conserves finite resources / cuts down on rubbish sent to landfill.

Q2 e.g. insulating glass wool / jars

3. Life Cycle Assessments

Page 225 — Application Questions

Q1 E.g. he is correct. Life cycle assessments require judgements to be made which are based on a person's values.

Q2 a) The wooden table as it is made out of a renewable resource and uses less energy to manufacture.
    b) There is no information regarding the other stages of the product's lifetime / the information given is subjective.

4. Potable Water

Page 227 — Fact Recall Questions

Q1 Potable water is water that is safe to drink.

Q2 e.g. chlorine gas / ozone / ultraviolet light

Page 227 — Application Questions

Q1 She is not correct. Tap water contains dissolved substances whereas pure water only contains H_2O molecules.

Q2 In the UK the majority of water comes from fresh water sources. It is then treated firstly by filtration to remove solid waste and then sterilisation to make sure it is safe to drink. However, in hot, dry countries fresh water is scarce so potable water may be produced via desalination of seawater. This is done by distillation or reverse osmosis.

5. Waste Water Treatment

Page 229 — Fact Recall Questions

Q1 E.g. organic matter and harmful microbes.

Q2 E.g. organic matter and harmful chemicals.

Q3 a) Large bits of material are removed as well as any grit.
    b) The water is allowed to stand in tanks causing the heavier suspended solids to sink to the bottom as sludge and the effluent floats on top.

Q4 Advantage: e.g. uses less energy than desalination. Disadvantage: e.g. requires more processing than treating fresh water so costs more / public may be against drinking recycled water.

Pages 232 — Using Resources
Exam-style Questions

1.1 E.g. the material comes from plants which are a renewable resource (1 mark).

1.2 E.g. they could be reused / recycled (1 mark).

1.3 E.g. for an LCA to be effective the entire life-cycle of a product must be considered. (1 mark).

2.1 A: sedimentation (1 mark)
     B: anaerobic digestion (1 mark)

2.2 The water is filtered by passing through a wire mesh and then gravel and sand beds to remove any solids (1 mark). The water is then sterilised to kill harmful microbes e.g. by bubbling chlorine gas through it or by using ozone or ultraviolet light (1 mark).

2.3 Distillation / reverse osmosis of salt water (1 mark).

Glossary

A

Accurate result
A result that is close to the true answer.

Acid
A substance with a pH of less than 7 that forms H^+ ions in water.

Activation energy
The minimum amount of energy that reactant particles must have when they collide in order to react.

Alkali
A substance with a pH of more than 7 that forms OH^- ions in solution.

Alkali metal
An element in Group 1 of the periodic table. E.g. sodium, potassium etc.

Alkane
A saturated hydrocarbon with the general formula C_nH_{2n+2}. E.g. methane, ethane, propane etc.

Alkene
A type of hydrocarbon that is more reactive than alkanes.

Alloy
A metal that is a mixture of two or more metals, or a mixture involving metals and non-metals.

Anion
A particle with a negative charge, formed when one or more electrons are gained.

Anomalous result
A result that doesn't fit with the rest of the data.

Aqueous
When a substance is in solution with water it is said to be aqueous.

Atmosphere
The layer of air that surrounds a planet.

Atom
A neutral particle made up of protons and neutrons in the nucleus, with electrons surrounding the nucleus.

Atomic number
The number of protons in the nucleus of an atom. It's also known as proton number.

Avogadro constant
The number of particles in one mole of a substance, which is 6.02×10^{23}.

B

Base
A substance that reacts with acids in neutralisation reactions.

Bias
Unfairness in the way data is presented, possibly because the presenter is trying to make a particular point (sometimes without knowing they're doing it).

Bioleaching
The process by which a metal is separated from its ore using bacteria.

Boiling
The transition of a substance from a liquid to a gas.

Boiling point
The temperature at which a substance changes from a liquid to a gas or vice versa.

Bond energy
The amount of energy required to break a bond (or the amount of energy released when a bond is made).

C

Calibrate
Measure something with a known quantity and set the instrument being used to that quantity.

Carbon footprint
A measure of the amounts of greenhouse gases released by a product, a service or an event.

Catalyst
A substance that can speed up a reaction without being changed or used up in the reaction.

Catalytic cracking
The process of breaking down long-chain hydrocarbons into shorter ones using a catalyst, often aluminium oxide.

Categoric data
Data that comes in distinct categories, e.g. blood type (A+, B–, etc.) or metals (copper, zinc, etc.).

Cation
A particle with a positive charge, formed when one or more electrons are lost.

Chemical bond
The attraction of two atoms for each other, caused by the sharing or transfer of electrons.

Chromatogram
The pattern of spots formed as a result of separating a mixture using chromatography.

Chromatography
An analytical method used to separate the substances in a mixture based on how the components interact with a mobile phase and a stationary phase.

Climate change
A change in the Earth's climate. E.g. global warming, changing rainfall patterns etc.

Collision theory
The theory that in order for a reaction to occur, particles must collide with sufficient energy.

Combustion
An exothermic reaction between a fuel and oxygen.

Compound
A substance made up of atoms of at least two different elements, chemically joined together.

Concentration
The amount of a substance in a certain volume of solution, given in units of 'units of amount of substance'/'units of volume'.

Condensing
The transition of a substance from a gas to a liquid.

Continuous data
Numerical data that can have any value within a range (e.g. length, volume or temperature).

Control group
A group that matches the one being studied, but where the independent variable isn't altered. The group is kept under the same conditions as the group in the experiment.

Control variable
A variable in an experiment that is kept the same.

Conversion factor
A number which you must multiply or divide a unit by to convert it to a different unit.

Correlation
A relationship between two variables.

Covalent bond
A chemical bond formed when atoms share a pair of electrons.

Covalent substance
A substance where the atoms are held together by covalent bonds.

Cracking
The process that is used to break long-chain hydrocarbons down into shorter, more useful hydrocarbons.

Crystallisation
The formation of solid crystals as water evaporates from a solution. For example, salt solutions undergo crystallisation to form solid salt crystals.

D

Delocalised electron
An electron that isn't associated with a particular atom or bond and is free to move within a structure.

Dependent variable
The variable in an experiment that is measured.

Discrete data
Numerical data that can only take a certain value, with no in-between value (e.g. number of people).

Displacement reaction
A reaction where a more reactive element replaces a less reactive element in a compound.

Displayed formula
A chemical formula that shows the atoms in a covalent compound and all the bonds between them

Distillation
A way of separating out a liquid from a mixture. You heat the mixture until the bit you want evaporates, then cool the vapour to turn it back into a liquid.

Double covalent bond
Two pairs of electrons shared between two atoms.

E

Electrode
An electrical conductor which is submerged in the electrolyte during electrolysis.

Electrolysis
The process of breaking down a substance using electricity.

Electrolyte
A liquid or solution used in electrolysis to conduct electricity between the two electrodes.

Electron
A subatomic particle with a relative charge of –1. In atoms, electrons are located in shells around the nucleus.

Electron shell
A region of an atom that contains electrons. It's also known as an energy level.

Electronic structure
The number of electrons in an atom (or ion) of an element and how they are arranged.

Electrostatic force
A force of attraction between opposite charges.

Element
A substance that is made up only of atoms with the same number of protons.

Empirical formula
A chemical formula showing the simplest possible whole number ratio of atoms in a compound.

Endothermic reaction
A reaction which takes in energy from the surroundings.

Energy level
A region of an atom that contains electrons. It's also known as an electron shell.

Energy level diagram
A graph that shows how the energy in a reaction changes as the reaction progresses (also known as a reaction profile).

Enzyme
A biological catalyst.

Equilibrium
The point at which the rates of the forward and backward reactions in a reversible reaction are the same, and so the amounts of reactants and products in the reaction container don't change.

Evaporation
The process where a liquid changes into a gas. Also, a physical separation technique used to remove a liquid from a solid.

Exothermic reaction
A reaction which transfers energy to the surroundings.

F

Fair test
A controlled experiment where the only thing that changes is the independent variable.

Feedstock
A raw material used to produce other substances through industrial processes.

Filtration
A physical method used to separate an insoluble solid from a liquid.

Finite resource
A resource that isn't replaced at a quick enough rate to be considered replaceable.

Flammability
How easy it is to ignite a substance.

Formulation
A useful mixture with a precise purpose made by following a formula.

Fraction
A group of hydrocarbons that condense together when crude oil is separated using fractional distillation. E.g. petrol, naphtha, kerosene etc.

Fractional distillation
A process that can be used to separate the substances in a mixture according to their boiling points.

Freezing
The transition of a substance from a liquid to a solid.

Frequency density
The height of a bar on a histogram. It is found by the frequency divided by the class width.

Gas
A state of matter where particles have weak forces of attraction and are therefore free to move with random motion filling the container they are held in. Gases have no fixed volume and no fixed shape.

General formula
A formula that can be used to find the molecular formula of any member of a homologous series.

Giant covalent structure
A large molecule made up of a very large number of atoms held together by covalent bonds (also known as a macromolecule).

Global dimming
The decrease in the amount of sunlight reaching the Earth's surface due to an increase in the amount of particulates in the atmosphere.

Global warming
The increase in the average temperature of the Earth.

Greenhouse effect
When greenhouse gases in the atmosphere absorb long wavelength radiation and re-radiate it in all directions, including back towards Earth, helping to keep the Earth warm.

Greenhouse gas
A gas that can absorb long wavelength radiation.

Group
A column in the periodic table.

H

Half equation
An equation which shows how electrons are transferred when a substance is reduced or oxidised. E.g. at an electrode during electrolysis.

Halide ion
An ion with a 1− charge formed when a halogen atom gains an electron. E.g. Cl^-, Br^- etc.

Halogen
An element in Group 7 of the periodic table. E.g. chlorine, bromine etc.

Hazard
Something that has the potential to cause harm.

Homologous series
A group of chemicals that react in a similar way because they have the same functional group. E.g. the alcohols or the carboxylic acids.

Hydrocarbon
A compound that is made from only hydrogen and carbon.

Hypothesis
A possible explanation for a scientific observation.

I

In excess
A reactant that is not used up during a reaction.

Incomplete combustion
When a fuel burns but there isn't enough oxygen for it to burn completely. Products can include carbon monoxide and carbon particulates. Also known as partial combustion.

Independent variable
The variable in an experiment that is changed.

Indicator
A substance that changes colour above or below a certain pH.

Insoluble
A substance is insoluble if it does not dissolve in a particular solvent.

Intermolecular force
A force of attraction that exists between molecules.

Ion
A charged particle formed when one or more electrons are lost or gained from an atom or molecule.

Ionic bond
A strong attraction between oppositely charged ions.

Ionic compound
A compound that contains positive and negative ions held together in a regular arrangement (a lattice) by electrostatic forces of attraction.

Ionic equation
An equation that shows only the particles that react and the products they form.

Ionic lattice
A closely-packed regular arrangement of particles held together by electrostatic forces of attraction.

Isotope
A different atomic form of the same element, which has the same number of protons, but a different number of neutrons.

J

Joules
The standard unit of energy.

L

Lattice
A closely-packed regular arrangement of particles.

Le Chatelier's principle
The idea that if the conditions of a reaction are changed when a reversible reaction is at equilibrium, the system will try to counteract the change.

Life cycle assessment
An assessment of the environmental impact of a product over the course of its life.

Limiting reactant
A reactant that gets completely used up in a reaction, so limits the amount of product that's formed.

Liquid
A state of matter where randomly arranged particles tend to stick closely together but are free to move past each other. Liquids have a fixed volume but no fixed shape.

Litmus
A single indicator that's blue in alkalis and red in acids.

M

Macromolecule
A large molecule made up of a very large number of atoms held together by covalent bonds (also known as a giant covalent structure).

Mass number
The total number of protons and neutrons in an atom.

Mean (average)
A measure of average found by adding up all the data and dividing by the number of values there are.

Melting
The transition of a substance from a solid to a liquid.

Melting point
The temperature of which a substance changes from a solid to a liquid.

Metal
An element that can form positive ions when it reacts.

Metal ore
Rocks that are found naturally in the Earth's crust containing enough metal to make the metal profitable to extract.

Metallic bond
The attraction between metal ions and delocalised electrons in a metal.

Mixture
A substance made from two or more elements or compounds that aren't chemically bonded to each other.

Mobile phase
In chromatography, the mobile phase is a gas or liquid where the molecules are able to move.

Model
Something used to describe or display how an object or system behaves in reality.

Mole
A unit of amount of substance — the mass of one mole of a substance is equal to the value of the relative formula mass of that substance in grams, and contains 6.02×10^{23} particles of the substance.

Molecular formula
A chemical formula showing the actual number of atoms of each element in a compound.

Molecule
A particle made up of at least two atoms held together by covalent bonds.

N

Natural resource
A resource formed without human input.

Negative ion
A particle with a negative charge, formed when one or more electrons are gained. Also known as an anion.

Neutral substance
A substance with a pH of 7.

Neutralisation reaction
The reaction between acids and bases that leads to the formation of neutral products — usually a salt and water.

Neutron
A subatomic particle with a relative charge of 0 and a relative mass of 1. Neutrons are located in the nucleus of an atom.

Noble gas
An element in Group 0 of the periodic table. E.g. helium, neon etc.

Non-metal
An element that doesn't form positive ions when it reacts with the exception of hydrogen.

Nuclear model
An accepted theory which describes the atom as having a tiny, positively charged nucleus surrounded by shells which are occupied by negative electrons.

Nucleus
The central part of an atom, made up of protons and neutrons.

O

Organic compound
A chemical compound that contains carbon atoms.

Oxidation
A reaction where electrons are lost or oxygen is gained by a species.

P

Paper chromatography
An analytical technique that can be used to separate and analyse coloured substances.

Peer-review
The process in which other scientists check the results and explanations of an investigation before they are published.

Period
A row in the periodic table.

Periodic table
A table of all the known elements, arranged in order of atomic number so that elements with similar chemical properties are in groups.

pH scale
A scale from 0 to 14 that is used to measure how acidic or alkaline a solution is.

Phytomining
The process by which a metal is extracted from soil by using plants.

Plum pudding model
A disproved theory of the atom as a ball of positive charge with electrons inside it.

Polymer
A long chain molecule that is formed by joining lots of smaller molecules (monomers) together.

Positive ion
A particle with a positive charge, formed when one or more electrons are lost. Also known as a cation.

Potable water
Water that is safe for drinking.

Precipitate
A solid that is formed in a solution during a chemical reaction.

Precise result
When all the data is close to the mean.

Prediction
A statement based on a hypothesis that can be tested.

Product
A substance that is formed in a chemical reaction.

Proton
A subatomic particle with a relative charge of +1 and a relative mass of 1. Protons are located in the nucleus of an atom.

Pure substance
A substance that only contains one compound or element throughout.

R

Random error
A difference in the results of an experiment caused by things like human error in measuring.

Range
The difference between the smallest and largest values in a set of data.

Rate of reaction
How fast the reactants in a reaction are changed into products.

Reactant
A substance that reacts in a chemical reaction.

Reaction profile
A graph that shows how the energy in a reaction changes as the reaction progresses (also known as an energy level diagram).

Reactivity series
A list of elements arranged in order of their reactivity. The most reactive elements are at the top and the least reactive at the bottom.

Redox reaction
A reaction where one substance is reduced and another is oxidised.

Reduction
A reaction where electrons are gained or oxygen is lost.

Relative atomic mass (A_r)
The average mass of the atoms of an element measured relative to the mass of one atom of carbon-12. The relative atomic mass of an element is the same as its mass number in the periodic table.

Relative formula mass (M_r)
All the relative atomic masses (A_r) of the atoms in a compound added together.

Reliable result
A result that is repeatable and reproducible.

Renewable resource
A resource that can be made at the same or similar rate as it's being used.

Repeatable result
A result that will come out the same if the experiment is repeated by the same person using the same method and equipment.

Repeating unit
The shortest repeating section of a polymer.

Reproducible result
A result that will come out the same if someone different does the experiment, or a slightly different method or piece of equipment is used.

Resolution
The smallest change a measuring instrument can detect.

Reversible reaction
A reaction where the products of the reaction can themselves react to produce the original reactants.

R_f value
In chromatography, the ratio between the distance travelled by a dissolved substance and the distance travelled by a solvent.

Risk
The chance that a hazard will cause harm.

S

S.I. unit
A standard unit of measurement, recognised by scientists all over the world.

Saturated
A molecule that contains only single bonds.

Scaling prefix
A word or symbol which goes before a unit to indicate a multiplying factor (e.g. 1 km = 1000 m).

Significant figure
The first significant figure of a number is the first non-zero digit. The second, third and fourth significant figures follow on immediately after it.

Simple distillation
A way of separating a liquid out from a mixture if there are large differences in the boiling points of the substances. You heat the mixture until the bit you want evaporates, then cool the vapour to turn it back into a liquid.

Simple molecule
A molecule made up of only a few atoms held together by covalent bonds.

Single covalent bond
A pair of electrons shared between two atoms.

Single indicator
Indicators that only contain one colour-changing compound, so have one distinct colour change at a particular pH.

Solid
A state of matter where particles are held close together with strong forces of attraction to form a regular lattice arrangement. Solids have a fixed volume and a fixed shape.

Solute
A substance dissolved in a solvent to make a solution.

Solution
A mixture made up of one substance (the solute) dissolved in another (the solvent).

Solvent
A liquid in which another substance (a solute) can be dissolved.

Solvent front
The point the solvent has reached up the filter paper during paper chromatography.

State symbol
The letter, or letters, in brackets that are placed after a substance in an equation to show what physical state it's in. E.g. gaseous carbon dioxide is shown as $CO_{2(g)}$.

Stationary phase
In chromatography, the stationary phase is a solid or really thick liquid where molecules are unable to move.

Steam cracking
The process of breaking down long-chain hydrocarbons into shorter ones by mixing the vapour of hydrocarbons with steam and heating to very high temperatures.

Strong acid
An acid which fully ionises in an aqueous solution.

Successful collision
A collision between particles that results in a chemical reaction.

Sustainable development
An approach to development that takes into the account the needs of present society while not damaging the lives of those in the future.

Systematic error
An error that is consistently made throughout an experiment.

Tangent
A straight line that touches a curve at a particular point without crossing it.

Theory
A hypothesis which has been accepted by the scientific community because there is good evidence to back it up.

Thermal decomposition
A reaction where one substance chemically changes into at least two new substances when it's heated.

Trial run
A quick version of an experiment that can be used to work out the range of variables and the interval between the variables that will be used in the proper experiment.

Triple covalent bond
Three pairs of electrons shared between two atoms.

U

Uncertainty
The amount by which a given result may differ from the true value.

Universal indicator
A wide range indicator that changes colour depending on the pH of the solution that it's in.

Unsaturated hydrocarbon
A molecule that contains two fewer hydrogen atoms than the equivalent alkane due to the presence of a double bond.

V

Valid result
A result that is repeatable, reproducible and answers the original question.

Viscosity
How runny or gloopy a substance is.

W

Weak acid
An acid which partially ionises in an aqueous solution.

Wide range indicator
An indicator containing a mixture of dyes that gradually changes colour over a broad range of pH, such as Universal indicator.

Y

Yield
The amount of product made in a reaction.

Z

Zero error
A type of systematic error caused by using a piece of equipment that isn't zeroed properly.

Acknowledgements

Photograph Acknowledgements

Cover Photo **Alexandre Dotta**/Science Photo Library

p 3 iStock.com/**StasKhom**, p 5 iStock.com/**YolandaVanNiekerk**, p 6 **Tony Craddock**/Science Photo Library, p 8 **Tony Mcconnell**/Science Photo Library, p 9 **Tek Image**/Science Photo Library, p 12 iStock.com/**tunart**, p 13 **Martyn F. Chillmaid**/Science Photo Library, p 21 **Pr. M. Brauner**/Science Photo Library, p 24 Science Photo Library, p 30 (top) **Andrew Lambert Photography**/Science Photo Library, p 30 (bottom) **Martyn F. Chillmaid**/Science Photo Library, p 34 Science Photo Library, p 35 Science Photo Library, p 37 **Martyn F. Chillmaid**/Science Photo Library, p 38 Science Photo Library, p 40 **Andrew Lambert Photography**/Science Photo Library, p 41 **Andrew Lambert Photography**/Science Photo Library, p 43 Science Photo Library, p 51 **Sputnik**/Science Photo Library, p 53 **Andrew Lambert Photography**/Science Photo Library, p 55 (top) iStock.com/**de-kay**, p 55 (bottom) iStock.com/**yanethgc**, p 57 iStock.com/**OvertheHill**, p 58 **Martyn F. Chillmaid**/Science Photo Library, p 62 **Andrew Lambert Photography**/Science Photo Library, p 63 **Andrew Lambert Photography**/Science Photo Library, p 64 iStock.com/**samaro**, p 75 **Charles D. Winters**/Science Photo Library, p 77 **Charles D. Winters**/Science Photo Library, p 79 **Friedrich Saurer**/Science Photo Library, p 81 **Andrew Lambert Photography**/Science Photo Library, p 83 iStock.com/**JanPietruszka**, p 84 **Charles D. Winters**/Science Photo Library, p 87 (top) **Lawrence Lawry**/Science Photo Library, p 87 (bottom) **Science Stock Photography**/Science Photo Library, p 89 **Victor Habbick Visions**/Science Photo Library, p 91 iStock.com/**elbold**, p 98 **Andrew Lambert Photography**/Science Photo Library, p 100 iStock.com/**AltoClassic**, p 105 **Martyn F. Chillmaid**/Science Photo Library, p 107 **Andrew Lambert Photography**/Science Photo Library, p 109 **Andrew Lambert Photography**/Science Photo Library, p 110 **Andrew Lambert Photography**/Science Photo Library, p 115 **Andrew Lambert Photography**/Science Photo Library, p 120 **GIPhotoStock**/Science Photo Library, p 125 (top) Science Photo Library, p 125 (bottom) **Martyn F. Chillmaid**/Science Photo Library, p 131 **Martyn F. Chillmaid**/Science Photo Library, p 134 **Charles D. Winters**/Science Photo Library, p 135 **Trevor Clifford Photography**/Science Photo Library, p 136 **Charles D. Winters**/Science Photo Library, p 138 iStock.com/**SalvadorGCubells**, p 140 **Martyn F. Chillmaid**/Science Photo Library, p 145 **Trevor Clifford Photography**/Science Photo Library, p 152 **Martyn F. Chillmaid**/Science Photo Library, p 153 (top) **Andrew Lambert Photography**/Science Photo Library, p 153 (bottom) **Martyn F. Chillmaid**/Science Photo Library, p 157 **E. R. Degginger**/Science Photo Library, p 160 **Charles D. Winters**/Science Photo Library, p 166 (top) **GIPhotoStock**/Science Photo Library, p 166 (bottom) **Trevor Clifford Photography**/Science Photo Library, p 167 **Laguna Design**/Science Photo Library, p 169 **Martyn F. Chillmaid**/Science Photo Library, p 170 (top) **Andrew Lambert Photography**/Science Photo Library, p 170 (bottom) **Andrew Lambert Photography**/Science Photo Library, p 176 **Andrew Lambert Photography**/Science Photo Library, p 182 **Martyn F. Chillmaid**/Science Photo Library, p 183 Science Photo Library, p 186 **Martyn F. Chillmaid**/Science Photo Library, p 189 (top) **Jerry Mason**/Science Photo Library, p 189 (bottom) **Martyn F. Chillmaid**/Science Photo Library, p 191 **Paul Rapson**/Science Photo Library, p 193 iStock.com/**photllurg**, p 194 **Paul Rapson**/Science Photo Library, p 195 **Paul Rapson**/Science Photo Library, p 199 iStock.com/**PavelIvanov**, p 202 **Alexandre Dotta**/Science Photo Library, p 203 (top) **Martyn F. Chillmaid**/Science Photo Library, p 203 (bottom) **Andrew Lambert Photography**/Science Photo Library, p 207 **Andrew Lambert Photography**/Science Photo Library, p 210 (top) iStock.com/**kn1**, p 210 (bottom) **NASA's Scientific Visualization Studio**/Science Photo Library, p 215 (top) **Simon Fraser**/Science Photo Library, p 215 (bottom) **Adam Hart-Davis**/Science Photo Library, p 221 **Dirk Wiersma**/Science Photo Library, p 225 iStock.com/**studiocasper**, p 227 (top) **Ashley Cooper**/Science Photo Library, p 227 (bottom) **Photostock-Israel**/Science Photo Library, p 228 iStock.com/**ewenjc**, p 229 **Ashley Cooper**/Science Photo Library, p 236 (top) **Andrew Lambert Photography**/Science Photo Library, p 236 (bottom) **Andrew Lambert Photography**/Science Photo Library, p 237 **Charles D. Winters**/Science Photo Library, p 238 **GIPhotoStock**/Science Photo Library, p 240 (top) **Martyn F. Chillmaid**/Science Photo Library, p 240 (bottom) **Martyn F. Chillmaid**/Science Photo Library, p 247 **Andrew Lambert Photography**/Science Photo Library, p 250 iStock.com/**AtomStudios**

Index

F

fair tests 10
filtration 37
fluorine 61
formula triangles 245
formulations 199
fossil fuels 191, 207, 209,
    212-214
fractional distillation 40, 191,
    192
freezing 100
fullerenes 88, 89

G

gas syringes 169, 170, 234, 236
gases 98, 99
geometry 248
giant covalent structures 85-88
giant ionic lattices 75-77
global dimming 214
global warming 209-211
gradients 171-174, 246
graphene 88
graphite 87
graphs 16, 17, 171-174, 246, 247
greenhouse gases 209
Group 0 64, 65
Group 1 56-58
Group 7 61-63
groups (of the periodic table) 52,
    53

H

half equations 142-144
halide ions 62
halogens 61-63
hazards 7, 8
heating substances 239, 240
histograms 16
homologous series 193
hydrocarbons 188-195
hydrogen 57, 134
   test for 203
hypotheses 2, 9

I

incomplete combustion 214
independent variables 10, 16
indicators 124, 125, 237
intercepts 247
intermolecular forces 83-85, 87
iodine 61
ionic bonds 29, 72-74
ionic compounds 57, 75-77
ionic equations 139
ions 23, 29, 70-74
iron 138
isotopes 27, 28, 51

L

lattices 79, 90
Le Chatelier's principle 188, 189
life cycle assessments 223-225
limewater 203
limiting reactants 114-116
liquids 101
litmus 129, 241

M

macromolecules 86
Marsden, Ernest 42
mass numbers 25
means (averages) 14
measuring
   energy transfer 153, 154
   mass 235
   pH 237
   temperature 237
   time 237
   volumes 235, 236
medians (averages) 14
melting 100
Mendeleev, Dimitri 50, 51
metal oxides 130-132, 137, 138
metals
   bonding 54, 55, 90, 91
   extraction 137, 138
methane 188, 209
mixtures 34-41
models 3, 75, 79
modes (averages) 14
moles 106, 107, 111-117

N

natural resources 218
negative correlation 17
negative ions 70
neutralisation reactions 125, 126,
    130-132, 152-154
neutrons 22-25, 43
nitrogen oxides 214
noble gases 64, 65
non-metals 54, 55, 70
nuclear model 22, 23, 42, 43
nuclei 22-24, 42, 43

O

ores 137
oxidation 137, 139, 140
oxides of nitrogen 214
oxygen (test for) 203

P

paper chromatography 35, 36,
    200-202
particle theory 97, 98
percentage masses 104, 105
percentages 242
periodic table 50-53
pH 124, 125, 128, 129, 237
photosynthesis 207
phytomining 220
pipettes 235
plum pudding model 42
polymers 85
positive correlation 17
positive ions 70
potable water 226, 227
precipitation reactions 168, 169,
    176, 177
precision 12
predictions 2, 9
propane 188
protons 22-25, 43, 70
purity 198